NORWICH and its Region

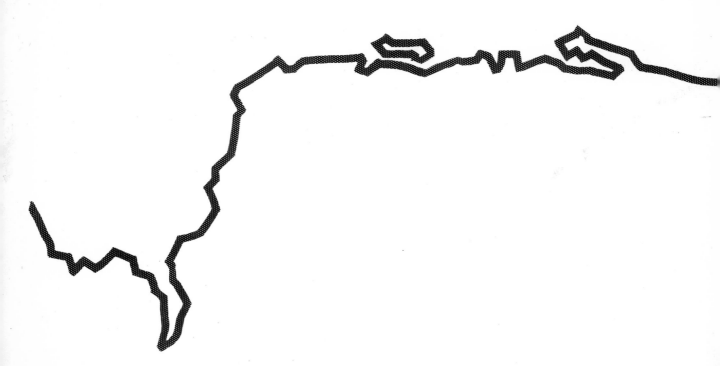

NORWICH

BRITISH ASSOCIATION
FOR THE ADVANCEMENT OF SCIENCE

and its REGION

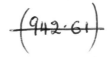

First edition August 1961

Second edition November 1961

DESIGNED AND PRINTED IN GREAT BRITAIN
BY JARROLD AND SONS LTD NORWICH

contents

THE COVER

The NORFOLK HORNED SHEEP is now nearly extinct; a flock has, however, been presented to Whipsnade. Sheep formerly grazed much of 'upland Norfolk' and their wool played its part in Norfolk's fifteenth century prosperity based on worsted weaving. To sheep and wool therefore Norwich and the region are still indebted for their many fine medieval buildings and magnificent churches. (Worstead, which gave its name to the cloth, is now a small agricultural village, map reference D8.) In the eighteenth century sheep were an essential part of the celebrated Norfolk Husbandry of Thomas William Coke and others.

Photo: Jarrold & Sons Ltd

MAGDALEN STREET in Norwich was formerly a somewhat neglected shopping street. In 1957 the Civic Trust proposed to the City Council that it should be the subject of a joint experiment in the re-decoration and general tidying up of a whole street under the guidance of a team of architects. This pioneer scheme was suc-cessfully carried through in 1959, with the full co-operation of the Council and most of the traders. The street is now a source of pleasure to all and the shops report in-creased turnover (see page 213).

Photo: Civic Trust

This 30 CWT MUSTARD BLENDER in the Carrow works of Reckitt & Colman Ltd carries out a stage in the processing of one of Norwich's oldest and best known pro-ducts, one whose bulk manufacture from a raw material of its region helped to bring a late and beneficent industrial revolution to the city, and was the forerunner of one of its most important modern industries – food manufacture. That Norwich's gradual evolution into an industrial centre has been in fact beneficent in every way is to some degree due to the example of the combina-tion of business sense with social responsi-bility shown by its first industrialist, Jeremiah James Colman, the man who brought mustard milling into Norwich.

Photo: J. & J. Colman Ltd

More HERONS breed in Norfolk than in any other county. 1959 was a record year with a total of 430 nests distributed in 22 heronries. The largest heronry was at Islington with 134 nests. A heron ringed at Denver in April 1958 was recovered six months later in Portugal.

Photo: R. Jones

BARLEY is the most characteristic cereal of the region. As with wheat, sugar-beet, carrots, celery, and strawberries more of it is produced in Norfolk than in any other English county. It is grown on 34% of Norfolk's arable acreage as against 15.9% for wheat and 12.4% for sugar-beet. It is used, of course, for brewing, both locally and nationally, and in the manufacture of feeding stuffs.

Photo: Fisons Ltd

LANGMERE, and its neighbour Ringmere, lie in a shallow Breckland valley. They, and the five other similar-sized meres, besides numerous ponds and swallow holes, are an interesting feature of this very dis-tinctive part of the region. It is now thought that the meres are filled by a rise in the saturation level of the subsoil, so that the water levels depend ultimately on rainfall. The beach effect caused by the fluctuations can be seen in the photograph. The Breck area itself is unique in Britain for the numerous continental species of its flora and for the near approach which it provides to 'steppe' conditions. Afforestation can be seen in the background.

Photo: Hallam Ashley

preface
FRANK BRIERS

IN *Norwich and its Region* an attempt has been made to produce something more satisfying than a collection of separate and self-contained articles. Contributors have been encouraged, within the inevitable limitations of space, to give full accounts of the present situation in their respective fields of study, and many have clearly taken advantage of the opportunity to summarize the results of very recent research. It is hoped that the publication will be welcomed as a balanced and reasonably comprehensive survey of the region, and one in which the reader will find much that is of interest and value.

The overall arrangement of the material has been very carefully considered and a continuous theme has been used, wherever possible, to give unity to its various sections. The fullest use has been made of photographs, maps, charts, and diagrams to illustrate the text of the articles, and many have been prepared specially for this occasion. Considerable thought has also been given to the problem of making the survey an attractive document to handle and to read.

The Editor's task has been made easier by the help and kindly forbearance of the contributors, as well as the many others who have been associated with the survey in all the stages of its development. In particular, he wishes to acknowledge with gratitude the support and encouragement of Mr M.W. Bulman, the Chairman of the Publications Committee. He is also greatly indebted to Mr A.R. Cartwright, to Mr R. Jones, and especially to Mr A.J. Stevens, for their willing and valuable collaboration. Mr M.D. Oliver, of Jarrold & Sons Ltd, has taken an unfailing interest in the production, which has benefited considerably from his helpful suggestions. Thanks are also due to Miss J. Egles, the Editor's secretary, who has done a great deal to help all those who have been concerned with the publication.

Generous advice and assistance has been given by many individuals and by representatives of organizations. These are too numerous to mention fully, but their help is, nevertheless, most gratefully acknowledged.

1 Introduction

an English province and its capital ERIC FOWLER

THIS SURVEY describes the region of Norfolk and north Suffolk which, in the local phrase, *looks to Norwich* as the centre of its administration, commerce, or recreation. From east to west this region is about sixty miles wide, extending from the seaport of Great Yarmouth to the Fens. From north to south it stretches for a good forty miles, from the sands and saltmarshes of the north Norfolk coast to the ploughlands of mid-Suffolk. It has a population of about 600,000, at least half of whom are concentrated in the eastern part, between Norwich and the coast.

The Norwich region as a whole is one of the richest and most progressive arable farming areas in Britain. The comparatively dry and sunny climate favours the growing of cereals. East Anglian farmers are experts in the cultivation of fine malting barley, and also of wheat, sugar-beet, and potatoes, but these main crops are diversified by fruit and vegetables, grown largely for canning and freezing factories. The region is also a great producer of milk, beef, pigs, and poultry. The coast has an historic fishing industry, now concentrated mainly upon the Suffolk port of Lowestoft.

Yarmouth, with more than 800 years of seafaring history behind it, has put on the cap and bells of the

ERIC FOWLER, of the *Eastern Daily Press*, is an essayist, journalist, and broadcaster

Blackpool of the East Coast. But both Yarmouth and Lowestoft have in modern times become industrial towns as well as seaports and holiday resorts. Away to the westward, the beautiful old town of King's Lynn, facing the Wash, acts as the capital and port of west Norfolk and the eastern Fens – and Lynn, too, enjoys a rising industrial prosperity.

As for Norwich, it is not only an historic cathedral city and a great market town. It has a history dating back to the fifteenth century as a centre of manufactures. Now it is one of the principal centres in Britain of the shoe industry, and has a tremendous variety of other light industries.

The most striking fact about Norfolk and Suffolk today is that both towns and countryside are in the midst of a second industrial and agricultural revolution, while at the same time the coast and the Broads have acquired an enormous popularity as holiday resorts. Quiet backwater though East Anglia may still appear to some of our visitors from London or the industrial Midlands, a resident is more conscious of the speed with which we are being drawn into the main stream.

The influence of the modern social and industrial revolution is all the more remarkable here by force of contrast, since the Industrial Revolution of the nineteenth century made but a belated and modified impact upon East Anglia. Not only remoteness from the coal and iron fields and the major seaports, but the conservatism of the people, and their obstinate resistance in the early nineteenth century to the new machines, prevented Norwich from any attempt to become another Manchester or Leeds – as its previous eminence as a centre of the wool and silk-weaving industry might well have dictated. And from 1870 onwards, while Norwich gradually adapted itself to new industries and the factory system, a prolonged agricultural depression so held back the social and economic progress of the countryside that modern educational and social reformers in the rural districts have often found themselves bridging the gap, not between the nineteenth and the twentieth, but between the eighteenth and the twentieth centuries.

Norfolk people – although resentful of the still not uncommon imputation that there is nothing north of

Ipswich but agriculture and ancient monuments – are fond of describing themselves as isolated. From the end of the Napoleonic Wars in 1815 to the beginning of the First World War in 1914 there was probably a good deal of truth in the description. The economic consequences for the artisans and labourers of that period were not happy. But it is possible for us who are living today to reflect that from an aesthetic point of view isolation had its advantages. The historic and beautiful centre of Norwich, which we now treasure, could hardly have survived the full impact of Victorian utilitarianism. Neither could the graceful high streets and market places of our country towns and villages. It is an open question, in 1961, how much will survive the utilitarianism of the twentieth century.

The Anglo-Saxons founded Norwich. They invaded East Anglia by sea and advanced up the river valleys. Having destroyed or abandoned the Romano-British cantonal capital of Venta Icenorum – whose overgrown ramparts now enclose fields of corn and sugar-beet at Caistor St Edmund's, three miles south of the present city – the invaders seem to have settled in a group of villages, or *wics*, near the lowermost ford of the river Wensum. And when the group grew together into a town, the *north wic* must have given its name to the whole community. That, at least, is the most likely theory as to the origin of the name, Norwich.

For the prehistoric peoples, the high road between East Anglia and the south and west of England was the Icknield Way, which runs from the Chiltern Hills, over the Newmarket Downs, and thence across west Norfolk to the mouth of the Wash (where there was possibly a ferry across to Lincolnshire). Neolithic man, who dug his remarkable flint-mines in the chalk of Grime's Graves, near Brandon, found it easier to cultivate the light, sandy soil in the west than to clear the more fertile but heavily forested land in central Norfolk and Suffolk. So, apparently, did the Iceni. And the Romans, having found it necessary as late as A.D. 61 to subdue with fire and sword those intractable survivors of the Iron Age, did not advance their civilization so far into this eastern cul-de-sac as they did along the main routes of England. They founded no big towns nor great and rich villas here in Norfolk.

The Anglo-Saxons, invading the Wash as well as the east coast, found the bulk of the population was still in the western part of East Anglia. But it was they and the Danes after them, coming by sea and pressing inland from the coast, who determined that the future centre of commerce and population should be in the east of the province. For they had the tools, the energy, and the farming skill to clear the richer soil of central Norfolk and Suffolk of its primeval forest, and bring it under the plough – even as they also had the ships to use the sea as a high road into this province.

'Domesday Book' shows that the eastern part of Norfolk, at the time of the Norman Conquest, was the most populous part of England. Norwich – having risen again from the ashes to which the Danes had reduced it in the year 1004 – was a big town with 1,320 burgesses, and hence with a population of five or six thousand. It was the commercial centre, and the huge earthen mound and outworks of Earl Ralph Guader's castle had perhaps made it the military centre of East Anglia. Norwich was confirmed in its position as a provincial capital in 1094, when the proud, ambitious, and able Bishop Herbert de Losinga decided to found his cathedral there – removing from Thetford the seat of his diocese, which then and until the beginning of the present century extended over both Norfolk and Suffolk.

In the days when the only clerks were those in holy orders, that must have determined the situation of the administrative as well as the ecclesiastical capital. Thenceforward Norwich prospered in its comparative isolation from the rest of England. Southward, it was a long and tiresome journey from London. Westward, it was an even more difficult journey across the Fens. But the city was the mercantile capital of a fertile province, which at that time produced large quantities of wool as well as barley. And eastward the sea, even though open to the dangers of storm and piracy, was the way to a rich trade with the great mercantile and manufacturing cities of the Low Countries.

Moreover, from the fourteenth century onwards, after Edward III had encouraged the immigration of Flemish weavers to propagate their craft among English artisans, Norwich itself became the centre of a great industrial district. Not only the city, but all the surrounding towns and villages, throve by the spinners' and weavers' skill. Worstead, now a small farming village with a magnificent church to remind us of the former wealth as well as piety of its inhabitants, gave its name to worsted cloth.

And, of course, the seaports also prospered. King's Lynn, with a domestic trade derived via the Great Ouse and its tributaries from seven English counties, and an overseas trade ranging from the Baltic to the Mediterranean, was at this time one of the richest ports in England. The evidence survives today in its wonderful treasure of historic buildings, whose fame is spread by a distinguished annual arts festival.

Great Yarmouth, at the mouth of the Yare, was the seaward outlet of Norwich. Not only that, but it could also have been said to have been founded like Amsterdam on a pile of herring-bones, for it was the headquarters of a great autumn herring fishery whose salted products supplied most of Europe with lenten diet. And indeed, there were still a thousand craft fishing out of Yarmouth in the autumn of 1913, to supply an enormous trade with eastern Europe. Though sadly diminished by the Russian Revolution, this trade persisted after 1918: but today, through an unaccountable disappearance of the herring shoals from their former grounds, the fishery has dwindled to a few score of boats. Yarmouth's new frozen food industry and its big factories of television and radio components have come in the nick of time to supplement its holiday trade and compensate for the decline of its historic fishery.

That, however, is a digression, which is intended to illustrate the maritime character of this province. Until the coming of the railways, and of larger ships than coasting brigs and schooners, a whole string of little ports flourished along the Norfolk and Suffolk coastline. It is probable that until the beginning of the nineteenth century as much of the commerce of East Anglia moved by sea and river as overland.

And in some respects isolation was an advantage. A traveller today, with an eye to history on his journeys from London to the west, the Midlands, or the north, finds himself passing along the routes of all the civil wars and domestic commotions in English history. But there are very few crossed swords on the map of East Anglia. Our social and economic history is full of interest – perhaps the more so because there have been so few violent disturbances of the relics of the centuries. But as far as military events are concerned, our history between

the time of the Plantagenets and the air raids of 1939–45 is of an enviable placidity.

Norfolk participated in two unsuccessful agrarian risings – the Peasants' Revolt of 1381 and Kett's Rebellion in 1549 (which latter was grievous not only to the landed gentry, but to the trade and property of the merchants of Norwich). But the building of so many splendid churches during the fifteenth century, not only in Norwich but in the surrounding countryside, suggests that the Wars of the Roses did not very deeply disturb its industrial and mercantile prosperity. And, jumping forward to the Civil War, we find that Colchester and Lynn stood siege on behalf of the King, but the rest of East Anglia was so deeply engaged in Cromwell's Eastern Association that it suffered no battles, and the worst that Norwich saw of the war was a riot.

Yarmouth ships composed a large part of Edward III's fleet at the battle of Sluys; little Blakeney is proud to have been one of the Norfolk ports that contributed ships and men to the defeat of the Armada; and no doubt hundreds of Norfolk and Suffolk men fought among Cromwell's Ironsides, and others among the Cavaliers. Nobody knows how many shouldered muskets under Marlborough, but Nelson was proud to have recruited most of his 'old Agamemnons' from his native county. And yet it must be counted one of the blessings of our local history, that we have for the most part been up a by-road, so that our men have seldom been called upon to fight on their own territory – save against their natural enemies of flood and storm.

Along with the maritime character of the province went a culture which, as far as outside influences were concerned, was predominantly Flemish. From the fifteenth century onwards the new light of the Renaissance percolated into East Anglia, not directly from the Mediterranean, but indirectly – along with their merchandise and craftsmen – from the great trading cities of Flanders and the Low Countries. Their influence is apparent in the decoration of our magnificent Perpendicular churches, where historians often find it difficult to determine how much is Flemish and how much is native East Anglian craftsmanship. Indeed, the very shape of Norwich, Yarmouth, and Lynn, with their great open market places, reminds modern tourists of Dutch and Flemish towns.

The flint-walled Guildhall of Norwich, built at the beginning of the fifteenth century, is dwarfed today by the towering neo-Georgian-cum-Scandinavian City Hall of the modern municipality, but the Guildhall can still be seen as a symbol of the early emancipation of a great manufacturing and mercantile city from the feudal domination of the Castle and the hierarchy of the Cathedral. For, church-builders though they were, the citizens of Norwich never submitted easily to the secular pretensions of the priesthood, and the Lollards found a receptive audience here.

Norwich in the fifteenth century was rising towards the position it was to hold for the best part of two hundred years, as the second city of England, after London. It was a sort of Manchester or Leeds of the age of handicrafts – from the early seventeenth century until about 1750, it was rivalled only by Bristol and York for size or affluence. Before the Reformation, this wealth, which permeated all the surrounding district, was exemplified by the building of churches. That is why some Norfolk and Suffolk villages, numbering only a few hundred inhabitants, still possess churches almost of the proportions of cathedrals. Norwich itself–which is today embarrassed as well as beautified by the possession of thirty medieval churches – contained many more at the time of the Reformation.

That religious and political upheaval coincided with a decline of the weaving industry, which Queen Elizabeth I sought to restore by encouraging a fresh immigration of Flemings to practice in England their finer crafts and more varied manufactures. But the Spanish persecution of Protestants in Holland and Flanders induced thousands of refugees to follow the emigrant craftsmen into England. The influx into Norfolk was so great that towards the end of the sixteenth century nearly a third of the population of Norwich (at that time about 15,000) was of foreign origin.

The Strangers, as they were called, had their own churches and their own cloth hall in Norwich. Even as late as the 1890's some of their descendants were still sufficiently conscious of their ancestry to hold an annual service in Dutch in Blackfriars' Hall – the east end of the former conventual church of the Dominican Friars, which in the sixteenth century was allotted to the Strangers as the Dutch church.

The massive immigration of Dutch- and French-speaking tradesmen and their families was greeted, as might be expected, with some resentment by the citizens of Elizabethan Norwich. It was, nevertheless, so thoroughly successful in re-establishing the local weaving industry that its impetus lasted until the beginning of the nineteenth century. Moreover, it is held that the subsequent fusion of Flemish, Walloon, and (in the seventeenth century) Huguenot craftsmen with the native East Anglian stock left an inheritance of handicraft skill that promotes the success of the largest present industry of Norwich, which is the manufacture of fine women's and children's shoes.

But the Flemish and Walloon immigrants did much more than establish a staple industry in Norwich and Norfolk. They had an abiding influence on the local character and even scenery. It is for instance obvious in the round or crow-stepped gables of so many of our fine brick houses, and in the name 'locum' (Fr. *lucarne*) which old Norfolk people still apply to attic windows. The Flemish weavers are said to have brought with them the famous Norwich canaries, which sang to the rattle of the looms – and the breed survived to cheer the labours of Victorian shoemakers in their garret workshops.

The first printing press ever set up in this city (about 1570) belonged to a Fleming, one Anthony de Soleme. The Strangers, too, are said to have fathered that love of flowers and gardens which causes Norwich still to rejoice in the name and reputation of 'the city of gardens'. It may well have been their skill in land drainage that helped to dot the marshes of east Norfolk with windmills.

Certainly, modern research into farming history credits the Strangers with having been pioneers in growing turnips as a field crop, and in some of the other improvements in agriculture and stock-feeding which later on, in the eighteenth and early nineteenth centuries, helped sustain the swarming urban population of the Industrial Revolution, and made Norfolk agriculture an example to Europe and America. According to this school of thought, 'Turnip' Townshend of Raynham (1674-1738), and the great Thomas William Coke of Holkham (1754-1842) were not so much innovators as patrons, exemplars, and propagandists of the best farming practices.

Coke, in particular – the great Whig aristocrat and

virtuoso, who did not disdain to wear a labourer's smock as he moved about the miniature principality of his Norfolk estate – settled it that the grand contribution of Norfolk to science should be made through the cultivation of its fields and care of its stock. The influence of his experiments was international, and the suggestion that he in turn owed something to the work of the Strangers 200 years previously throws a new light on those ingenious people as agriculturists as well as manufacturers.

At any rate, thanks to the impetus their craftsmanship had given it, Norwich, until well past the middle of the eighteenth century, was one of the wealthiest and most industrious cities in Britain, in the centre of one of the most prosperous districts. It had the large population, for those days, of 38,000, and there was a big export as well as home trade in Norwich textiles. Not only did the city prosper, but its industry permeated all the surrounding countryside, where the earnings of the women and children at the spindle and the weaver at his loom handsomely supplemented the produce of the husbandman in the fields.

The elegant Assembly House (built in 1756) testifies to the wealthy and cultivated society of which Norwich was at that time the centre. The story of the rapid decline, during and after the Napoleonic Wars, of the city's staple industry, and the gradual emergence, during the Victorian era, of its modern commerce and manufactures, is told in the industrial chapters of this survey. Suffice it here to say that at the passing of the Reform Acts in the 1830's this once opulent city was sunk in political corruption and industrial poverty and decay.

Strangely enough, it was during this period of decline that John Crome and John Sell Cotman developed their genius as leaders of the Norwich School of Painting – the only distinctively local school in the history of English painting. Neither of them was richly rewarded in his lifetime – Crome was a drawing master: and Cotman was employed in laboriously illustrating the researches of Dawson Turner, the antiquarian banker of Yarmouth. But they found patrons here for landscapes which – in their appreciation of the qualities of light and the open air, as against the heavy classicism which was the fashion of the time – are held to have been forerunners of the work of the Impressionists.

One can only surmise that, with Norfolk farmers prospering under the influence of Thomas William Coke's improvements, the wars, and the Corn Laws, Norwich was upheld against its industrial decay by its commerce as a market town and county capital. For it was also during this impoverished period (in 1824) that the Norfolk and Norwich Triennial Music Festival was founded – with popular success, and under royal patronage. And at this time, too, Sir James Smith, the purchaser of the Linnaean Collection and founder of the Linnean Society, lived here, as also did William Taylor, the German scholar.

The Quaker Gurneys, who had prospered in the eighteenth century as wool merchants, were rising to eminence alike as bankers and philanthropists – and Elizabeth Fry, the future prison reformer, was one of seven pretty Gurney daughters at Earlham Hall, who were taking drawing lessons from Mr Crome. A moody, gifted youth named George Borrow was playing truant from a lawyer's office in St Giles to wander among the gipsies on Mousehold Heath. And that lively Quakeress, Amelia Opie, was holding a literary *salon* at her house in Castle Meadow.

Harriet Martineau, who lived opposite the old Gurney house in Magdalen Street, sniffed at the pretensions of early-nineteenth-century Norwich to call itself a little Athens. But out of the ashes of the eighteenth-century prosperity, a new, thoughtful, and cultivated middle class was growing up, with time to spare for the arts and sciences, even while it struggled to interpret to a stubborn city the meaning of the Industrial Revolution. Commercially, it is significant that at this time also Thomas Bignold and his son Samuel were founding the fortunes of the Norwich Union Life and Fire Insurance Societies.

Politically and industrially the new order found its local leaders towards the middle of the century in two Radical Nonconformists, Jacob Henry Tillett and Jeremiah James Colman. Tillett was a handsome, eloquent, and deeply religious lawyer – a descendant of a Huguenot family who escaped to England and settled in Norwich after the Revocation of the Edict of Nantes. In 1845 he took the lead in establishing a newspaper dedicated to civil, religious, and commercial freedom. And until his death in 1892 he employed platform, pulpit, and pen towards the reformation of the government, morals, and education of his native city. Norwich – by no means unanimously grateful – sent him briefly and belatedly to Parliament in 1880. It seemed like the malice of fate that he, the warrior against corruption, had twice been unseated after previous elections, because of corrupt practices by his agents.

Jeremiah James Colman was the practical, wealthy, and influential ally Tillett needed, and was also his lifelong friend. Colman was one of a family of country millers, who had discovered and begun to develop an international market for mustard. In 1856 he moved the family concern into Norwich, and founded Carrow Works, which before the end of the century employed 2,000 people under conditions that in many respects anticipated the Welfare State. He was an eminently practical idealist, and a pioneer of slum clearance and re-housing, technical education, electrification, and industrial welfare schemes. He may be said to have introduced the Industrial Revolution to Norwich in its most beneficent aspect.

J. J. Colman and his family were moreover looked up to as the grand local patrons of philanthropic causes and of the arts and sciences. Before his death in 1898 the now renascent city seems to have regarded him as its patriarch. It may help to indicate the mind of the man that – being for twenty-four years a Member of Parliament for Norwich and three times Mayor – he regarded the first visit of the British Association to Norwich, during his mayoralty in 1868, as possibly the greatest event of his civic career.

Victorian Radicalism and the Nonconformist conscience were thus two of the strongest influences in forming the character of modern Norwich, cathedral city though it is. But for the beginnings of that character we have to look again to those all-pervasive Strangers of the sixteenth century. They were Protestants of a stubbornness that had been tempered in the fires of persecution, and in the seventeenth century they were no more disposed to yield in matters of conscience to the autocracy of Charles I and Archbishop Laud than they had been to surrender to Spain and the Holy Inquisition. A Norfolk man cherishes his freedom to 'du different' – as he says in his dialect. And the non-conformity of the local temperament – with which went an obstinate insistence on civil as well as religious liberty – was undoubtedly toughened by fusion with the Strangers.

And so it was a matter of historical continuity that, in the nineteenth century, a Puritan and Radical Norwich was led towards political reform and industrial recovery by two men whose religious Nonconformity was the mainspring of their politics. Neither can we consider it a freak, but rather an outcome of the old Radicalism, that the proud cathedral city of today has been governed for the past thirty years by a Council with a Labour majority – yet without any prejudice at all to a hearty conservatism of outlook on all changes, among a substantial majority of the citizens.

And that conservatism may also have its value in maintaining the historic beauty of Norwich, without detriment to its modern progress. For progress it has, in the great variety of its present industries, in its prosperity as an agricultural market, and in its eminence as the capital of a highly distinctive province. The growth of motor transport, and the situation here of radio and television stations serving the whole of East Anglia, have enlarged the city's sphere of influence.

If we count the population in the outer suburbs, as well as within the municipal boundary which Norwich has long overflowed, this is now a city of more than 150,000 people, serving another quarter of a million as a centre for shopping, professional and commercial services, and recreation. Moreover, it prides itself upon its culture and its beauty.

The Cathedral is not merely admired as a monument: it is used by congregations of thousands from all over the county as the great central church of a widespread diocese of 600 parishes. The Norwich museums are not just repositories of exhibits – the Castle is the centre of a lively interest in the arts and in scientific research. Neither is the Norwich School of Painting a dead tradition – the School of Art fosters a strong and vigorous modern practice of painting and sculpture. The City College, built since the war, has 7,000 students. The Triennial Musical Festival is the glorification of a widespread local enjoyment not merely of listening, but of music-making. The Assembly House, since its restoration in 1951, has been a genuine success as an artistic and social centre, and is used for the meetings of 200 local societies. The new Central Library, now being built, will not only be a municipal lending and reference library, but a centre for city and county, for the care and study of one of the finest collections in the country of local historical records.

But perhaps the outstanding local artistic achievement of the past fifty years has been the foundation by the late Nugent Monck of the little Maddermarket Theatre, where the Norwich Players – amateurs, with a professional producer – have performed the entire cycle of Shakespeare's plays, and in addition a great part not simply of the English but of the world's drama. (As Monck once put it: 'Anything from Aristophanes to Anouilh.')

Such are the considerations on which Norwich, two years ago, successfully based its claim to become the home of a new university, which it is hoped will receive its first students in 1964. The University of East Anglia is an aspiration Norwich has actively cherished for half a century. It is seen as a necessary counterpart to material progress: and moreover it is felt to be something towards which local history has been working for nearly a thousand years.

Norwich is full of contrasts such as this in Princes Street – fine old buildings on one side with St George Tombland tower in the background and a modern boot and shoe factory across the street

2 The Physical Background

geology G. P. LARWOOD | B. M. FUNNELL

A COMPREHENSIVE *review of the geology of Norfolk is due to be published in 1961 as a separate publication of the* Transactions of the Norfolk and Norwich Naturalists' Society. *In the present short account we emphasize the results of recent research and we regret that this compels us to omit reference to the extensive investigations of earlier workers. A summary of this earlier work is given by Boswell (1935). The localities mentioned in the present account are shown on the map accompanying the section on the physiography of Norfolk.*

Advances in our understanding of the Pleistocene deposits have been particularly rapid in the last few years and are likely to continue; therefore some of the statements concerning the Pleistocene in this account are inevitably interim in character.

MESOZOIC

THE PALAEOZOIC FLOOR
AND BURIED MESOZOIC ROCKS

Upper Jurassic Kimmeridge Clay is the oldest deposit exposed at the surface in Norfolk. The *pre-Kimmeridgian* sequence is known, however, from five deep borings in East Anglia, at North Creake, Southery, Lowestoft, Culford, and Cambridge, and from shallower borings at other localities. Both deep and shallow borings reveal a sequence of Mesozoic sediments resting on an irregular surface which cuts across Palaeozoic or older rocks. Variations in the form of this Palaeozoic floor to the south and south-west of Norfolk have also been determined by seismic methods. More recently the Geological Survey has completed gravity and magnetic surveys over East Anglia revealing strong gravity and magnetic anomalies in and around the Wash.

In an account of the deep boring at North Creake, P. E. Kent has compiled a map showing the probable south-eastern limits of the buried Mesozoic rocks in East Anglia; these boundaries, and a north–south cross-section, are shown in fig. 1. At North Creake the Palaeozoic floor is at −2,435 feet, and, from here, it rises steadily southward to an east–west ridge beneath Culford culminating at −355 feet at Cambridge.

The Triassic sediments, near the base of the deep boring at North Creake, rest upon Precambrian (Charnian) volcanic rocks and consist of pale grey Bunter Sandstone with variegated Keuper Marls above. These marls are overlain by thick grey shales, clays, and thinner muddy limestones, calcareous sandstones and occasional ironstones of the Lower and Middle Lias which, in turn, passes up into thinner bituminous Upper Lias shales. Great Oolite limestones rest directly upon these and are succeeded by grey clays and shales with a thin development of Cornbrash limestones above. Kellaways Beds of calcareous sandstones and grey shaly clays rest upon the Cornbrash and are overlain by thicker Oxford Clay deposits of grey shales and clays with subsidiary muddy limestones. A hard, grey limestone marks the base of the overlying Corallian Clay sequence which passes up into thinner Kimmeridge Clay with shales. The succeeding 700 feet of Cretaceous sediments rest unconformably on the Kimmeridge Clay.

JURASSIC

The surface outcrop of the *Kimmeridge Clay* in west Norfolk extends from Hilgay to north of King's Lynn,

G.P. LARWOOD is a member of the staff of the Department of Geology, University of Cambridge. B.M. FUNNELL is a Research Worker in the Department of Geodesy and Geophysics, University of Cambridge

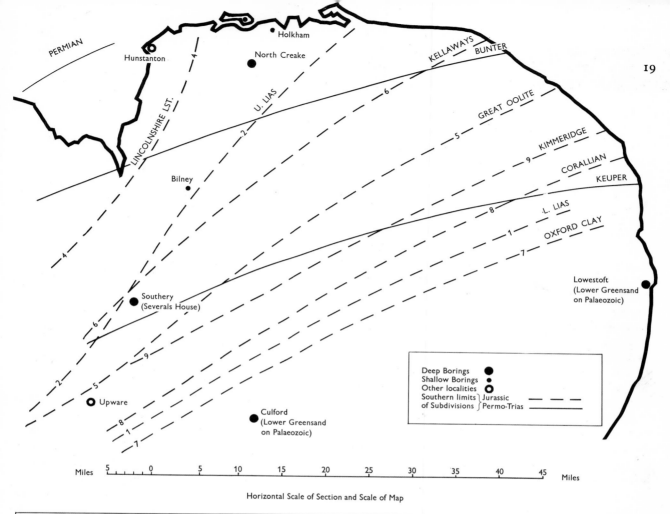

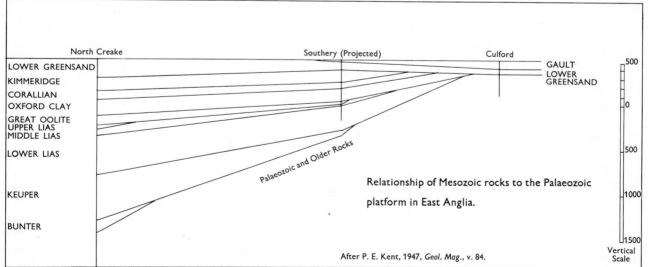

Relationship of Mesozoic rocks to the Palaeozoic platform in East Anglia.

After P. E. Kent, 1947, *Geol. Mag.*, v. 84.

Fig. 1 *Probable south-eastern limits of buried Mesozoic rocks in East Anglia*

but it is discontinuous and narrow. Eastward it passes beneath the Lower Greensand and westward it is covered by Fenland peats, silts, and clays. The Kimmeridge formation consists of blue-grey shaly clays containing fragmentary ammonites characteristic of a high zone and the remains of crushed lamellibranchs and, occasionally, fish and marine reptiles. The deposit accumulated in a muddy sea which may have completely submerged the ridge of Palaeozoic rocks to the south.

No Jurassic rocks which are younger than the Kimmeridge Clay outcrop in Norfolk. After Kimmeridge times slight earth movements tilted the area, exposing it to erosion until Lower Cretaceous times when it was again submerged by the advance of a sea from the north. The deposits of this sea were laid down unconformably on the eroded edges of the Kimmeridge Clay and in the process phosphatized ammonites and fragments of mineralized wood were washed from it into the base of the newer Lower Cretaceous sediments – the Lower Greensand.

LOWER CRETACEOUS

Neocomian. In north-west Norfolk the *Lower Greensand* sequence is about 170 feet thick, its outcrop extending from just south of Downham Market to Hunstanton (fig. 2). North of West Newton three divisions are recognizable: the basal Sandringham Sands, about 100 feet thick, being separated by about 30 feet of Snettisham Clay from the overlying 40 feet or so of Carstone. The *Sandringham Sands* form a prominent rise east of the Fenland and are well exposed in several localities. They are generally unfossiliferous, pale coloured or iron stained orange-brown quartz sands, with occasional very thin clay streaks. Their irregular bedding is typical of sediments laid down in shallow, current-swept water. The attitude of the current-bedding units and the presence of distinctive mineral grains suggests that the sands were derived from a land area not far to the north-west or north-north-west rather than from the south.

The very narrow outcrop of the succeeding *Snettisham Clay* may be traced southwards from Heacham to nearly one mile south-east of West Newton. The clay is silty in parts and locally has a thin basal pebble bed with small, rolled phosphatic nodules. It is pale grey when fresh, but weathers a reddish-brown and contains clay-ironstone nodules which occasionally enclose the remains of ammonites and a variety of lamellibranchs. The ammonites are important in that they are Neocomian forms and show that the Snettisham Clay, and the underlying Sandringham Sands, were deposited before the Lower Greensand beds of southern England. South of West Newton the Snettisham Clay apparently passes laterally into thinly-bedded sandstones, and it is very difficult to distinguish these from the Sandringham Sands or from the overlying Carstone sequence. The Snettisham Clay is now only very poorly exposed at Heacham and Snettisham.

Aptian and Albian. The *Carstone* forms the base of the cliffs at Hunstanton and outcrops on the foreshore, and from here it can be traced to just south of Downham Market. In the north it is a coarse and pebbly, ferruginous, ginger-brown sandstone, but from south of Dersingham to Downham Market it is noticeably finer grained. The ammonites which have been found in phosphatic nodules in its basal pebble bed at Hunstanton are known to occur at several horizons in the Lower Greensand of southern England, and their presence in the base of the Carstone shows that in Aptian times a southern sea finally spread northward across the Palaeozoic ridge to link up with the sea in which the Carstone was accumulating. The age of the unfossiliferous upper part of the Carstone is not known, but it may extend up into the Albian.

The outcrop of the Albian deposits which overlie the Carstone is extremely narrow from Hunstanton to Dersingham. Beyond Dersingham the outcrop widens into an irregular band of clay land extending south to Narborough and thence south-west to Crimplesham and to the west of Stoke Ferry. Small outlying patches also occur south of Castle Rising, east of Middleton, and south-east of Downham Market.

In the cliffs at Hunstanton, immediately above the Carstone, is the most prominent bed of the Lower Cretaceous sequence – the *Hunstanton Red Rock.* It contains a very varied fauna of ammonites, nautiloids, belemnites, lamellibranchs, echinoderms, polyzoa, and sponges, some of which show it to be a condensed deposit

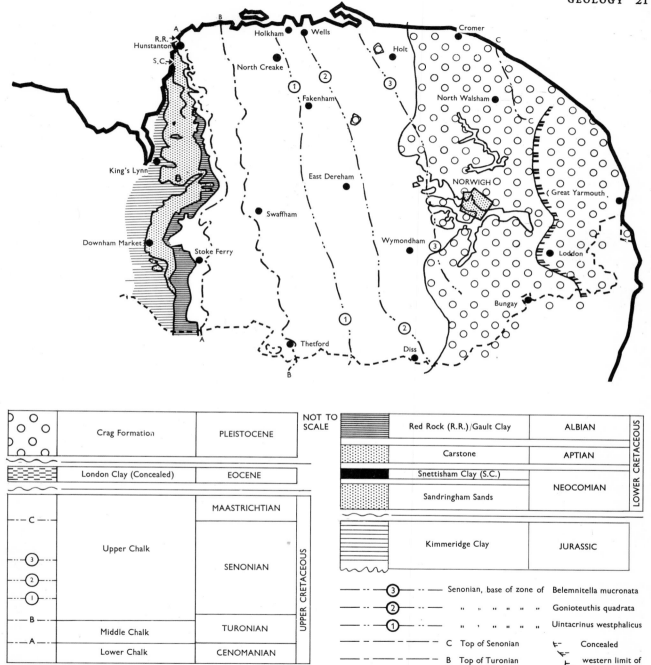

Fig. 2 *Geology of Norfolk (Drift and Post-glacial Deposits omitted)*

equivalent to much thicker Albian deposits to the south-west. In Bedfordshire the Albian sequence consists of 230 feet of dark, blue-grey *Gault Clay*, but as it is traced north-eastwards it thins to 150 feet at Cambridge, and is further reduced to 60 feet of paler marly clay at West Dereham. This thinning continues northwards to 20 feet at Grimston, beyond which there is a more marked change in lithology. At Roydon the Gault is also about 20 feet thick, the lower part being a series of grey marls with small red patches and the highest part a bed of hard, pale yellowish limestone. Four miles farther north, at Dersingham, the Gault Clay sequence is only 7 feet thick and consists of soft, greenish-white, cal-careous marls at the top passing down into harder yellow, brownish, and red marls beneath. From Ingoldisthorpe to Hunstanton the Albian consists of only 4 feet of Red Rock – an iron-rich, pebbly limestone.

Ammonites which are characteristic of the Lower Gault elsewhere apparently occur in the lowest 10 inches of the Red Rock and the rest of it is equivalent to the Upper Gault. Many lydite and quartz pebbles are present in the lower band which grades very rapidly down into the underlying Carstone. The upper part of the Red Rock is rather nodular, with fewer scattered quartz and lydite pebbles and its junction with the overlying Chalk is slightly irregular but sharply defined. The red colour reflects a high iron content, as much as 40 per cent, but usually about 10 per cent. This iron is thought to be derived from the erosion of a lateritic land surface. The heavy minerals of the Red Rock are identical with those of the Carstone, but Rastall also found mineral grains of a different type in the thin, dark red layer between the Red Rock and the Chalk and suggested that these were introduced by derivation from a newly exposed land area at the very end of Red Rock times. He found none of these distinctive mineral grains in the lowest bed of the overlying Chalk.

In the deep boring at North Creake, twelve miles south-east of Hunstanton, the Red Rock was found to be the same as in the coast section, passing down directly into Carstone, but a shallow boring at Holkham, thirteen miles east of Hunstanton, passed through about 8 feet of Red Rock resting on 10 feet of normal grey Gault Clay, showing that here the Red Rock type of deposition began later than in the Hunstanton area.

It is evident that during Neocomian, Aptian, and Albian times rather peculiar sediments accumulated in the area now occupied by west and north-west Norfolk. These Lower Cretaceous sediments have distinctive lithologies which cannot be matched exactly in beds of the same age elsewhere in the British sequence. Their faunas, although including species which occur in more widespread and normal Lower Cretaceous deposits, also contain some new and distinctive species. These faunal and lithological changes, and the thinning of the deposits, may be related to the stability of the area during Lower Cretaceous times. J.M. Hancock has indicated that similar changes may be traced in the Chalk of Norfolk.

UPPER CRETACEOUS

Chalk is the dominant, most widespread and, super-ficially, the most uniform of the Cretaceous rocks. In Norfolk it reaches a thickness of about 1,350 feet and outcrops over a great area. In the west its lower beds extend southward from Hunstanton to Lakenheath, and, as the formation dips gently eastward, increasingly higher zones are exposed at the surface in that direction (fig. 2). It underlies the younger deposits of east Nor-folk and in a boring at Great Yarmouth the eroded surface of the Chalk was penetrated at −506 feet O.D. In Norfolk the Chalk is often covered by Glacial Drift deposits and glacial erosion probably accounts for its generally subdued topography, although, in the west, where the Drift cover is thinner or patchy, the Chalk forms gently rising ground flanking the Gault Clay outcrop and the Fens.

The Chalk is almost pure calcium carbonate. M. Black has shown that 'The calcite of typical soft chalk . . . appeared to be provided entirely from organic skeletons, the coarser fractions coming from the shells of in-vertebrates, the finer from planktonic algae.' He has also pointed out that the proportions of micro-constituents of chalk vary considerably within certain limits, and that these variations account for chalks with noticeably different bulk properties. Thus, gritty textured, friable chalk usually contains a large number of *Inoceramus* prisms and other shell fragments; harder, nodular chalks are often rich in the tests of Foraminifera, and the commoner, soft chalks have a preponderance of coccolith

THE FOLLOWING DEPOSITS ARE PRESENT IN THE AREA

Formations, Zones, and Deposits	Stages	Periods and Systems	
Barrier Islands and Spits Broadland and Fenland Deposits	Post-glacial	HOLOCENE	
Hunstanton Till and Outwash Deposits	Last (Hunstanton) Glaciation	PLEISTOCENE	
Morston Raised Beach	Ipswichian Inter-glacial		
Gipping Till and Outwash Deposits	Gipping Glaciation		
Nar Valley Clay Nar Valley Freshwater Beds	Hoxnian Inter-glacial		
Lowestoft Till Corton Beds Cromer Till and Norwich Brickearth *Leda myalis* Bed	Lowestoft Glaciation		
Arctic Freshwater Bed Cromer Forest Bed Series	Cromerian Inter-glacial		
Weybourne Crag Norwich Crag { Upper Division / Lower Division }	Icenian		
Ludham Crag	?Butleyan		
London Clay	Ypresian	EOCENE AND PALAEOCENE	
Reading Beds	Sparnacian		
?Thanet Sands	?Thanetian		
Zone of *Belemnella lanceolata*	Maastrichtian	UPPER	CRETACEOUS
Zone of *Belemnitella mucronata* Zone of *Gonioteuthis quadrata* Zone of *Marsupites testudinarius* Zone of *Uintacrinus westphalicus* Zone of *Micraster cor-anguinum* Zone of *Micraster cor-testudinarium*	Senonian		
Zone of *Holaster planus* Zone of *Terebratulina lata* Zone of *Inoceramus labiatus*	Turonian		
Zone of *Holaster subglobosus* Zone of *Schloenbachia varians*	Cenomanian		
Red Rock and Gault Clay	Albian	LOWER	
Lower Greensand { Carstone	Aptian		
Lower Greensand { Snettisham Clay Sandringham Sands	Neocomian		
Kimmeridge Clay	Kimmeridgian	JURASSIC	

material – the calcareous remains of the minute plank-tonic algae mentioned above.

In early Upper Cretaceous times, at the beginning of the Cenomanian, there was a very widespread marine submergence establishing the sea in which the Chalk accumulated until the end of the Cretaceous period. The Norfolk area was far from any shoreline, and little or no land-derived detritus is to be found in the Chalk. In this area, as elsewhere, three main divisions may be recognized, each comprising a number of zones charac-terized by particular assemblages of invertebrate fossils. The courses of some of these zones across Norfolk are shown in fig. 2.

Cenomanian. In west Norfolk the rather irregular and narrow outcrop of the *Cenomanian Chalk* extends from Old Hunstanton southwards to Lakenheath; it is widest north of Stoke Ferry. The southward widening of the outcrop in part reflects the thickening of both zones of the Cenomanian Chalk in that direction. The lower zone, containing the ammonite *Schloenbachia varians*, is coincident with the Chalk Marl which is only 18 feet thick at Hunstanton. This is a tough, sometimes nodular, greyish chalk which reaches 75 feet in thickness at Stoke Ferry. At the base of the Chalk Marl at Hunstanton there is 18 inches of hard, white chalk with peculiar, irregularly branching structures similar to those of the top of the underlying Red Rock. The echinoid *Holaster subglobosus* characterizes parts of the upper zone of the Cenomanian which thickens from about 40 feet at Hunstanton to about 50 feet at Stoke Ferry. At its base is the local equivalent of the Cambridgeshire Burwell Rock, a pale, brownish-grey, nodular layer, and this is overlain by thinly-bedded Grey Chalk which extends to the top of the zone.

Turonian. The succeeding *Turonian Chalk* is about 100 feet thick in Norfolk in contrast to 200 feet in Bedford-shire. From Titchwell, on the north coast, its upper boundary extends south-south-east to Thetford and west of here its outcrop is at its widest. Three feet of greyish marls, containing the belemnite *Actinocamax plenus*, mark the base of its lowest zone which is charac-terized by the lamellibranch *Inoceramus labiatus*. This zone is comparatively thin and its outcrop narrow and

irregular. Immediately above the band of Belemnite Marls the *I. labiatus* Chalk is hard and nodular with a distinctive yellow colour. This horizon is a thinner equivalent of the Melbourn Rock of Bedfordshire and Cambridgeshire. The remainder of the zone of *I. labiatus* and the succeeding, thicker zone of *Terebratulina lata*, a small brachiopod, include a variety of chalk litho-logies. Black flint nodules occur along the bedding planes of the chalk in the upper part of the zone of *T. lata* and in the succeeding zone. The highest zone of the Turonian is named after the echinoid *Holaster planus*, which it contains. Again the lithology of the chalk is varied, and the bottom of the zone coincides with the base of the Chalk Rock which is the lowest unit of the Upper Chalk.

The Chalk Rock is a hard, sometimes nodular, pale yellow-brown rock which contains casts and moulds of a varied and distinctive invertebrate fauna. This fauna and the lithology indicate that it accumulated in shallow, current-disturbed water.

Senonian and Maastrichtian. East of the upper bound-ary of the Turonian the Upper Chalk underlies the whole of Norfolk. Most of this great thickness belongs to the Senonian stage, but on the north-east coast, there are exposures of Chalk referable to the succeeding Maas-trichtian stage. Most of the *Senonian Chalk* is soft and white, though it may be stained yellow-brown by water percolating from overlying limonitic sands and gravels. Flint occurs throughout the Upper Chalk as irregular nodules or in thin sheets. The large, vertical, cylindrical flint masses with a chalk core, known as paramoudras, which may be 2 or 3 feet in diameter and several feet long, are restricted to the chalk of the highest zone of the Senonian.

There is a great variety of well-preserved fossils in the Upper Chalk. Almost all invertebrate groups are present and, with the exception of ammonites, are common at various horizons. Fish remains may be frequent at some levels and the teeth and skeletal fragments of large, marine reptiles also occur. Six zones are recognized in the Senonian. The heart-shaped echinoids *Micraster cor-testudinarium* and *M. cor-anguinum* characterize the lowest zones which extend as far east as Burnham Overy and Sculthorpe, in the north, and nearly to Garboldis-ham, in the south of the county. The succeeding two zones are thinner than the *Micraster* Chalk and are named after the crinoids *Uintacrinus westphalicus* and *Marsupites testudinarius*. From just west of Wells, on the north coast, the upper boundary of the younger zone runs south-south-east to just west of Guist and Attleborough and thence south-eastward to Diss. The remaining zones of the Senonian are much thicker and both are named after belemnites. The older zone is that of *Gonioteuthis quadrata* and its boundary with the overlying zone of *Belemnitella mucronata* extends from just west of Morston, on the north coast, to about four miles west of Norwich. About seven miles south of Norwich the boundary apparently swings to the east and the Chalk is concealed by younger deposits.

The *Belemnitella mucronata* Chalk is about 250 feet thick, and is well exposed in various pits around Norwich and on the north coast between Weybourne and Sheringham where it outcrops at the base of the cliffs. This thick zone can be further subdivided on variations in its abundant invertebrate faunal assemblages.

The *post-Senonian Chalk* exposed at Trimingham and Mundesley resembles the Senonian Chalk in lithology and similarly it contains flint nodules, though these and its numerous fossils are commonly crushed and broken – presumably by the passage of ice during the Pleistocene. The Trimingham Chalk has a very rich and varied invertebrate fauna like part of that of the younger Chalk of north-west Germany. It is correlated with part of the belemnite zone of *Belemnella lanceolata* of the Maastrichtian stage, and is the only chalk of this age in Great Britain.

After the Chalk was deposited earth movements tilted and warped the accumulated sediments which formed a land area exposed to erosion until it was submerged again in early Caenozoic times.

CAENOZOIC

PALAEOCENE AND EOCENE

The earliest post-Cretaceous deposits occur at depth under eastern Norfolk. Resting on the Chalk beneath Great Yarmouth at −506 feet O.D. are 46 feet of greensands passing up into grey clays with lignite. They have usually been referred to the *Reading Beds*, but some of the greensand at the base contains green-coated flints and may be equivalent to the *Thanet Sands*. No fossils have been recorded, and the suggested correlation with formations known in the London Basin is based on similarities in lithology and stratigraphical position. The deposits are probably deltaic, marine at the base but becoming fluviatile towards the top.

Overlying the Reading Beds at Great Yarmouth is 310 feet of *London Clay*. At this point its base lies at −460 feet O.D., but the formation thins westward and comes to rest directly on the Chalk. At its western limit, about ten miles from the coast (fig. 2), its base has risen to approximately −100 feet O.D. It consists of brown, brown-grey, and grey clays, sometimes micaceous and sandy, with pyrites and courses of septaria, exactly like the same formation in the London Basin. No fossils are known, but there is little doubt that it is a marine deposit.

PLEISTOCENE

The Pleistocene deposits of Norfolk comprise an exceptionally complete and varied record of that period. The early Pleistocene is represented by the marine deposits of the Crags (shelly sands), and the later Pleistocene by glacial and inter-glacial deposits.

THE CRAGS

The Crag formation underlies almost all of Norfolk east of Norwich, and its western limit runs as a sinuous line from Weybourne to Diss (fig. 2). The base of the Crag, which rests either on the London Clay or the Chalk, is rather diversified. It rises to as much as +100 feet O.D. at its western margin, but in a depression trending north-east from South Burlingham towards Winterton it descends to depths of more than −150 feet O.D. A second, similar depression, separated from the first by an elevation under Limpenhoe, appears to run under Ellingham towards Thurlton. The thickness of the Crag formation approaches 200 feet towards the North Sea; it is largely controlled by the contours of its base.

The lithology exhibits considerable variation in detail. At the surface localities around Norwich the deposit consists of shell beds, sands, alternating sands and clays, clays, and gravels, all of which are stained yellow or brown by ferric iron compounds. Towards the east, at depth, it consists of shelly sands and silty and micaceous clays, which are also sometimes shelly; these are stained grey by ferrous iron compounds.

Only the *Upper Division* of the *Norwich Crag* and the *Weybourne Crag* are found at surface localities, but earlier deposits have recently been recognized at depth in east Norfolk. The Foraminifera of samples obtained from water-supply borings at Ludham have been examined, and in 1959 the Royal Society financed a boring at the same site to enable a comprehensive investigation of the pollen, Foraminifera, and Mollusca of this important sequence to be undertaken.

The Crag at Ludham rests on London Clay at −165 feet O.D. Between approximately −90 feet O.D. and the bottom the foraminiferal assemblages resemble those of the *Red* and *Scrobicularia Crags* of Suffolk. The lowest 50 feet most closely resembles the Butleyan Red Crag, and, like that deposit, it consists principally of coarse, shelly sands with occasional thin gravelly layers containing flint and phosphate (coprolitic) pebbles; there is no marked basement bed of large flints as there is where the Crag rests on the Chalk. The succeeding 25 feet more nearly resembles the Butleyan *Scrobicularia* Crag and there is an increasing proportion of clay in the sediment. Both the Foraminifera and the pollen contain Pliocene-relict forms and probably indicate an inter-glacial climate; no indication has so far been found of the cold episode known from the Neutral Farm horizon of the Butleyan Red Crag of Suffolk. The sediments were probably deposited as sub-littoral shell banks, the water becoming shallower as deposition proceeded.

Above −90 feet O.D., for approximately 20 feet, the deposit consists of grey silty clay and the foraminiferal assemblages become increasingly impoverished as a consequence either of ecological or climatic changes or both. The foraminiferal assemblages in the lower portion of this part of the sequence are comparable with those found in the *Lower Division* of the *Norwich Crag* in Suffolk. Pliocene-relict forms are no longer found amongst the Foraminifera, but inter-glacial conditions are still indicated, at least in the lower portion. There appears to be no justification for referring to this or any other clay bed in the Norfolk Crag succession as Chillesford Clay. Clay beds with similar lithological characteristics occur at several horizons in the succession. (The Chilles-

ford Crag of Suffolk, which contains a specialized, probably tidal-flat assemblage of Foraminifera, is difficult to correlate, but will possibly prove to be referable to the Lower Division of the Norwich Crag.)

At about −70 feet O.D., in the Ludham sequence, the foraminiferal assemblages become comparable with those obtained from the *Upper Division* of the *Norwich Crag* at surface localities in Norfolk. From −70 feet O.D. to −40 feet O.D., the sediment consists of grey shelly sand with layers of clay, and the Foraminifera indicate a climatic deterioration exactly similar to that found in the Bramerton section. Abnormal, distorted Foraminifera and Mollusca in the Bramerton sediments indicate deposition at the head of a bay subject to periodic influxes of fresh water.

Between −40 and −30 feet O.D. the sediment consists of grey clay. The Foraminifera indicate very cold, glacial conditions and a cold climate is also suggested by the pollen. No actual glacial deposits are present, but the degree of cold implies glaciers in Scotland and the north of England. Similar foraminiferal assemblages are found as limonitic casts at the top of the Bramerton section above the prominent clay bed.

The *Weybourne Crag* also contains a similar foraminiferal assemblage and identical climatic conditions are implied. There is, however, some question as to whether all the deposits which are attributed to the Weybourne Crag (because of the occurrence of the mollusc *Macoma balthica*) belong to the same horizon.

THE GLACIALS AND INTER-GLACIALS

Cromerian Inter-glacial. The *Cromer Forest Bed Series* of the Norfolk coast has long been renowned for the wealth of mammalian remains it contains. It consists of a *Lower Freshwater Bed*, which is only infrequently seen, a middle *Estuarine Bed* containing the bones and teeth of large mammals, and an *Upper Freshwater Bed* which can usually be seen outcropping at the base of the cliff at West Runton.

Pollen analysis of the Upper Freshwater Bed has shown that a sequence of climatic changes occurred during its accumulation. This sequence comprises a lower, boreal, coniferous phase (birch and pine), a middle, temperate, mixed oak forest phase (elm, oak, alder, lime, and hazel), and an upper, boreal, coniferous phase (pine and birch). Such a sequence of climatic changes is characteristic of the inter-glacials of the later Pleistocene and this is called the Cromerian Inter-glacial. The flora of this inter-glacial is characterized by the presence of the water-fern *Azolla filiculoides* and the absence of exotic Pliocene elements. It differs from subsequent inter-glacial successions in various ways, but principally in the low representation of hazel and the absence of silver fir.

It is not yet clear whether the whole of the Cromer Forest Bed Series belongs to the Cromerian Inter-glacial, neither is it certain that the Weybourne Crag represents the glacial phase immediately preceding it.

Following the Upper Freshwater Bed and leading on to the Lowestoft Glaciation is the *Arctic Freshwater Bed* which contains remains of arctic birch and arctic willow.

Lowestoft Glaciation. A short marine episode, represented by the *Leda myalis Bed*, preceded the arrival of the glaciers of the Lowestoft Glaciation. It contains an arctic marine fauna of molluscs and Foraminifera, together with a flood of derived Jurassic, Cretaceous, and early Pleistocene Foraminifera.

The Cromer Advance (fig. 3a) brought glacier ice over north-east Norfolk, moving south-eastwards and depositing the *Cromer Till* series of the coastal sections and the *Norwich Brickearth* inland. The erratics include rhomb porphyry from the Oslo region of Norway, but much of the matrix of these two deposits is of more local origin.

On the coast very large erratics of Chalk which were caught up in the Cromer Advance can be seen today in the cliffs between West Runton and Mundesley. Also in these cliffs can be seen gigantic contortions which extend towards Fakenham, and which were possibly caused by the interaction of the ice of the Cromer and Lowestoft Advances.

The Lowestoft Advance (fig. 3b) brought glacier ice over the whole of the remainder of Norfolk. Initially, during the first stage, the ice was travelling south-eastwards parallel to the Cromer Advance, but subsequently, during the second stage, it turned north-eastwards to occupy much of the region previously covered by the Cromer Advance. This change in direction is recorded

as a change in the orientation of the stones in the *Lowestoft Till*. The Lowestoft Till of Norfolk exhibits two facies. Both are chalky boulder clays but, owing to the oblique course of the glacier ice across the Jurassic and Cretaceous outcrops, the matrix of the more southerly facies is predominantly blue Kimmeridge Clay, whereas the more northerly is a much more chalky, grey clay. The boundary between the two facies runs approximately east–west from New Buckenham towards Lowestoft, but is deflected north-eastwards from the Waveney valley towards Ormesby, probably as a consequence of the direction of movement of the ice during the second stage of this advance.

Sub-glacial channels, eroded erratically to depths as great as —350 feet O.D. are a feature of the Lowestoft Advance. An example at Trowse, near Norwich, extends to —80 feet O.D. They are thought to have been excavated by sub-glacial meltwater streams operating under pressure, and subsequently filled by glacial deposits. The resultant valleys must originally have had a similar appearance to the tunnel valleys of Denmark, but their former topographic expression has long since been destroyed, although they are frequently followed by present-day river valleys, such as the Yare and Waveney. The occurrence of low-lying Lowestoft Till in these channels is not evidence of inter-glacial erosion between the Cromer and Lowestoft Advances.

The *Corton Beds*, which intervene between the glacial tills of the Cromer and Lowestoft Advances in eastern Norfolk, contain a marine fauna. This has been claimed as an indigenous fauna indicating inter-glacial conditions. It is unlikely that this interpretation can be upheld. Its microfauna, which exhibits considerable similarities to that of the *Leda myalis Bed*, contains an abundance of derived Jurassic and Cretaceous specimens; it also contains many warm indicators from the early Pleistocene which could easily have been derived from the extended Crag succession, now known in eastern Norfolk, by sub-glacial streams eroding to depth and upwelling at the margin of the Lowestoft Till glacier. It is possible that a proportion of the cold indicators may be indigenous, which would suggest that the glaciers of both the Cromer and Lowestoft Advances were advancing into a pro-glacial sea. This would be consistent with the lack of disturbance frequently observed where the tills

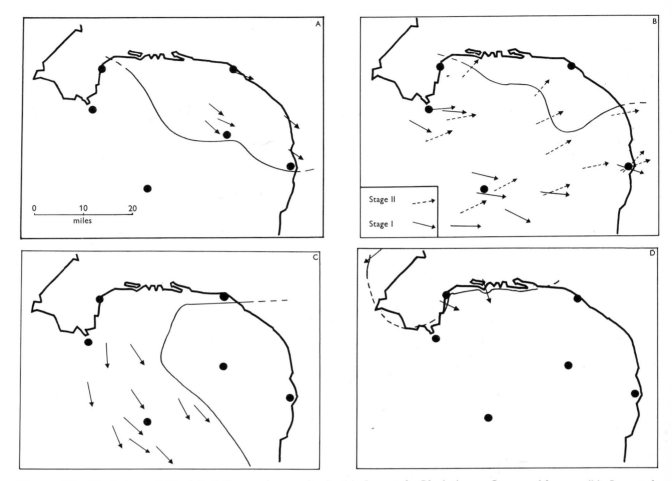

Fig. 3 *The Glaciations of Norfolk (after various authors):* (a) *Lowestoft Glaciation – Cromer Advance;* (b) *Lowestoft Glaciation – Lowestoft Advance;* (c) *Gipping Glaciation – Gipping Advance;* (d) *Last (Hunstanton) Glaciation – Hunstanton Advance*

of these glaciers are found resting on unconsolidated sands.

Hoxnian Inter-glacial. The Nar valley inter-glacial deposits, which occur between tills attributed to the Lowestoft and Gipping Glaciations in west Norfolk, consist of the *Nar Valley Freshwater Beds* below and the *Nar Valley Clay* above. Pollen analysis of these deposits has shown that the freshwater beds cover a period of climatic amelioration from park tundra to mixed oak forest conditions, with a climate at least as warm as the present day. The estuarine clay indicates a marine transgression (inter-glacial eustatic rise in sea-level) following

the climatic optimum and contains the first indications of the climatic deterioration leading to the next glaciation.

Similar vegetational successions are also known from lacustrine deposits of the same interglacial at Hoxne and St Cross South Elmham on the Suffolk side of the Waveney valley. All these successions differ from the Cromerian Inter-glacial in the abundance of hazel and the presence of silver fir.

Gipping Glaciation. The Gipping Advance (fig. 3c) only extended as far south as the Cromer-Holt ridge in north-east Norfolk, but it spread south across western Norfolk into Suffolk. The ice of this advance travelled southwards, principally along the strike of the Cretaceous rocks, and the *Gipping Till* which it deposited is a chalky boulder clay. It underlies large stretches of heath in Breckland but is often decalcified or podzolized.

The Kelling and Salthouse outwash plains near Holt, the Blakeney ridge, and the kames and kame terraces of the Glaven valley are probably the products of outwash from the Gipping glacier at its margin in north-east Norfolk. Other outwash deposits are known east of its supposed margin in mid-Norfolk, but these have not yet been adequately investigated. In the Waveney valley there is a fluvio-glacial terrace extending eastwards from Harleston towards Beccles, which is probably related to the Gipping Advance. In the lower levels of the deposits of this terrace remains of mammoth, woolly rhinoceros, Irish elk, and arctic plants have been found.

Ipswichian Inter-glacial.   No deposits representing this period are definitely known from Norfolk, although the marine March Gravels of neighbouring Cambridgeshire are generally attributed to it. It is possible that the so-called raised beach at Morston is referable to this period. It contains no fauna, but it is composed of grey flints, thought to be derived from the Gipping Advance, and it is covered by the succeeding Hunstanton Till. Another deposit possibly dating from this period is the *Mundesley Freshwater Bed.*

Last (Hunstanton) Glaciation.   The Hunstanton Advance (fig. 3d) only just reached the north coast of Norfolk. It deposited the *Hunstanton Till,* a reddish-brown boulder clay, containing erratics from the Cheviot Hills, which very closely resembles the Hessle Till of Yorkshire and Lincolnshire. The Hunstanton Park esker was deposited near the margin of this ice. The period of the Hunstanton Advance was the last occasion on which west–east through-drainage is likely to have been carried by the Little Ouse-Waveney valley.

The production of peri-glacial features, such as stone polygons and stone stripes, was widespread in Norfolk during the Hunstanton Glaciation. Some of the best examples occur in Breckland.

Late glacial deposits occur at Lopham Little Fen and possibly also at Old Buckenham Mere.

HOLOCENE

The post-glacial period in Norfolk has seen the accumulation of the deposits of Fenland and Broadland, and the evolution of the present coastal features.

The Fenland deposits consist of peat beds which interfinger with marine silts and clays towards the Wash. There have been two principal periods of marine transgression which correspond broadly, but not exactly, with the Lower and Upper Clay transgressions of Broadland. The first transgression occurred towards the end of the Neolithic period (c. 2000 to 1500 B.C.) and the second during Romano-British times (c. A.D. 0 to 500).

A consideration of the deposits of Broadland and the evolution of the present coastal features will be found elsewhere.

REFERENCES

GENERAL

1. BOSWELL, P.G.H. (1935). 'Geology of the Norwich District.' Part VII of a scientific survey of Norwich and District. Appendix to *Rep. Brit. Assoc. Adv. Sci. for 1935* (Norwich), pp. 49–58.

2. CHATWIN, C.P. (1954). *British Regional Geology: East Anglia and Adjoining Areas.* Third Edition, v and 99 pp., 8 pls.

MESOZOIC

3. BLACK, M. (1953). 'The Constitution of the Chalk.' *Proc. Geol. Soc. Lond.,* No. 1499, pp. lxxxi-ii, lxxxv-vi.

4. Director's Report (1959). *Summ. Prog. Geol. Surv. for 1958,* p. 8.

5. HANCOCK, J.M. (1957). 'The Cretaceous Setting of East Anglia.' *Paramoudra Club Bull.,* No. 7, pp. 3–6.

6. HEY, R.W. and PERRIN, R.M.S. (1960). *The Geology and Soils of Cambridgeshire.* Cambridge Nat. Hist. Soc., v and 52 pp.

7. KENT, P.E. (1947). 'A Deep Boring at North Creake, Norfolk.' *Geol. Mag.,* **84,** 2–18.

8. PRINGLE, J. (1923). 'On the Concealed Mesozoic Rocks in South-West Norfolk.' *Summ. Prog. Geol. Surv. for 1922,* pp. 126–39.

9. RASTALL, R.H. (1930). 'The Petrography of the Hunstanton Red Rock.' *Geol. Mag.*, **67**, 436–58.

10. SCHWARZACHER, W. (1953). 'Cross-bedding and Grain Size in the Lower Cretaceous Sands of East Anglia.' *Geol. Mag.*, **90**, 322–30.

CAENOZOIC

11. BADEN-POWELL, D.F.W. (1948). 'The Chalky Boulder Clays of Norfolk and Suffolk.' *Geol. Mag.*, **85**, 279–96.

12. BADEN-POWELL, D.F.W. (1950). 'Field Meeting in the Lowestoft District.' *Proc. Geol. Assoc.*, **61**, 191–7.

13. BADEN-POWELL, D.F.W. and WEST, R.G. (1960). 'Summer Field Meeting in East Anglia.' *Proc. Geol. Assoc.*, **71**, 61–80.

14. DOWNING, R.A. (1959). 'A Note on the Crag in Norfolk.' *Geol. Mag.*, **96**, 81–6.

15. FUNNELL, B.M. (1958). 'The Yare Valley "Buried Glacial Channel".' *Trans. Nfk. & Norwich Nat. Soc.*, **18**, pt. 7, 10–14.

16. STEVENS, L.A. (1960). 'The Interglacial of the Nar Valley, Norfolk.' *Quart. J. Geol. Soc. Lond.*, **115**, 291–312.

17. STRAW, A. (1960). 'The Limit of the "Last" Glaciation in North Norfolk.' *Proc. Geol. Assoc.*, **71**, 379–90.

18. SUGGATE, R.P. and WEST, R.G. (1959). 'On the Extent of the Last Glaciation in Eastern England.' *Proc. Roy. Soc. Lond.*, Ser. B, **150**, pp. 263–83.

19. TALLANTIRE, P.A. (1953). 'Studies in the Post-glacial History of British Vegetation XIII. Lopham Little Fen, a Late-glacial Site in Central East Anglia.' *J. Ecol.*, **41**, No. 2, 361–73.

20. TALLANTIRE, P.A. (1954). 'Old Buckenham Mere. Data for the Study of Post-glacial History: XIII.' *New Phytol.*, **53**, No. 1, 131–9.

21. WATT, A.S. (1955). 'Stone Stripes in Breckland, Norfolk.' *Geol. Mag.*, **92**, 173–4, pl. viii, figs. 1, 2.

22. WEST, R.G. (1957). 'Notes on a Preliminary Map of some features of the Drift Topography around Holt and Cromer, Norfolk.' *Trans. Nfk. & Norwich Nat. Soc.*, **18**, pt. 5, 24–9.

23. WEST, R.G. (1958). 'The Pleistocene Epoch in East Anglia.' *J. Glaciol.*, **3**, 211–16.

24. WEST, R.G. (1960). 'The Ice Age.' *Adv. Sci.*, No. 64, pp. 428–40.

25. WEST, R.G. and DONNER, J.J. (1956). 'The Glaciations of East Anglia and the East Midlands: a Differentiation based on Stone Orientation Measurements of the Tills.' *Quart. J. Geol. Soc. Lond.*, **112**, 69–91.

26. WEST, R.G. and DONNER, J.J. (1958). 'A Note on Pleistocene Frost Structures in the cliff section at Bacton, Norfolk.' *Trans. Nfk. & Norwich Nat. Soc.*, **18**, pt. 7, 8–9.

physiography
J. A. STEERS

A GLANCE at a map of Norfolk suggests that it is flat and uninteresting; a quick journey across the county shows that there is much variety in the scenery, and a little study soon emphasizes that the problems involved in explaining the landscape are far from simple.

The previous chapter has shown that the rocks range from the Upper Jurassic to the most recent, and also that, excluding the Fen deposits, the age of the rocks decreases from west to east. It is therefore convenient, as a first step only, to survey the country from the Wash eastwards. Facing the Fenland there is a narrow outcrop of the Kimmeridge Clay which rises but little from the Fens, and is backed by a low escarpment of the Lower Greensand, a feature fairly well developed near Downham Market. Farther north, alongside the Wash, the outcrop is wider, and includes the Carstone, the Snettisham Clay, and the Sandringham Sands. The sands give rise to pleasant heathy country near Wolferton and Sandringham. The old cliff line is conspicuous, and is varied by small, steep valleys. Locally the Snettisham Clay has been used for brick-making, but it has comparatively little effect on the scenery. The Carstone is seen at its best in the cliffs and foreshore at Hunstanton. The rock is locally used as a building stone.

There is a discontinuous and narrow belt of the Gault Clay between the Lower Greensand and the Chalk, but it has an insignificant effect on the scenery, apart from the local and spectacular occurrence in the cliffs at Hunstanton where it is represented by the Red Rock.

The Chalk underlies most of Norfolk, but only in the west does it appear as a surface rock; partly as a minor scarp, and partly, in the Breckland (q.v.), as a low and dissected plateau. At Ringstead the Chalk has been cut by a glacial overflow valley and downland-like characteristics prevail. East of a line through Docking, Little Massingham, Castle Acre, Swaffham, and Thetford the Chalk is buried beneath glacial deposits, and these largely determine the scenery, except in some of the valleys where the Chalk is exposed. But despite the surface details referable to the overlying beds the Chalk is mainly responsible for High Norfolk and High Suffolk. Roughly east of a north–south line through Norwich the dip of the Chalk increases, and in the eastern part of the county it is below sea-level. It reaches a maximum height (in Norfolk) of about 250 feet near Swaffham, whereas at Great Yarmouth it is 506 feet below sea-level.

In the eastern part of the county, and continuing into Suffolk, the Crags, shelly sands and gravels, overlie the Chalk and form the basement on which the superficial deposits rest. From the point of view of scenery, there is little to distinguish Crag deposits from glacial sands and gravels. The former may be more regularly bedded, and locally indurated, but both give rise to heathy country, seen perhaps at its best in Suffolk behind Dunwich and Southwold.

The cover of glacial beds has already been described in terms of origin. It remains to emphasize their role in producing the present landscape. Over much of High Norfolk, a flat plateau-like area varying between 150 and 200 feet, and falling to 50 feet near the Broadland and the Waveney, the boulder clay is spread as a thick layer in which the streams have cut small valleys.

It was originally forest-covered, and the soils are heavy and tenacious. The best development of this type of country is between Broadland and Breckland. To the

J.A. STEERS is Professor of Geography in the University of Cambridge

north-west it extends and rises somewhat in height. It terminates northwards in the area dominated by the Cromer Ridge. Most of the country is arable.

Westwards the boulder clay lightens in texture and gives place in north-western Norfolk to a sandy area, the average altitude of which is about 200 feet. The sands represent a local facies of the boulder clay. Up to the beginning of the eighteenth century it was a region of desolate heaths and commons, but as a result of the improvements made by Coke and Townshend it has become one of the famous agricultural areas, not only of Britain, but of the world. It was Townshend who first gave it the name 'Good Sands' region – underneath the sandy cover he exploited a rich marl which gave the great increase in fertility.

There is also a comparable change on the east of the boulder-clay country. In north-east Norfolk, with which may be included the Hundreds of Flegg, the Crags come in between the Chalk and the glacial deposits. The area includes Norwich, and the soils throughout are good and fertile, and it is often referred to as the loam region, since the best soils are loamy with associated sands and gravels. It is lower than the regions so far discussed, much of it is below the 50-foot contour. It passes gradually into the Broadland.

Thus we may think simply of : (1) the heathy and

Fig. 1   *Cromer Moraine near Cromer*

broken country of the western Greensand belt; (2) the narrow Chalk outcrop; (3) the sandy region, now of great agricultural significance; (4) the higher and heavier boulder-clay land in the centre, and extending beyond the county boundary into Suffolk; (5) the loam region falling to the Broadland of the east and north-east.

But such a simplified scheme omits some of the most interesting regions – the Breckland, the Broads, the coast, and the local, but often extensive, features of glacial origin such as the Cromer Ridge.

Since we have mentioned the general distribution of the flat-lying glacial deposits, we may now turn to the more conspicuous features produced by the ice. The best known is the moraine landscape behind Cromer and Sheringham. Viewed from the cliff-top the 'moraine' appears as a steep-sided ridge facing north, extending almost to the river Glaven in the west, and beyond Cromer to the east. Part of the abrupt north face suggests an ice-contact slope and part possibly deposition in an ice-ponded lake. The ridge is composed of sands and gravels (no attempt is made here to discuss their stratigraphy) including the well-known cannon-shot gravel. Southwards the ridge falls more gradually. Kelling Heath and Salthouse Heath are true outwash plains with very gradual slope, and composed of bedded sand and gravels. Associated with them are some prominent gravel ridges of which the Blakeney 'esker' is the most conspicuous. The most recent description of it suggests that it is perhaps a terminal moraine rather than an esker. Similar, but smaller, gravel ridges diversify the coastal area near Stiffkey and Wells.

The abrupt north side of the Cromer Ridge is, especially in the western part, furrowed by small valleys, and there are a few on the south side where it is steeper than normal. They are all erosion features and may have originated under peri-glacial conditions by spring-sapping at the junction of the permeable sands and gravels of the ridge with the underlying impermeable drift. Associated with the ridge-front are more conspicuous hills – Skelding, Beeston, and Muckleburgh. The last is possibly a kame, and the two former may be remnants of a push-moraine. The whole region is one of beauty and interest, and necessitates much detailed work before any final answer to its many problems can be given.

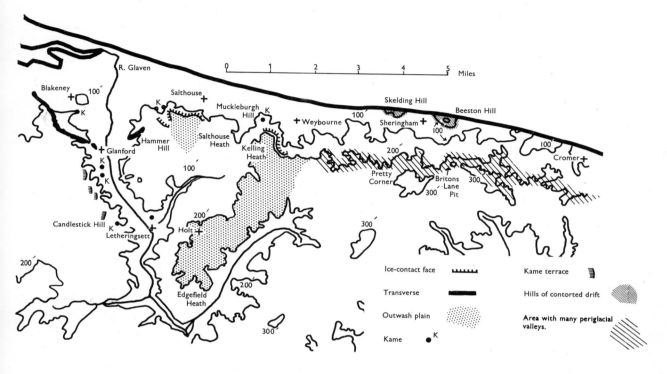

Fig. 2 *Drift Topography of the Cromer-Holt Area* *After West*

The Cromer Ridge is not only the most prominent glacial feature in Norfolk, but also forms the highest ground in the county. But many minor sand and gravel ridges occur, especially in the western parts of the county. We may perhaps regard them as marginal ridges to an ice-sheet, but it is not possible to tie them into the glacial sequence with any precision. Those near Crimplesham and Stoke Ferry, or those near Massingham and Castle Acre suggest a kame-like origin. Burrow Hills make a conspicuous feature near the main road between Swaffham and Fakenham. They are in some ways similar to ridges in the Lin valley near Cambridge where Sparks's recent work has overset older ideas. Whatever the origin of all these features, they give considerable local variety to the scenery, and are all too frequently overlooked in most accounts of it.

The Breckland is a region unique in these islands, and much of it is in Norfolk. The Chalk underlies all of it, and is thinly covered with sands and gravels of glacial origin. Since the Chalk is almost horizontal or gently undulating, the surface of the Breck forms a low plateau, dissected by fairly fast-flowing rivers, and on its western side merges almost imperceptibly into the Fenland. Facing the Fens, in the southern part of the Breck, there is a line of gravel-capped hills up to about 100 feet high.

At least two boulder clays occur in Breckland separated by sand, loess, and brickearth. Both boulder clays are very chalky, and leaching has left the insoluble material on the surface, thus producing a sandy soil. There is a fair amount of variation in the soil, but the differences are chemical rather than physical. Podzols are found in all stages of development, especially in the valleys of the Lark and Little Ouse, and also facing the Fens. At one time boulder clay was locally spread over mobile sands, and now the stones from this clay are sometimes found in layers at any depth down to about 10 feet, as a result of the erosion of the sand beneath. A feature still noticeable in the Breck is the sand

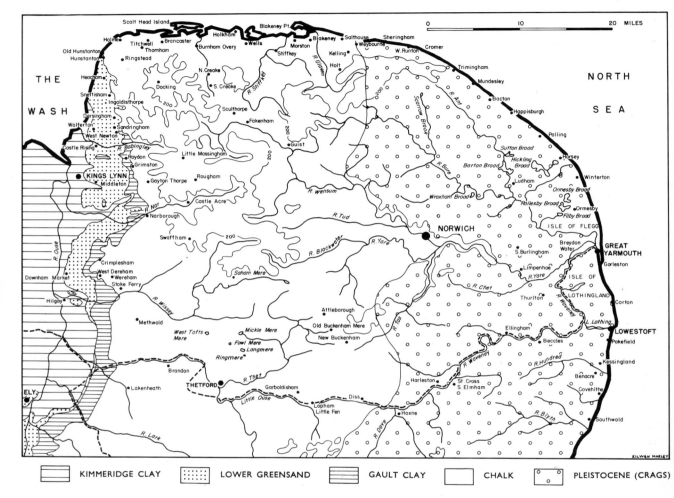

Fig. 3 *Sketch-Map of the Geology and Physiography of Norfolk*

blowing, especially in dry springs. In the past this phenomenon was widespread, and often serious. There was a destructive storm, lasting several days, in 1650, and W. Gilpin relates in 1769, perhaps with some exaggeration, the difficulty of travelling, even in a four-horse carriage, over sand-covered roads.

Watt believes that the sand is derived directly from the two boulder clays and the fluvio-glacial sands. Even today there are some parts of the Breck so thickly covered in mobile sand that true dunes occur. Watt has investigated the formation of blow-outs, and also the

general nature of wind erosion in the area. He distinguished two distinct types of wind erosion. The one is seen during windy days in March or April when sand is drifted from newly tilled fields; the other type is produced by cyclonic and often intense winds of local origin. These cause erosion and produce furrows and blow-outs. The first type affects the whole area. The whirlwinds which make the blow-outs have considerable lifting power, but they show no relation to topography, soil, or vegetation. Moreover, unlike what was frequently believed to be common in coastal dunes, no blow-out in the Breck has ever been shown to have had any relation to rabbit activity. Blow-outs never form where there is a continuous plant cover, but where the vegetation is degenerate and patchy. Nevertheless, a blow-out once formed may widen sideways into ground closely covered with plants, and thus bring about further degeneration. Watt made certain measurements of this process between December 1931 and 1935, and found in three separate blow-outs the total retreat was 25, 25, and 36 inches, or an average of 7.2 inches a year. An analysis of the sand shows that it is distinctly more angular than that found in dunes at Scolt Head Island, and also there is a greater range of particle size in Breck sands in the fraction passing the 0.5 mm. sieve. Both these factors allow of closer packing and binding than is the case in coastal dunes.

Blow-outs vary a good deal in size, depth, and age. On Lakenheath Warren small ones up to 20 feet in depth are found inside a large one, more than half a mile broad; their axes trend south-west to north-east. In 1668 Thomas Wright recorded that ' . . . these wonderful sands . . . first broke prison', and that some thirty or forty years earlier they had reached, and partly buried, the village of Santon Downham.

The interrelation of plant distribution and physiography is beautifully shown in another feature of the Breck. Parallel strips of *Calluna* were often noted before the Second World War. In the war the soft sandy and calcareous soil was taken away from one such area, and subsequent erosion revealed 'low ridges each about 5½ yards wide, consisting of hard compact boulder clay with numerous flints aggregated towards the middle line. The ridges were separated from each other by shallow furrows about 3½ yards wide of softer more sandy calcareous material with flints scattered on the surface.' These stone stripes are now a recognized feature of the Breck and have been effectively revealed by air photography. Now that their general nature is recognized it is easy to trace them in many places. They are fossil stone stripes, and were produced when the Breck area was undergoing peri-glacial conditions.

The meres of Breckland are interesting, and they occur in two shallow valleys – with the Devil's Punch Bowl, Fowlmere, Home Mere, the Wretham Park meres and Mickle Mere in one, and Langmere and Ringmere in the other. The small meres are simple in outline, but some have been altered in shape by man. Many small ponds and swallow-holes also occur, the swallow-holes being embryo meres which may have originated as sandpipes or by subsidence. It appears more likely, since the boulder clay in which they are situated is decalcified, that they were formed by solution. There are several hollows near Roudham Junction. The boundary of the boulder clay and chalk was near them when they were formed, but erosion has shifted the boundary upstream, eliminating the clay from the hollows and fostering solution. It is now usually assumed that the meres are filled by a rise in the saturation level – the rise and fall in the meres reflecting, to some extent, fluctuations of the water-level in the subsoil. Rainfall is ultimately the determining factor. These hollows are post-glacial and are still being formed.

Broadland is another distinct region of East Anglia, and most of it lies within Norfolk. Long arms of alluvium extend up the valleys of the Bure, Yare, Waveney, and their tributaries. These areas form low-lying ground, some still marshy, and much reclaimed. The higher ground enclosing the valleys forms a low plateau, almost entirely in the loam regions of Flegg and north-eastern Norfolk (*q.v.*). The drained alluvium affords good grazing ground, and is a valuable adjunct to the upland farms.

J.K. St Joseph. Crown Copyright Reserved

Fig. 4 *Barton Broad showing balks*

It is an extraordinary fact that the origin of the Broads, perhaps the best-known lakes in Britain, was not understood properly until a few years ago. Samuel Woodward in 1834 and H.B. Woodward in 1881, had suspected the artificial origin of Barton and Hickling Broads; and J.N. Jennings in 1952 also considered that they might be man-made, but the final answer that they represent the sites of former great excavations for peat, came later from Dr Lambert who was working in close collaboration with Jennings.

There are roughly three types of broad, as far as appearance is concerned. All lie in valleys which still find their outlet through Breydon Water to Yarmouth Haven. Breydon Water is entirely natural and is the unfilled part of an estuary. It is tidal, and is gradually contracting through the encroachment of vegetation and the deposition of fine water-borne material. Fritton and Flixton lie in side valleys and were formerly explained by the deposition of alluvium in the main river causing dams. They, like all the Broads except Breydon Water, are now regarded as having originated as peat-cuttings in medieval times.

Until this was realized, the usually accepted views of the origin of the Broads were those of J.W. Gregory who suggested that those around Wroxham were all that remained of an open estuary which had been partially filled by delta-like sedimentation that had isolated small lake-like expanses. But this and any other early explanations did not take account either of the sequence of deposits in the valleys, or of the full significance of the ecological factors at work in the area. Moreover, the archaeological and historical evidence had not been assessed in relation to the origin of the lakes.

Apart from local developments, the general sequence of deposits in the valleys is as follows: (1) A compact Basal Peat in an incised channel cut in the valley floors and corresponding to Zones V, VI, and Early VII of the British post-glacial forest history: it may begin earlier in deeper parts; (2) a thin lower clay, penetrated by reed growth, and also confined to the incised channel. It may represent the landward facies of an estuarine transgression; (3) a Middle Peat spreading over the whole width of the valley: it corresponds with the top of Zone VII and Transition Zone VII–VIII; (4) an Upper Clay, representing an extensive transgression, and mainly corresponding with Zone VIII. This was probably contemporaneous with the Romano-British transgression in the Fenland; (5) an Upper Peat (Zone VIII). Upstream the bottom two deposits are replaced by coarse detritus mud. Downstream there is presumably more Lower Clay, and the Upper Clay fills the whole width of the valley.

These deposits imply changes in the relative levels of land and sea, the peats representing relative standstills or possibly slight downward movements, and the clays incursions of the sea. But although they give us a fairly clear idea of the history of the valleys in which the Broads lie, they do not of themselves throw any light on their origin. When Jennings made his investigations, largely by means of bore-hole analysis, he was occasionally impressed by suggestions of rather abrupt ending of deposits in a given section. But his bores were put down to determine the sequence of deposits. Later Dr Lambert, in studying the ecology of the Broads, found it necessary to put down bores at very short distances apart. In doing so, she frequently found sudden lateral transitions between deep freshwater muds and vertical walls of peat, or peat and clay, which marked the limits of the basins of the Broads. Similarly, upstanding islands or ridges of peat with vertical sides were often found within the basins themselves. The stretches of undisturbed peaty deposits between the Broads and the rivers form the ronds, the explanation of which gave rise to so many difficulties in the past; the minor ridges clearly represent balks of uncut peat left standing between adjacent diggings.

Once it was realized by Dr Lambert that the Broads were the flooded parts of former peat excavations it was but natural that corroborative evidence should be sought. C.T. Smith examined the historical evidence: 'Much that would otherwise be inexplicable became clear in the light of the theory that the Norfolk Broads are ... flooded and abandoned turf pits. The transitions in nomenclature of land from turbary to fen and to water and marsh; the appearance of valuable fisheries in properties which had formerly included productive turbary; the frequent medieval references to turbary and turf-production in parishes which now contain broads but few or no deposits of peat; the absence of early references to the broads in place-names or documents; the existence

Ranworth and Malthouse Broads (Bure valley)

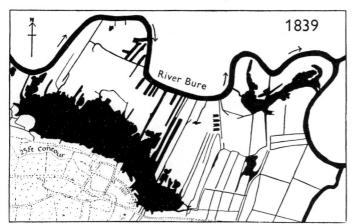

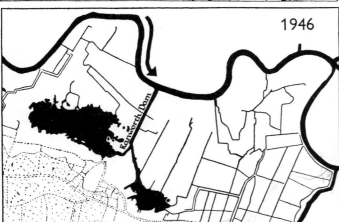

Surlingham Broad (Yare valley)

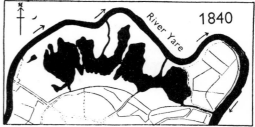

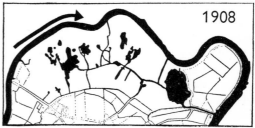

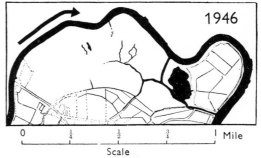

The diagrams for 1839 and 1840 are reduced from large-scale maps produced for each parish by the Tithe Redemption Commission during the survey of Britain which followed the Tithe Commutation Act of 1836 (these being generally more accurate in detail than the Ordnance Survey maps of comparable date, which are of much smaller scale)

The diagrams for 1907 and 1908 are reduced from direct tracings from the second edition of the six-inch Ordnance Survey maps

The diagrams for 1946 are based on tracings made from Air Ministry vertical aerial photographs

NOTE: In order to bring the series of diagrams to a more comparable basis, some slight adjustment has been necessary to standardize both the Tithe maps and the photograph tracings against ruling points on the Ordnance Survey maps – in the former case to counteract small discrepancies in surveying, and in the latter to compensate for tilt distortion

J.M. Lambert, Journ. Ecol., Vol. 36, 1951

Fig. 5   *The Shrinkage of the Broads*

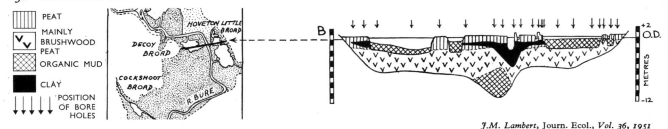

J.M. Lambert, Journ. Ecol., *Vol. 36, 1951*

Fig. 6   *Generalized Section in the Alluvium of the Middle Bure valley including Decoy and Hoveton Little Broads*
(*Vertical Exaggeration* × 20)

of turf-pits and even the extraction of timber from the horizon of brushwood peat at Martham all confirm the theory. . . .' The flooding of the pits to make the Broads almost certainly occurred in the fourteenth century; on the other hand there is little evidence of turf-cutting before the twelfth century. Are we to assume that at the end of the thirteenth century relative movements of land and sea made the flooding of the old peat diggings easy? Since the Broads have been lakes vegetation has formed around their margins and has gradually reduced their area. Some Broads have entirely disappeared, others are rapidly lessening in area. These changes can often be traced on tithe and other maps. Dr Lambert thinks that in many a critical phase has been reached, and that the shallowing now attained in most Broads allows a much quicker inward spreading of vegetation so that changes are taking place much more rapidly. This is a problem which may well have severe practical and economic repercussions in relation to the Broads as one of the main holiday resorts of the country.

The coast of Norfolk presents features unique in this country in at least two respects. Marshland is more fully developed than elsewhere, and the series of barrier beaches is unmatched. The cliffs between Weybourne and Happisburgh afford a magnificent section of glacial deposits and also exemplify the intricacies of erosion in rapidly varying beds.

The coast of the Wash is not unlike that of the marshland. Near the embouchure of the Ouse it is nothing else than the continuation of the Fenland, but farther north there is a transition to more marine conditions, and the old cliff can be traced inside the marshes near Wolferton and Snettisham. The Heacham river is deflected southwards by a spit of shingle showing that the littoral drift is southwards. North of Heacham the Lower Greensand

gradually rises, and at Hunstanton is the famous cliff section of the Carstone (Lower Greensand), the Red Rock (Gault), and the Lower Chalk at the top. The Carstone also forms a fine rock platform, and the disposition of the beds of the foreshore shows the two sets of joints at right angles to one another. These also appear in the cliff, where they are seen in vertical section. A study of the platform and cliffs illustrates the relation of structure and erosion in not very resistant rocks extremely well. The dip of the beds is to the east at a slight angle, although there is also a northerly component as can be seen if the cliff section is followed from south to north. At Old Hunstanton there is no longer any cliff at the back of the beach, but the former line can be traced all the way from Hunstanton to Weybourne behind the marshes; the main coast road roughly follows it.

The marshes are usually within a series of barrier beaches built by the waves. It is possible to distinguish several stages in the evolution of these beaches. The simplest types are seen off Stiffkey. There, on the wide sand flats, are small sand and shell ridges which remain mobile or semi-mobile for some time: later they may be destroyed or become stable. However, in their early stages they form low ridges behind which deposition of mud or fine material may take place. This is sooner or later colonized by *Salicornia* and other plants. The second stage is seen to great advantage at Thornham. On the west side of the harbour there is a crescent-shaped island of sand and shell, with a little shingle. It has existed for fifty years at least and has been mapped on several occasions. Storm waves override its mid-part, but at the two ends there is a considerable development of dune. Inside it, marsh has developed rapidly since the war: in 1939 there was but a thin spread of *Salicornia* and *Suaeda maritima* in the middle and east parts, and virtually bare sand flat with a little mud elsewhere. Farther west another ridge has developed and shows some signs of becoming stable.

A later stage occurs at Wells. The island, known as Lodge Marsh, on the east side of the harbour, has been altered a good deal by man. At one time there was a farm there. The island itself is complex in structure; there is a fair amount of shingle, and towards the north-east two or three lateral ridges.

Scolt Head Island is the most elaborate of the barriers. It is basically a long low ridge of shingle and sand bearing on its inner side a magnificent series of laterals, each of which was at one time the western end of the island. The island has grown from east to west, but that there have been many vicissitudes in its growth is made clear by the changes in the form of its western end, which has been mapped and recorded on many occasions since 1924. The island is but one part of a shingle complex. On the landward side of Norton Creek, the channel separating the island from the mainland, there are some old ridges which by their disposition imply a growth to the east. The ridges forming Brancaster golf links have also grown, and are still growing, to the east. The direction of beach drift on the outer parts of the coast is to the west, but if the position of the golf-course ridges is considered, it will be appreciated that the island protects these from all but north-westerly winds which provoke easterly beach drifting. Farther west, beyond the club house, the drift again is to the west, and careful examination of this part of the coast reveals an old beach now incorporated in the mainland.

East of Scolt the dunes at Holkham, now largely planted with conifers, rest on comparable beaches; Holkham Gap represents the space between two distinct units. The foreshore is wide and sandy, and the seaward slope extremely gentle. The dunes are prograding (i.e. growing seawards), and since the war a new ridge, a high tide island, has grown up, partly around masses of dannert wire which were dumped there.

Blakeney Point is different from all the other barriers. It is formed primarily of shingle which is far more abundant there than elsewhere. The shingle is continuous from the Far Point to Weybourne and beyond. The western part of Blakeney is fronted by wide sand flats and thus resembles the coast to the west. A mile or so to the east, at Cley, the shingle falls directly into the water, which, at Weybourne, is deep close inshore. It may well be that a shingle spit extending westward from Weybourne eventually joined itself to a barrier beach which formed in what is now the Headland area of Blakeney Point. On the other hand a continuously westward growing spit is a possibility. In either case, a series of laterals was thrown out. Those which form the Marrams are short and close together; the Hood stands apart, and those at the Headland and beyond are long and partly dune-covered, and resemble those at Scolt.

Within all these various types of barrier beach, salt-marshes have grown up. In parts reclamation has taken place, and the marshes are now valuable grazing land, bearing a relation to the upland farms similar to that of the Broadland marshes to the high ground near them. The Norfolk saltings have grown on sand flats, and are for the most part composed of firm and compact mud which may reach several feet in thickness. The early stages of marsh growth occur where algae spread over the surface and form a trap for seeds carried by the flowing tides and in other ways. Mud begins to settle in such places and also in sheltered spots, and gradually increases in amount as the plants colonize the initial patches and spread upwards and outwards. Creeks begin to form at an early stage, but at first are wide and rather formless; as the marsh develops they are more and more enclosed and gradually take on the familiar form seen in well-developed marshes. There is a close interrelation too, between the nature of the plant covering and the height and structure of the marsh (see pages 53 and 54).

The upward growth of marshes is mainly dependent upon the interaction of the vegetation and the silt and fine material brought in by the tides. Their rate of growth has been measured at Scolt, and varies with the nature of the plant covering and the number of times a marsh is covered by high waters. The rate of upward growth is fastest in those marshes which have already attained a close plant cover, over which the water spreads at most high tides.

The cliffs which extend from Weybourne to beyond Happisburgh have been shown in the previous article to be of great significance in elucidating the glacial sequence. Here it is relevant to call attention to their composition, ranging from strong clays with few pebbles

Fig. 7   *Cliffs east of Trimingham*

near Happisburgh to abundant sands and gravels with little clay near Cromer and Sheringham. At the eastern end of the cliffs the bedding is simple and often horizontal, so that the various beds yield to erosion just as would those in a normal sedimentary series. But in the Cromer area the beds are contorted and twisted, and complicated by great rafts of what may have been part of the sea-floor carried bodily forward by later movements of the ice and dumped on previously formed deposits. Since, too, the variation in lithology is great in this part of the cliffs, erosion both by the sea and land water draining out through the cliffs is not only serious, but leads to cliff falls, the formation of gullies, and short-lived stacks in some of the harder bands near sea-level. The beach is steeper than off the marshland coast, and usually there are masses of coarse flints on its upper part. At Sheringham there is an offshore platform cut in the Chalk. Eastwards of Sheringham the direction of littoral drift is to the east.

Beyond Happisburgh the cliffs soon disappear, and give place to the single line of dunes that fringes the coast near Eccles, Palling, and Horsey. Since the great floods of 1938 and 1953 these dunes have been protected by a sea wall which is often buried in the sand. The Hundred river used to run out at Horsey, and the coast there has always been liable to flooding. A little farther south-east erosion gives place to accretion, and the interesting foreland of Winterton Ness has been built, partly in front of the line of cliffs which reach the sea at Hemsby. Here begins another line of low and easily destroyed cliffs. At Caister the high ground gives place to the former wide estuary of the Yare, Bure, and Waveney. Yarmouth has been built on a sandbank which was thrown up by wave action across the mouth, so that for a time there was a northern entrance, Grubb's or Cockle Haven, near Caister, as well as the main entrance to the south. The northern entrance silted up and disappeared; the southern entrance became more and more deflected by the southward growing spit, and at one time (1347) extended to between Gunton and

Corton. The present harbour mouth of Yarmouth is within about a quarter of a mile of that made in the reign of the first Elizabeth. Since the fixing of the haven, the Denes, the name given to the spit, have widened and the fine beach at Yarmouth has grown at the expense of these both to north and south. When borings were made a few years ago for the grid pylons, it became clear from the deposits passed through that the sandbank has had a longer and more varied history than was formerly suspected.

It would be easy to extend this account of the physiography of Norfolk, but only two other features can be mentioned. The rivers fall into three groups. The first flows directly to the Great Ouse and the Wash down the scarp of the Chalk, and are probably Pliocene in age. They are obsequent streams. The second group (Burn, Stiffkey, Glaven) contains the minor streams associated with the Cromer Ridge and, therefore, of presumably very recent origin. The third group includes those flowing in a generally east or south-east direction to the North Sea. They are in one sense dip streams since they flow down the dip of the Chalk, but their history is more complicated as a result of glacial conditions. The subsequent evolution of the valleys is shown by their terraces which imply periods of aggradation following erosion. The terraces in the Yare stand at about 50 feet. On the Norfolk–Suffolk border is the interesting through valley of the Little Ouse and Waveney. These two rivers rise near Lopham Ford, and the valley in which they run is wide and open and unlike an ordinary river valley. The suggestion has been made that it is a glacial overflow.

The Fens have been omitted: they only fringe Norfolk and any adequate account would extend this paper too much. But one general point remains to be re-emphasized – how frequently in Norfolk the study of the physiography is closely interrelated with that of ecology. The connexion has been indicated briefly in the account of the coast and Breckland; it is just as emphatic in the Broads and the Fenland.

REFERENCES

In addition to those references listed on page 58 which are concerned in part with physiography, the following are of direct interest, and each contains a bibliography:

1. LAMBERT, J.M., JENNINGS, J.N., SMITH, C.T., GREEN, C., HUTCHINSON, J.N. (1960). *The Making of the Broads*. R.G.S., Research Series No. 3.

2. WATT, A.S. *Studies in Breckland Ecology*.

3. WATT, A.S. (1936). (i) 'Climate, Soil and Vegetation.' *J. Ecol.*, **24**, 17.

4. WATT, A.S. (1937). (ii) 'On the Origin and Development of Blow-outs.' *J. Ecol.*, **25**, 91.

5. SPARKS, B.W. (1957). 'The Evolution of the Relief of the Cam Valley.' *Geog. J.*, **123**, 188.

6. STEERS, J.A. (1942). 'The Physiography of East Anglia.' *Trans. Nfk. & Norwich Nat. Soc.*, Presidential Address.

7. STEERS, J.A. (1948). *The Sea Coast*. Cambridge. Chapters 9, 10, 12, 14.

8. STEERS, J.A. (1960). *Scolt Head Island*. Heffer.

9. MARR, J.E. (1913). 'The Meres of Breckland.' *Proc. Cambridge Phil. Soc.*, **17**, 58.

10. JONES, O.T. and LEWIS, W.V. (1941). 'Water Levels in Foulmere and other Breckland Meres.' *Geog. J.*, **97**, 158.

11. GREEN, C.T. (1961). 'East Anglian Coast-line Levels since Roman Times.', *Antiquity*, **35**, 21.

climate   A. T. GROVE

NORFOLK, lying on the east side of the British Isles and so farther from the Atlantic, has a more Continental climate than most of the country. Its winters are rather cool, its summers rather warm inland; mean annual rainfall, partly on account of the low relief, is only about 25 inches and skies are clearer than in the west.

Average monthly temperatures range over some 22°F.; a degree or two more than in most parts of England, and daily ranges of temperature are also relatively high, partly on account of the clear skies. July and August are usually the warmest months. January has the lowest mean temperatures, but in many years such as 1956 February is colder.

The sea has a tempering effect on coastal climates, particularly well-marked in early summer when the surface temperature of the North Sea is only 50°F. At that season, onshore winds bring mists, called frets, to districts within a few miles of the coast while the sun shines brightly farther inland. On fine days, with a few cumulus clouds high in the sky, a cool sea breeze springs up about midday and undercutting the warm air penetrates several miles inland, occasionally reaching as far as Norwich. As a result, mean daily maxima and minima for June in the Yarmouth area are 63° and 51°F. as compared with 68° and 49°F. in Breckland. Temperatures on the open stretches of Breckland are more extreme than elsewhere, partly because the dry sands are poor conductors of heat and therefore warm up and cool down quickly at the surface. Late frosts are frequent there, and when a cold air mass covers East Anglia, minimum temperatures in Breckland are known to sink 15°F. lower than on the coast.

Mean annual rainfall totals vary between about 23 inches on low ground and 27 inches at the highest levels, with rather rapid increases inland from the coast at Hunstanton to the hilly country near Sandringham, and from Sheringham to the ridge behind the town. Light showers are quite common with winds off the sea, and the north-east of the county experiences rain on some 200 days of the year, twenty or thirty more than most parts of lowland England.

In some years as little as 15 inches of rain may be recorded, in others as much as 35 inches. According to the monthly means, rain is fairly evenly distributed throughout the year, with a higher percentage falling in summer than in most parts of the country; much of the summer rain comes as heavy downpours associated with thunderstorms. The first six months of the year are generally drier and sunnier than the last six months; but occasionally, as in 1951, a wet spring is followed by a dry autumn. Mean monthly rainfall totals are very little guide to what can happen in any particular year.

The potential losses of water from the surface in the period April to September average 17 to 18 inches, as compared with rainfall totals of about 11 to 14 inches over the same period. During these months there is little or no surplus water percolating deep into the soil, and so additional supplies of water are required most years for optimum crop growth. The need is particularly great in summers following unusually dry winters, when the soil at depth has not been adequately recharged with water and crops are liable to suffer severely from drought. Irrigation is being used ever more widely, but in certain areas the large volumes of water used by farmers and gardeners from underground or piped supplies cause additional problems to other users.

A.T. GROVE is a Lecturer in the Department of Geography, University of Cambridge

Snow falls on low ground an average of seventeen days in the year, and is found lying there on about ten mornings. Showers of snow are commonly experienced on the coast at times when none falls inland, but it usually melts quickly.

Thick fogs with visibility less than 220 yards occur some five times a year, less frequently than in most parts of the country, and coastal districts are notably free from fog in the winter months.

Unusual weather conditions are as important in the climate of a place as the average conditions. In Norfolk, violent departures from the means are uncommon, but the storm of 25–26 August 1912 was quite exceptional, and it seems appropriate to mention it here because it indicates what can happen on occasion. More than 3 inches of rain fell over the whole of Norfolk, and a small area between Norwich and Brundall received more than 8 inches. In the low-lying parts of Norwich, flood-water reached higher than for 300 years, the level rising 15 inches above the mark for 1614 inscribed on a tablet in the wall of the city. Much damage was done to bridges, but the Broads absorbed a great deal of the flood-water and prevented serious flooding at Yarmouth.

	SPROWSTON, NORWICH* THIRTY YEAR MEANS			ORMESBY ST MICHAEL 1950–59†
	Rainfall Ins.	Sunshine Hrs.	Mean Temp. °F.	Evaporation Ins.
January	2·31	50·7	38·3	0·28
February	1·67	67·9	38·8	0·20
March	1·56	126·7	42·2	0·68
April	1·72	148·4	46·8	1·52
May	1·80	194·8	51·9	2·32
June	1·76	197·2	57·8	2·34
July	2·44	195·3	61·8	2·85
August	2·16	183·1	61·7	2·26
September	2·19	146·9	57·6	1·59
October	2·37	109·5	50·6	0·96
November	2·97	55·7	44·5	0·57
December	2·12	46·0	39·8	0·34

* By courtesy of Norfolk Agricultural Station.   † By courtesy of Great Yarmouth Waterworks Company.

soils   R. M. S. PERRIN

THE FIRST soil map of Norfolk was given by Young in his *General View of the Agriculture of the County of Norfolk* published in 1804. This map was of course an agricultural rather than a pedological map, but, although much generalized, it still has some validity as a rough guide to the agricultural soils of the county.

In an account of the soils and agriculture of Norfolk, Newman (1911) related the soils to the surface geology as shown on the Survey maps. He gave mechanical compositions and chemical analyses carried out by the conventional methods of agricultural chemistry in use at the time.

In 1933 the Cambridge University Farm Economics Branch published a soil texture map of the eastern counties. That part of the map which shows the county of Norfolk and also Young's earlier map are reproduced in Mosby (1938), where the soils of the county are briefly considered in relation to land utilization.

Studies of the soils of the county from a pedological point of view have been mainly confined to the Breckland area (Watt 1936, 1937, 1938, 1940; Perrin 1955, 1957). The Soil Survey of England and Wales is at present mapping two one-inch sheets (173 and 174), which include some of the Norfolk Fens and Breckland.

In connexion with the production of a soil map of Europe by the Food and Agriculture Organization of the United Nations, C.A.H. Hodge and the author made a brief reconnaissance survey of East Anglia in 1957. The map of the county shown in fig. 3, which must be regarded as very generalized and tentative in character, is mainly based on that reconnaissance. Such generalized surveys unfortunately pose more problems than they solve: owing to the great complexity of the surface geology (which is far more intricate than would

appear from the one-inch geological maps), no really satisfactory account of the soils of the county will be possible until a very large amount of pedological research and detailed mapping have been completed or, for that matter, started.

THE FORMATION OF SOILS IN NORFOLK

In such a brief account it is possible to indicate the formation of soils in only the most general terms. With some important exceptions, however, the processes have been fairly similar to those in the adjacent county of Cambridgeshire where they have been discussed in a little more detail by Hey and Perrin (1960).

As a result of recent geological history, none of the land surfaces in the county are very old and some are extremely young. The influence of parent material on soil development is thus strong and the great variations in surface geology, coupled with differences in drainage conditions due to topography, give rise to a highly complex pattern of soils.

At the outset it is useful to make a distinction between soils formed on pre-Hunstanton deposits, where there has been time for climate to exert appreciable effects on weathering and soil-formation and those developed on surfaces and materials of post-glacial origin where climatic influence has been relatively unimportant. The latter soils are mainly confined to the Fen Basin, the coastal marshes and sand deposits, Broadland and the alluvial flats of major rivers, while the soils on pre-Hunstanton materials occupy the whole of the rest of the county.

R.M.S. PERRIN is Lecturer in Soil Science at the School of Agriculture, University of Cambridge

SOILS ON PRE-HUNSTANTON DEPOSITS

The oldest surfaces are probably to be found on the Norwich Brickearth, which in places has the appearance of a till-plain and is deeply weathered. However, even if these areas were never wholly covered by Lowestoft or Gipping ice, numerous patches of later drifts are found in the region and it seems very unlikely that soil-formation could have proceeded undisturbed since this material was first exposed.

In the broad belt of country lying between the Brickearth and the Fen Basin the majority of soils appear to be formed on parent materials wholly or partially derived from the Gipping Till or its outwash. Study of the surface soils in progress at present suggests that the Gipping ice brought a rather uniform sandy material, containing flints and other erratics, into north Norfolk, and that this became progressively mixed with debris from pre-existing solid and drift deposits as it passed south. Thus, on the Cretaceous sands one finds parent materials containing flints, quartzites, etc., in which the sand fractions appear to be in part of local, and in part of extraneous, origin.

In the area shown as Chalk on the geological maps soils are never derived from the Chalk itself but from sandy, or sometimes gravelly, drifts of very varying thickness which have locally assimilated considerable amounts of chalk. These drifts appear to represent deposits of Gipping Till or its outwash resting directly on a Chalk surface.

In the boulder clay region which stretches from north Norfolk down into Suffolk it seems that the Gipping ice passed over the high-lying remnants of the Lowestoft Till, which had been weathered in the Hoxnian Inter-glacial, incorporating increasing quantities of its debris as it progressed. Owing to the change in facies in the Lowestoft Till, referred to in the section on the Geology of the County on p. 27, the parent materials are sandy and, prior to decalcification, very calcareous in the north and become heavier and less calcareous in the south of Norfolk and especially in Suffolk. Even there, however, the soils are never as heavy and poorly drained as those found on the Jurassic Clays and the Gault in Cambridgeshire. The drift surface is very variable in detail and the Gipping material is locally very thin indeed, but its presence is indicated all through this area

by a loamy surface soil containing sand with a characteristic particle size distribution that could not possibly derive from weathering of the heavier till beneath. The evidence from the composition of the soils suggests that the Gipping ice may perhaps have travelled a little farther east than is suggested by Baden Powell (1948).

The Breckland is an area overlying Chalk from which the Lowestoft Till appears to have been largely eroded before the arrival of the Gipping ice-sheet. The latter here seems to have been carrying exceptionally sandy material (possibly in part derived from the Sandringham Sands and Carstone farther north) which became more or less mixed with the local Chalk. Leaching of this peculiar till has been especially easy due to the virtual absence of clay, and the resultant sandy residue, having already a mechanical composition similar to that of a blown sand, has been readily redistributed by wind.

Throughout the belt between the Brickearth and the Fen Basin soil-formation commenced during the Ipswichian Inter-glacial, perhaps of the order of 150,000 years ago. On sloping sites these soils were probably largely removed by solifluxion in the peri-glacial conditions associated with the Hunstanton Advance but in flat plateau areas the partly weathered material, although much disturbed by frost-heaving, probably survived in part. In post-glacial times soil-formation thus recommenced on disturbed inter-glacial soils on hill-tops and on deep spreads of solifluxion debris or 'head' on lower-slope sites. These lower-slope soils have therefore developed from pre-Hunstanton *materials* but on post-Hunstanton *surfaces*: one may therefore find relatively young soils on quite well-weathered parent materials.

Although the climate has varied considerably in post-glacial times it was probably sufficiently mild and humid for the dominance of mixed oak forest by about 4500 B.C. and has remained essentially so ever since. Apart from the very low-lying swampy areas and coastal marshes this forest probably covered all the county, although the botanical composition and density would have varied considerably according to the parent material and drainage conditions of the soil. At the present time the potential annual percolation rate varies from about 7 inches in the east to about 11 inches in High Norfolk. If we can assume that such percolation rates are not greatly different from the average value in post-glacial time, it implies that there has been a steady, but not rapid, removal of soluble salts, exchangeable cations, and calcium carbonate where it was present. The ability of the soil to resist the effects of this leaching depends on its texture and permeability, and its initial base status, particularly its content of calcium carbonate.

Non-calcareous parent materials. In free-draining conditions under the prevailing climate the development of the soil and the associated vegetation proceed together from the colonization of the bare parent material by pioneer species through *immature soils* to *brown forest soils* or *brown earths* under deciduous forest.* This final stage represents a fairly stable system in which the loss of soluble ions is partly offset by efficient re-cycling via the leaf litter and an active soil population. As will be seen from the soil map, these 'zonal' brown earths are widespread in the county on a variety of parent materials. Immature soils, on the other hand, are confined to sites where recent erosion has occurred or to freshly deposited parent materials such as sand dunes in the Breckland or on the coast (areas 11 and 4).

Where the parent material is specially light and permeable leaching is more effective and normal brown earths are replaced by more acid varieties showing incipient podzolization (*podzolic brown earths*) or in extreme cases by *humus podzols*. As would be anticipated, such soils are particularly common on deep non-calcareous sands in the Breckland, or over the Sandringham Sands (area 6) and on some glacial sands and gravels especially those of the Cromer Ridge and the Blakeney 'esker' (area 13). In East Anglia it seems probable that true podzols are confined to sites which have been colonized by heath vegetation following clearance of scrub oak by man in early times (Godwin 1944).

Where the parent material is heavier and less permeable (areas 15 and 17) slight impedance may produce gleying or rusty mottling in the subsoil (*brown earths with gleying*). On the heaviest materials of all (parts of area 17) brown earths are replaced by *surface-water gleys*.

On the flanks of river valleys or adjacent to extensive low-lying tracts such as the Fen Basin or Broadland,

* Some writers suggest restricting the latter designation to those soils which have been modified by a long history of cultivation, but this distinction is not generally accepted and in this country the two terms tend to be used synonymously.

there are often well-marked catenas in which the brown earths on well-drained sites pass laterally into brown earths with gleying then *ground-water gleys* and sometimes *peaty gleys* and *basin peats*. Such a sequence when seen in the county is not usually an example of a *soil association* on a constant parent material owing to the complexity of the surface drift pattern. For example, the freely drained brown earth might be on a light till or outwash, the imperfectly drained brown earth with gleying on 'head' and recent colluvium, and the poorly drained gley on alluvium.

The relationships discussed above are summarized diagrammatically in fig. 1.

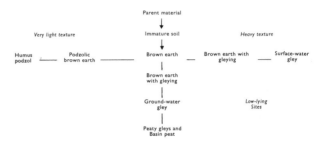

Fig. 1   *Soil-formation on non-calcareous parent material*
NOTE. The arrows represent a development sequence in time. Soil types joined by dotted lines are related but differ in texture of parent material or in topographical situation.

Similar considerations apply in the area of humus podzols which pass into *gley podzols*, etc., in low-lying areas (e.g. margins of area 6).

There is, of course, no primeval woodland left in Norfolk so that original brown forest soils have everywhere been modified to 'agricultural brown earths' in which cultivation has produced a fairly uniform topsoil sharply separated from the subsoil. Owing to oxidation of organic matter these cultivated topsoils have a colour nearer to that of the parent material and the structure is less stable. These changes tend to be reversed in plantations of deciduous trees or by a spell under grassland. Likewise, where podzols have been maintained in arable, liming and cultivation have tended to obliterate their original character and render them more akin to the 'agricultural brown earths'. The same can be said of gleyed soils; here improvement of aeration due to drainage has largely removed the signs of impedance in the cultivated topsoil, although mottling remains in the subsoil.

Calcareous Parent Materials. On calcareous parent materials the course of soil-formation is a little more complicated. *Immature calcareous soils* develop into shallow *rendzinas* and further decalcification and weathering produce deeper *brown calcareous soils* superficially resembling brown earths but containing much free carbonate (e.g. area 5). The two former soils are not common as the available time and rate of leaching have sufficed for these stages to be passed. Immature calcareous soils and rendzinas do occur locally but their existence is normally due to human disturbance or erosion on slopes.

Complete decalcification leads to the development of brown earths, this stage being reached more rapidly on materials of light texture and low carbonate content. On light parent materials the last stages of decalcification are often accompanied by the migration of fine clay to give a textural B horizon or clay pan, often of a rich reddish-brown colour (*brown earth with textural B horizon*). The removal of this clay renders very sandy topsoils liable to erosion by wind or to podzolization *in situ*: both these processes have occurred in the Breckland. The various development stages are summarized in fig. 2.

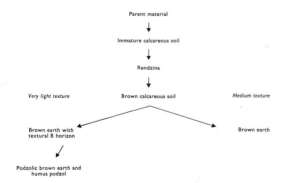

Fig. 2 *Soil-formation on calcareous parent materials*

Differences in texture or in topographic situation have effects similar to those noted for non-calcareous parent materials: for example brown calcareous soils may pass laterally into *brown calcareous soils with gleying* and calcareous surface-water or ground-water gleys.

Throughout the areas of soils formed on calcareous materials one finds that calcium carbonate lost by leaching has been more or less replaced either by the ploughing-up of thinly covered chalk or calcareous drift or by marling from deeper pits. Old pits in fields, often now represented by shallow depressions or tree-filled hollows, are a conspicuous feature of this part of the Norfolk landscape – the 'Good Sands' region of Young.

SOILS ON POST-GLACIAL MATERIALS AND SURFACES

Because of the youth of these soils the broad influence of climate already noted has had but little effect: they are dominated by the special conditions of parent material and topography and, in most cases, by considerable modification by man.

Basin Peats. Ponding back of fresh water by relative rise of sea-level in post-glacial times led to development in the Fen Basin, to a lesser extent in Broadland, and occasionally in river valleys, of basin peats from the partial decay under anaerobic conditions of aquatic, swamp, or carr vegetation. Most of these peats formed in calcareous ground water and are eutrophic *fen peats*, well humified and black in colour. There are, however, smaller patches of oligotrophic basin peats as well.

A peat may be regarded either as a special type of soil or as a geological deposit which is the potential parent material of a soil after drainage. In the Fens of Norfolk and Cambridgeshire, the basin peats have in fact all been intensively drained and cultivated from the seventeenth century onwards and the present soils are in a large measure artificial. Where the original peat was deep (area 9) good black fen still remains in spite of much shrinkage and oxidation. But seawards (area 3), and round the margins of the Basin and against the islands, the peat was never very deep and mineral matter is now being ploughed up in increasing quantities; such soils are locally known as 'skirty'.

In the upper reaches of the Broadland valleys, on the other hand, it would appear from the work of Lambert noted on p. 54, that much of the original peat has been dug and the small remaining areas have not been worth exploiting for agriculture intensively. Fresh peat is, of course, now forming in the Broads as they fill up.

Fen Silts and Coastal Marshes. Along the southern and south-eastern margins of the Wash, and in the coastal marshes of the north (area 1), silty or fine sandy mud is trapped at high tide by the saltmarsh vegetation (*Spartina, Salicornia,* etc.). The level gradually builds up until the surface is flooded only by the highest tides. A *marsh gley* develops, often under the valuable grazing grass *Puccinellia.* This soil is characterized by its high salinity and by an inky black gley horizon containing abundant ferrous sulphide.

Exclusion of the sea and partial drainage, as practised in the 'freshwater marshes' of the northern coast, removes the salt from the topsoil and leads to better aeration. With full-scale reclamation, which has been carried on at the south end of the Wash for centuries (area 2), efficient drainage is instituted and oxidation of sulphides proceeds to completion. Some of the calcite in the mud is dissolved and exchangeable calcium replaces the original sodium. The saline marsh gley is converted in a few years into a deep, freely drained soil of a characteristic pinkish-brown colour, still containing a little free calcium carbonate. At depths below those at which drains are effective, gleying and soluble salts may still be present. These valuable, largely artificial, soils on Fen Silt are not easy to classify: tentatively they are termed *brown warp soils.*

Blown Sands. Associated with the coastal marshes and on the east coast of the county there are tracts of more or less stabilized sand dunes (area 4). On these (and, as mentioned above, on dunes in the Breckland and on the Sandringham Sands) there are immature *raw sand soils.* Given a sufficient period of stability these soils trend towards podzolic brown earths, and under suitable vegetation, to humus podzols.

Recent Alluvium. Soils on recent alluvium occur in most of the river valleys and especially wide tracts are found in the lower reaches of the Broadland valleys. Such soils vary in their degree of development according to their situation on the alluvial flats. Adjacent to the stream, where drainage is better and where deposition is most abundant, there are usually found narrow strips of *immature alluvial soils* with little profile development. Under permanent pasture these soils gradually begin to

acquire the characteristics of brown earths, or brown calcareous soils, with slight gleying. Away from the stream in more poorly drained sites and occupying most of the alluvial deposit will be found ground-water gleys. Occasionally there may be small pockets of basin peat in hollows.

CLASSIFICATION OF THE SOILS

The provisional system of classification given is based as far as possible on that used by the Soil Survey in Cambridgeshire and west Norfolk so as to avoid confusion when the detailed one-inch maps appear.

Major Group	Sub group
Podzolized Soils Group	Humus podzol Gley podzol
Brown Earth Group*	Brown earth Podzolic brown earth Brown earth with textural B horizon Brown earth with gleying Brown warp soil
Calcareous Soils Group*	Rendzina Brown calcareous soil Brown calcareous soil with gleying
Gley Soils Group	Surface-water gley Ground-water gley Peaty gley
Organic Soils Group	Basin peat
Immature Soils Group	Immature calcareous soil Immature alluvial soil Raw sand soil

* Soils intermediate between typical brown earths and brown calcareous soils and containing only traces of free carbonates are arbitrarily assigned to the Brown Earth Group. The Calcareous Soils Group is reserved for those containing substantial quantities.

Key to the soil map

The different soil patterns are numbered 1–18 on the map. Each area is specified in terms of one or two, or occasionally more, dominant sub-groups and the parent materials are given in italics. Where other sub-groups are of significant extent they are mentioned in the notes.

The most widespread drainage conditions in each area are stated but it must be appreciated that they will locally be quite different. For example, in an area where freely drained brown earths predominate, brown earths with gleying and ground-water gleys will be expected in stream and river valleys.

The tentative character of the map must be strongly emphasized.

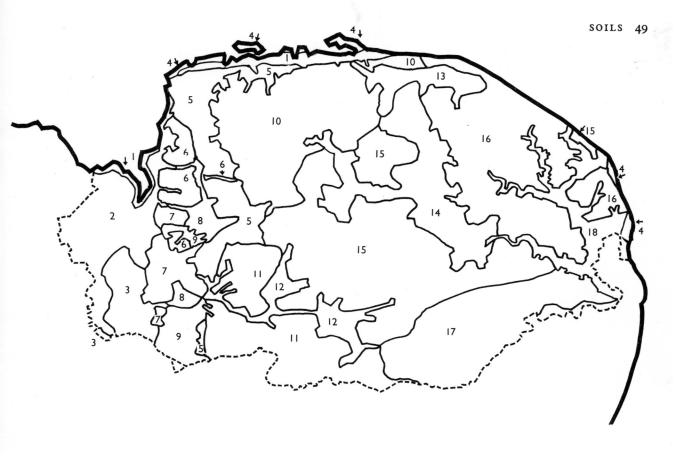

Fig. 3 *Soil map*

Area No.	Main features of the soil pattern

1 MARSH GLEYS

Estuarine or coastal fine-sandy or silty muds.
Very poorly drained soils under saltmarsh vegetation.

2 BROWN WARP SOILS

Fen silt (reclaimed estuarine muds).
Free drainage; water removed by artificial drains to tidal sluices.

3 PEATY GLEYS AND BASIN PEATS

Variable but generally shallow fen peat over various substrata.
Originally swamp, now freely drained; water removed by artificial drains and pumping to rivers.

4 RAW SAND SOILS

Coastal sand dunes.
Free to excessive drainage.

5 BROWN EARTHS WITH TEXTURAL B HORIZONS AND BROWN CALCAREOUS SOILS

Variable depths of more or less calcareous sandy drift over chalk.
Free drainage. Locally very chalky young soils occur; these usually result from disturbance. Decalcified soils have mostly been marled from local pits.

6 HUMUS PODZOLS AND PODZOLIC BROWN EARTHS

Sandringham Sands, Carstone, and very sandy drifts associated with them.
Free drainage. Gley podzols occur in poorly drained low-lying sites.

7 BROWN EARTHS

Light loamy or sandy drifts, probably of Gipping Age, overlying Sand-ringham Sands, Carstone, or Lowestoft Till; gravels along the Fen margin.
Free drainage in general; imperfect locally where heavy till lies near to the surface and along the Fen margin. Soils are more loamy and of a higher base status than those in area 6.

8 GROUND-WATER GLEYS AND BROWN EARTHS WITH GLEYING

Sandy or gravelly drifts mainly over Gault or Nar Valley Clay.
Poor or imperfect drainage due to impermeable substrata and/or low-lying sites.

9 BASIN PEATS AND PEATY GLEYS

Deep fen peat over various substrata.
Originally swamp, now freely drained; water removed by artificial drains and pumping to rivers.

10 BROWN EARTHS WITH AND WITHOUT TEXTURAL B HORIZONS

Sandy Gipping Till and associated outwash over Chalk or the calcareous facies of the Lowestoft Till.
Free drainage. Deep decalcification of the sandy parent materials has taken place, followed by clay migration in many cases. Most of these soils have been marled from local pits.

Area No.	Main features of the soil pattern
11	**PODZOLIC BROWN EARTHS, BROWN EARTHS WITH TEXTURAL B HORIZON, RAW SAND SOILS, ETC.** *Sandy, more or less calcareous Gipping Till over Chalk; associated sands and gravels; blown sand.* The Breckland complex of soils. Free drainage except in river valleys. Decalcification to varying depths and with varying degrees of peri-glacial and human disturbance has produced a range of soils including rendzinas, brown calcareous soils, and brown earths, often with textural B horizons. Podzolic brown earths and humus podzols are found on stabilized dunes and other non-calcareous deposits with very low clay contents. Raw sand soils occur on recent blown sand. The same general pattern is found in area 12 but, since much of it is low-lying, ground-water gleys are very prominent and peaty gleys occur locally.
12	See area 11.
13	**BROWN EARTHS, PODZOLIC BROWN EARTHS, AND HUMUS PODZOLS** *Sands and gravels of the Cromer Moraine and the Blakeney 'Esker'.* Free drainage.
14	**BROWN EARTHS** *Glacial sands and gravels probably mainly of Gipping origin.* Free drainage except in the major river valleys where ground-water gleys occur. The soils are very variable in detail but mainly light. Locally where they are specially sandy there are humus podzols. Outcrops of Chalk shown in valleys on geological maps are generally too deeply buried under drift to have had any influence on soil-formation.

Area No.	Main feature of the soil pattern
15	**BROWN EARTHS AND BROWN EARTHS WITH GLEYING** *Thin Gipping Till or outwash over Lowestoft Till.* Free or imperfect drainage. Textures generally are heavier than in area 10 and have checked clay migration. Calcareous soils are found locally.
16	**BROWN EARTHS** *Norwich Brickearth, Crags, and various thin drifts.* Free drainage, locally imperfect. Fine sandy loams are found on the Brickearth, coarse sandy loams on the Crag. Ground-water gleys are conspicuous in the major valleys.
17	**BROWN EARTHS WITH GLEYING AND SURFACE-WATER GLEYS** *Thin sandy Gipping Till overlying and partially mixed with the heavy facies of the Lowestoft Till.* Drainage is variable due to varying thicknesses of lighter Gipping material over the impermeable substratum. This has inhibited leaching and lowering of base status in these soils.
18	**GROUND-WATER GLEYS AND BASIN PEATS** *Alluvium and peat of the Broadland valleys.* Drainage poor to very poor. The lower reaches of the river valleys are occupied mainly by the ground-water gleys and the upper reaches by the peat beds.

REFERENCES

1. BADEN POWELL, D.F.W. (1948). 'The Chalky Boulder Clays of Norfolk and Suffolk.' *Geol. Mag.*, 85, 279–96.

2. Cambridge University Farm Economics Branch (1933). Report No. 22. *An Economic Survey of Agriculture in the Eastern Counties of England.*

3. GODWIN, H. (1944). 'Age and Origin of the Breckland Heaths of East Anglia.' *Nature*, 154, 6–7.

4. HEY, R.W. and PERRIN, R.M.S. (1960). *The Geology and Soils of Cambridgeshire.* Camb. Nat. Hist. Soc.

5. MOSBY, J.E.G. (1938). *Report of Land Utilisation Survey of Britain. Part 70, Norfolk.*

6. NEWMAN, L.F. (1912). 'Soils and Agriculture of Norfolk.' *Trans. Nfk. & Norwich Nat. Soc.*, 9, pt. 3, 349–93.

7. PERRIN, R.M.S. (1955). Studies in Pedogenesis: Part II: On Calcareous Till in the Breckland District. Ph.D. thesis. University of Cambridge.

8. PERRIN, R.M.S. (1957). 'The Clay Mineralogy of some Tills in the Cambridge District.' *Clay Min. Bull.*, 3, 193–205.

9. WATT, A.S. (1936). 'Studies in the Ecology of the Breckland.' *J. Ecol.*, 24, 117–38.

10. WATT, A.S (1937). Ibid., 25, 91–112.

11. WATT, A.S. (1938). Ibid., 26, 1–37.

12. WATT, A.S. (1940). Ibid., 28, 42–70.

13. YOUNG, A. (1804). *General View of the Agriculture of the County of Norfolk.*

the chief Norfolk habitats

J. M. LAMBERT

IN A RICHLY arable county such as Norfolk, it may seem surprising to visitors to find so much natural and semi-natural vegetation still relatively well-preserved. Admittedly the range of classic vegetation types is slight, compared with some parts of Britain. There are only limited areas of acid heath and bog, few stretches of unmanaged woodland, small fragments of chalk down, no rocky crags or moors. Yet against this must be set a series of ecologically important habitats which are only imperfectly matched elsewhere in the British Isles – the wide and varied belt of coastal vegetation in north Norfolk, the big tracts of fen and carr in the east Norfolk river valleys, and the unique expanse of Breckland to the south-west. Indeed, the coastal flats, the Broads, and the Breck, with their particular physiographical and ecological problems, have provided the focus for much detailed scientific work during the past half-century. The present conspectus of Norfolk habitats may thus justifiably concentrate on these, at the expense of minor habitats which, though of local interest, are either inadequately worked or are better represented elsewhere.

In most counties with generally fertile soils and a strong agricultural bias, the only remaining tracts of relatively unspoilt vegetation are either the legacy of historical preservation (as in the ancient Royal Forests and most common land), or else occupy areas which are too wet, too dry, or otherwise inappropriate, for full economic exploitation. The three areas under consideration here fall into the second category: the coastal flats and Broadland valleys provide an impressive range of aquatic and marshy habitats, while the other extreme is represented in the arid communities of the Breck.

As far as the north Norfolk coast is concerned, it is not only the sheer size and continuity of the coastal plain which gives it ecological importance. Its significance lies more particularly in the fact that the drowned coast is here predominantly an area of rapid accretion, to give an unrivalled series of maritime communities at all stages of successional development. From Weybourne to Hunstanton it is fringed by barrier beaches of sand and shingle which act as nuclei for dune establishment upon them and for saltmarsh formation on their landward side; and the very fact that the physiographic sequence has been so clearly demonstrated gives exceptional confidence in assessing the status of the associated vegetation.

The best-developed and most continuous shingle bank is that which stretches westwards from Sheringham to form the long spit ending eventually beneath the Headland dunes of Blakeney Point. The substratum varies in texture along its length, with large, bare stones at its eastern end, and with a greater proportion of smaller pebbles mixed with much sand farther west. Although the bank is overtopped by exceptional tides and material is thereby periodically washed landwards, much of the ridge forms a reasonably stable habitat for typical shingle plants such as *Glaucium flavum*, *Rumex crispus*, *Honkenya peploides*, and *Sedum acre*. Other barrier beaches of shingle and sand at different stages of development and colonization can be seen at Scolt Head, Thornham, and Wells.

Sand dunes in Norfolk are not limited to the north coast, but occur also along the low-lying eastern seaboard between Yarmouth and Happisburgh. Here the dune systems lie roughly parallel to the beach, and just south

J.M. LAMBERT is a Lecturer in the Department of Botany, University of Southampton

Hallam Ashley, August 1934

Fig. 1   *A close-up of pioneer dunes at Blakeney Point, showing sand accreting over shingle round plants of* Salsola *and* Ammophila

of Winterton there is a line of high dunes in front of the former sea cliff with a long, straight valley between, while an older and broader tract occurs north of the village. The north Norfolk dunes are more sporadically developed and more irregular in distribution, a reflection of the greater physiographical complexity of this part of the coast; but as a result, they often show a very complete series of developmental stages within a relatively small area. Thus on Scolt Head Island, an excellent series can be demonstrated from embryo-dune formation round drift-line plants of *Cakile maritima* and *Salsola kali*, through colonization by *Agropyron junceiforme* and

subsequently by *Ammophila arenaria* to give the conspicuous yellow-dune hills, with further enrichment and closure of the vegetation cover at the later, more stable, grey-dune stage. Grey dunes, with their characteristic components of *Carex arenaria*, various grasses, and abundant mosses and lichens, are well represented at Scolt, both on the main ridge and on many of the laterals, whereas at Blakeney the only remaining grey-dune system is at the Hood. In both areas, moreover, the sand has been secondarily removed by wind from older parts of the shingle skeleton to give an interesting series of degradation communities. The denuded

Fig. 2 *General view of Scolt Head Island and adjacent marshes at low tide, looking east along the coast*

shingle ribs bear a very different set of species from the primary shingle banks. The plants are markedly zoned, but with saltmarsh plants often growing in close juxtaposition to those more characteristic of shingle or sand. *Suaeda fruticosa*, usually mixed with *Halimione portulacoides*, *Limonium binervosum*, and *L. bellidifolium*, generally forms a dense belt along the edge, while patches of such carpet-forming plants as *Armeria maritima*, *Frankenia laevis*, and *Silene maritima* are frequent on the low crests.

The saltmarshes themselves form the most extensive set of maritime communities along this coast. They are broadly of two types: 'open' marshes along the more exposed stretches, and 'closed' marshes between adjacent shingle hooks. The former are flooded by tidal water along a relatively wide front, while tidal inflow and outflow to the latter are restricted to a narrow opening, so that scour is decreased over the marsh as a whole, sedimentation is correspondingly greater, and the various successional stages are passed through more quickly. There is also an important physiographical and ecological distinction between those marshes which form immediately behind the offshore bars and extend in a landward direction, and those which grow out from the

shore to meet them. The former contain a higher proportion of sand in their substrata, while the soils of the latter are much more silty.

The detailed floristic composition of the different marshes depends not only on their relative height above sea-level and concomitant differences in tidal régime, but also on differences in the soil. The complex interrelationships have been worked out fully by V.J. Chapman. All that can be said here is that in general algal communities, chiefly of species of *Enteromorpha*, occupy the lowest and youngest zones, with *Zostera nana* frequent in the more muddy patches; that these give place in turn to *Salicornia* (mainly the annual *S. stricta*) and to *Aster tripolium*; that the vegetation then becomes progressively richer and consists of a mixture of such plants as *Puccinellia maritima*, *Limonium vulgare*, *Halimione portulacoides*, and *Armeria maritima*; and that finally a community dominated by *Juncus maritimus* may be attained. On many parts of the coast, the older saltmarsh areas have been reclaimed, so that the last stage is only intermittently represented.

The general saltmarsh sequence is now, moreover, being very considerably modified, particularly in the lower zones, by the recent establishment and rapid spread of *Spartina townsendii* along the coast. The fertile form of this vigorous marine grass, first recorded from Hampshire in the latter half of the last century, has been widely planted for reclamation purposes in various

Fig. 3 *General view of a* Salicornia *marsh at Blakeney Point, with a ridge of yellow dunes in the background*

parts of Britain, and has spread extensively from many of these sites. In Norfolk, it is known to have been planted in the Wells area in 1907 and again in 1931, on the mud-flats north of King's Lynn in 1910 and more recently in other parts of the Wash, and on the mainland opposite Scolt Head in 1931-2 whence it apparently reached the island by 1939. At Blakeney, it was introduced by seed in 1925, and although deliberate efforts were made to eradicate it in this area two years later, it is more than probable that the great stretches now present on the Blakeney flats are the result of survivals from this introduction. Not only has the presence of *Spartina* greatly increased the rate of mud accretion on the previously bare flats which it has colonized, but it is invading established saltmarsh communities and is proving a serious competitor to other saltmarsh species of long standing.

The picture of coastal communities in Norfolk, however, should not be interpreted solely in terms of short-term development and relatively recent changes. In contrast to the newer marshes behind the offshore bars, it has been demonstrated at Brancaster that the landward marshes are based on a considerable depth of silt with freshwater peat beds interdigitated. The thickness of deposit and alternating upward sequence from one type of community to another here can best be explained in the light of long-term changes in the relative levels of land and sea. Whether a normal saltmarsh progression

J.N. Jennings, July 1949

Fig. 4 *Reedswamp of* Typha angustifolia *at Hoveton Great Broad, with* Nymphaea alba *and* Nuphar lutea *in the foreground*

can eventually end in non-maritime communities in the absence of land/sea-level changes is a matter for dispute; but it is significant in this connexion that a landward gradation from saltmarsh to freshwater marsh is seen in the present surface vegetation at both Brancaster and Thornham.

The indirect effect of land/sea-level changes in determining present vegetational patterns is much more marked when the Broadland picture is considered. Here we have valleys filled with great thicknesses of brushwood and fen peat, interrupted at two levels by tapered horizons of clay representing past marine transgressions. Today the area is covered by a patchwork of reedswamp, fen, and carr, whose relationship to the remaining open water of the broads is apparent only when the history of the valleys is reconstructed in detail from the stratigraphical horizons. It is now known, from the disposition of the estuarine clay and from the shapes of the basins of the broads themselves, that these sheets of water are not the relics of a former great estuary as once supposed; instead, they represent the sites of great medieval peat pits cut down into the brushwood deposits at a time when, according to available evidence, the land stood somewhat higher in relation to sea-level than it does at present. Subsequent sinking of the land was probably at least partly responsible for later flooding of the pits, to form the lakes which now we know as broads. The present vegetation can thus no longer be regarded as part of a single hydrosere from a large, continuous sheet of open water: instead, an important distinction must be made between the communities encroaching directly on the broads and those which occupy the solid peat between their basins.

The basins of most of the broads are roughly 10-12 feet deep from the present surface of the fenland, and it is significant that most of them appear to have retained their original outline until comparatively recent times. This can reasonably be explained when it is realized that the basins have roughly rectangular profiles instead of the concave shapes of natural lakes, so that organic ooze has settled fairly uniformly over their floors through the centuries, and has only recently reached the critical level of 3-4 feet from the water-surface when reedswamp plants can invade. Some of the shallower broads, such as Sutton and Dilham, attained this critical level some

J.K. St Joseph, June 1951. Crown Copyright Reserved

Fig. 5 *General view of the Yare valley in the region of Surlingham (extreme right) and Rockland (centre distance) Broads. Note the extensive invasion of former mowing-marsh by carr*

fifty or sixty years ago and are now practically extinct; others, like Barton and Ranworth, are approaching the danger stage; while in the deep side-valley broads of Fritton and the Ormesby-Rollesby-Filby complex, the mud-level is still well below the water-surface and there is comparatively little marginal encroachment.

The aquatic and reedswamp communities which invade the open water are followed at later stages by primary fen and carr, but the actual floristic composition of these various phases is by no means uniform for all the broads. In the Yare valley, for instance, where there is considerable tidal rise and fall, the marginal vegetation is largely composed of *Glyceria maxima* and *Phragmites communis*, the first forming semi-floating rafts of 'hover' where scour is not too strong, and the second more characteristic of scoured areas and also invading *Glyceria* from behind at a later stage in the succession. In less strongly tidal broads, the primary reedswamp plant is either *Typha angustifolia* or *Schoenoplectus lacustris*, followed by *Phragmites*, and then either by *Carex paniculata*, *C. acutiformis*, or *Cladium mariscus*. The tussocky form of *Carex paniculata* allows precocious invasion by sallow and alder bushes, so that the resulting carr is only precariously supported on a thin fen mat and forms an extremely unstable and swampy woodland known as 'swamp carr'; the rhizomatous *C. acutiformis* builds up a thicker fen mat before the trees gain entry, to give 'semi-swamp' alder carr; while *Cladium* produces a massive dead-leaf mattress and provides a strong platform of coarse, fibrous peat on which ash and oak as well as sallow and alder can become established.

In other broads with still less water movement, the reedswamp is somewhat reduced in vigour, and species of smaller stature, like *Juncus subnodulosus*, become the dominant fen plants. Each broad, in fact, has an individuality of its own, depending largely on the degree of water circulation to which it is exposed; and the plant communities themselves can be placed ecologically in linear order in relation to this factor.

Whereas human interference is at a minimum in the treacherous, swampy regions round the broads, past economic utilization of the adjacent fens has had a considerable effect on the vegetation of the solid peat between them. Not only is the fenland surface riddled with overgrown 'turf-ponds' (shallow peat cuttings quite distinct in scale from the deep excavations forming the broads), but much of the fen was formerly used as mowing-marsh, with rushes and grasses cut for litter and hay, and reeds and sedges harvested for thatching. Natural progression to carr was thus arrested, and the herbaceous communities themselves became modified and adapted to cutting-pressure. Recent changes in the economy of Broadland from direct utilization or sale of fenland produce to the more lucrative boat-letting trade have now caused much of the former mowing-marsh to revert to carr; but the change is by no means yet complete, and the whole area is still in a transitional state.

Moreover, as with *Spartina* in the saltmarshes, a new arrival in Broadland – this time an animal – is seriously changing the ecological balance of the region. A number of coypu 'rats' (*Myocastor coypus*) escaped from fur farms in the early years of the last war, and have become naturalized in great numbers throughout the whole Broads area, causing much damage to reedbeds, sedge fens, and even osier carrs. Admittedly they have helped to arrest some of the natural overgrowth of the broads, but in places their depredations are so intense that they are now considered a very serious pest.

The most interesting ecological features of Breckland fall into a different category from those of either the coastal habitats or the Broads. Whereas the two latter regions are particularly characterized by their superb representation of rapidly developing seral vegetation, the Breckland heaths might be regarded as comparatively stable, and represent a series of treeless communities established in broad outline by forest clearance as far back as Neolithic times. Much of the ancient history of the area has been elucidated from pollen sequences in the peaty deposits of Hockham Mere, where H. Godwin and his colleagues have reconstructed the origin of the adjacent heaths from changes in type and proportion of pollen grains preserved in successive horizons, correlated with an exceptional abundance of archaeological evidence.

The essentially open character of much of Breckland has been retained through the ages by widespread grazing, formerly by sheep and later by rabbits, accompanied by natural wind erosion. Agricultural inroads on the area have been intermittent, with periods of exploitation of marginally productive land followed by reabandonment. Latterly much of this marginal land has been afforested, so that the whole region now consists of a diffuse patchwork of plantations, fields, and residual heathy areas, with the latter becoming progressively more restricted in extent.

Although part of the Breck lies over the border in Suffolk, it forms a natural geographical and ecological region, and may therefore be considered most usefully here in its entirety. Its particular ecological interest lies in the semi-Continental nature of its climate, combined with the very sandy nature of its soils. The whole area, centred on Thetford and comprising some 400 square miles, is based on Chalk with a blanket of glacial drift. The latter belies its name of Chalky Boulder Clay in that it consists pre-eminently of a sand/chalk mixture with very little clay, and the derived soils are therefore extremely light and overdrained. This, in conjunction with the low rainfall of the region as a whole, makes it exceptionally liable to summer drought, while an overall susceptibility to frost accentuates the rigour of the general habitat conditions. Breckland is thus not only unique in the large number of Continental species, many rare in other parts of Britain, which are assembled together in its flora; it also provides a set of habitats with the nearest approach to 'steppe' conditions to be found in Britain,

Hallam Ashley, March 1948

Fig. 6   *A typical Breckland 'wind-break' of pine near Barton Mills*

and the dwarfed, open communities of drought-resistant or drought-escaping plants form excellent research and demonstration material for comparison with other areas with a more Oceanic climate. Moreover, since several of the commoner heathland species are near the limits of their tolerance, the chief ecological factors determining their range can be more easily identified, and their behaviour under limiting conditions in the field more easily studied.

Much of our knowledge of Breckland vegetation comes from the extensive investigations of A.S. Watt. Briefly, he distinguishes four main communities on the heaths, the first three dominated respectively by bracken (*Pteridium aquilinum*), heather (*Calluna vulgaris*), and sand-sedge (*Carex arenaria*), and the last comprising a mixed grass-heath of variable constitution but characterized by sheep's fescue (*Festuca ovina*) and the two bents (*Agrostis canina* and *A. tenuis*). Their detailed distribution depends largely on local variations in depth and development of the soil, which ranges from the un-leached, calcareous parent material to highly podzolized sand. In many places, moreover, former mature soil profiles are overlain by mobile, wind-borne layers, sometimes with actual dune-formation, while in others the lighter grains have been blown away to leave a comparatively stable erosion pavement of flints from the glacial drift. Superimposed on these soil differences

are other locally determining factors, such as the presence of frost pockets, or former differences in rabbit pressure, so that often a very complex mosaic of communities results. The pattern is further complicated by local secondary successions, and by the developmental cycles of the constituent species themselves; and it is noteworthy that detailed observations on Breckland communities provided much of the basic material on which Watt founded his classic 'pattern and process' theory of cyclical changes in vegetation.

Since the maintenance of the Breckland heaths has been attributed largely to rabbits, the recent drastic reduction in their numbers by myxomatosis must have far-reaching results. The full effects of rabbit removal have not yet been thoroughly assessed, and colonies may become re-established before the lag in vegetational adjustment is overcome; nevertheless, as with coypu effects in Broadland, Breck vegetation may well be entering a new phase in response to a powerful biotic factor other than direct human activity – this time, however, with the change in the opposite direction in that a factor has been removed instead of added. Change in

J.K. St Joseph, June 1958. Crown Copyright Reserved

Fig. 7   *Oblique air view of Weeting Heath in Breckland, with extensive afforestation of the surrounding country. Note the invasion of the heath by bracken and scrub, and the conspicuous 'stone-stripes' picked out by the vegetation in the foreground*

any natural or semi-natural community is inevitable over the centuries, but it is an interesting coincidence that the three chief Norfolk habitats are simultaneously entering a rather critical phase through independent causes. The spread of *Spartina* in the saltmarshes, the increasing depredations of the coypu in the Broads, and the disappearance of the rabbit from the Breck, are all phenomena of the last few years: they may all have serious repercussions on the communities which we know, and which many wish to preserve in their present familiar aspect.

REFERENCES

THE NORTH NORFOLK COAST

1. CHAPMAN, V.J. (1938, 1939, 1941, 1959). 'Studies in Salt-marsh Ecology, I–V, VIII, IX.' *J. Ecol.*, **26, 27, 29, 47.**

2. STEERS. A.J. (Ed.) (1960). *Scolt Head Island.* Second Edition, Cambridge. This book contains all the important references to the very extensive literature on Scolt Head, Blakeney Point, and other parts of the north Norfolk coast.

THE BROADS

3. ELLIS, E.A. (1949). 'The Broads as a Relict Marsh.' *New Nat.*, **6.**

4. GODWIN, H. and TURNER, J.S. (1933). 'Soil Acidity in Relation to Vegetational succession in Calthorpe Broad, Norfolk.' *J. Ecol.*, **21.**

5. LAMBERT, J.M. (1946, 1948, 1951). Various papers on Broadland vegetation. *J. Ecol.*, **33, 36, 39.**

6. LAMBERT, J.M. (1953). 'The Past, Present and Future of the Norfolk Broads.' *Trans. Nfk. & Norwich Nat. Soc.*, **17.**

7. LAMBERT, J.M. *et al.* (1960). *The Making of the Broads.* R.G.S., Research Series No. 3.

BRECKLAND

8. CLARKE, W.G. (1925). *In Breckland Wilds.* Second Edition revised and rewritten by R.R. Clarke, 1937. Cambridge.

9. FARROW, E.P. (1925). *Plant Life on East Anglian Heaths.* Cambridge.

10. GODWIN, H. (1944). 'Age and Origin of the "Breckland" Heaths of East Anglia.' *Nature*, **154.**

11. WATT, A.S. (1936–40). 'Studies in the Ecology of Breckland, I–IV.' *J. Ecol.*, **24–6, 28.**

12. WATT, A.S. (1947). 'Pattern and Process in the Plant Community.' *J. Ecol.*, **35.**

13. WATT, A.S. (1949). 'The Ecology of Breckland.' *New Nat.*, **6.**

flowering plants E. L. SWANN

CLIMATIC CONTRASTS coupled with soil differences and varying vegetation types ensure that a county the size of Norfolk can still show nearly three-quarters of the British flora. In common with other counties there have been many losses due to drainage, building, and intensive cultivation but the gains by way of new discoveries and segregates have steadily kept pace with the losses. The last *Flora of Norfolk* published in 1914 listed 1,029 plants, and it is estimated that a modern work would fall little short of this total.

Botanists will no longer find *Senecio paludosus* in the fen-ditches and the Broads, but *Sonchus palustris* and *Najas marina* are both slowly extending their areas of distribution. The Continental northern element represented by such plants as *Lathyrus palustris*, *Peucedanum palustre*, and *Hammarbya* has its main centre in the Broads district where a new member of the same component, *Eriophorum gracile*, was brought to light as a result of the intensive campaign organized for the Maps Scheme by the Botanical Society of the British Isles. A small colony of the rare and decreasing orchid, *Liparis loeselii*, has been discovered in a calcareous fen in west Norfolk, increasing its known stations.

In the Breckland of south-west Norfolk the greatest losses have occurred due, mainly, to the afforestation programme. Here the peculiar Continental climate favours the so-called 'steppe' species such as the spring annuals, *Veronica verna* and *V. triphyllos*, both now considerably reduced in frequency. Intensive search, however, has revealed additional stations for other members of the Continental component. Among these are *Carex ericetorum*, *Phleum phleoides*, *Medicago falcata*, *Apera interrupta*, *Herniaria glabra*, and *Veronica spicata*. In the 1914 *Flora* one station only was given for *Scrophularia*

umbrosa but the latest information shows it to be locally abundant along some of the upper reaches of the smaller streams. A recent loss is *Scleranthus perennis* from Barnhamcross Common where it was last seen in 1958.

The disastrous sea-floods of 1953 caused relatively little damage to the total flora but yearly cliff-falls have reduced the numbers of *Orobanche purpurea* whilst *Mertensia maritima* has not been seen since 1931. As a result of introduction to help consolidate the breaches in sand dunes there are now additional stations for *Ammocalamagrostis baltica* whilst a recent visit to Holme-next-the-Sea has shown at least fifty colonies of *Corynephorus canescens*. Another of the results due to flooding has been the temporary increase of *Puccinellia fasciculata* in the exposed, muddy soils. First recorded almost 200 years ago, *Juncus acutus* still persists along the coast near Brancaster, Thornham, and Burnham Deepdale. This member of the Oceanic southern element with others such as *Festuca uniglumis* and *Polygonum raii* contribute to the rich coastal phanerogamic flora.

In more than one place along the north Norfolk coast, there are flourishing colonies of the Mediterranean element in *Frankenia laevis* and *Limonium bellidifolium* growing between masses of *Suaeda fructicosa* on the margins of the saltmarsh, whilst the lows between the sand dunes at Burnham Overy Staithe provide the only remaining station for *Gnaphalium luteo-album*, where it has persisted for almost eighty years.

Among the very few components of the northern montane and Arctic-alpine elements, *Calamagrostis neglecta*, of the former, is abundant at Hockham Mere and *Eriophorum vaginatum*, of the latter, persists in places

E.L. SWANN is Joint Botanical Recorder to the Norfolk and Norwich Naturalists Society

such as Roydon Common. Indeed, places such as the margins of the Breckland meres and the many small calcareous valley fens in other parts of Norfolk often provide habitats for a rich helophytic flora containing many species absent or only poorly represented in the more extensive peaty stretches round the Broads. For instance, on East Winch Common, an area of peat overlying glacial gravel, a recent discovery was *Deschampsia setacea* in the low-lying peat bog; although originally described by Hudson in his *Flora Anglica* from Norfolk

material there have been no other records since the middle of the eighteenth century. Again, though all the Fenland bordering the Wash is now cultivated, there still remain small areas where *Lactuca saligna* and *Althaea officinalis* persist, while the wet heaths and *Sphagnum* bogs of Roydon Common and Wolferton Fen provide representatives of more acid-loving species such as *Anagallis tenella*, *Narthecium ossifragum*, all three species of *Drosera*, and *Oxycoccus palustris*.

Recent immigrants to Norfolk, not included in the 1914 *Flora*, include two species of *Galingsoga*, *Impatiens capensis*, *Sisymbrium orientale*, *Hirschfeldia incana* in the forest tracks and sandy soils of the Breckland around Weeting and Santon, *Bromus diandrus*, and *Epilobium adenocaulon*; this last species was not recorded until 1952 but has been found to be widespread and hybridizing freely with associated species, notably *E. montanum*. Moreover, during the Second World War there was a considerable influx of aliens from America by way of Lease-Lend agreement on import of seeds, chiefly carrots; but none of these has persisted, except that occasionally a few plants of *Echinochloa crus-galli* are still to be found in carrot-fields.

As already pointed out in the previous contribution, it is the three classic Norfolk areas, the north Norfolk coast, the Broads, and the Breck, which provide the most important natural and semi-natural habitats of the region, and it is only to be expected that the bulk of Norfolk phanerogamic records come from these parts. From a floristic point of view, however, the smaller areas of bogs and heaths and valley fens, even of ponds and fields and hedgerows, must not be forgotten, since these also contribute in no small measure to the richness of plant life in the region as a whole.

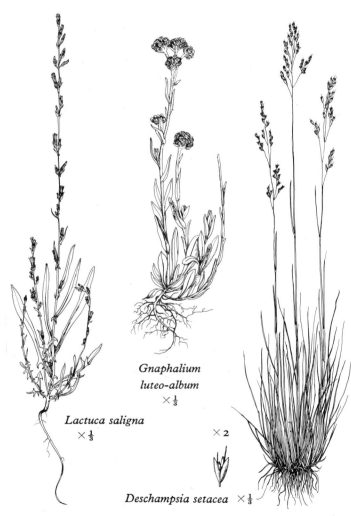

Gnaphalium luteo-album
× ⅓

Lactuca saligna
× ⅓

× 2

Deschampsia setacea × ⅓

Fig. 1

Drawn by Susan Puddy

REFERENCES

1. CLAPHAM, TUTIN, and WARBURG (1952). *Flora of the British Isles.*

2. HUDSON, W. (1778). *Flora Anglica.*

3. MATTHEWS, J.R. (1937). 'Geographical Relationships of the British Flora.' *J. Ecol.*, **25**, No. 1.

4. NICHOLSON, W.A. (1914). *A Flora of Norfolk.*

5. SWANN, E.L. (1955). 'An Annotated List of Norfolk Vascular Plants.' *Trans. Nfk. & Norwich Nat. Soc.*, **18**, pt. 1.

fungi　E. A. ELLIS

IN SPITE of its low rainfall, Norfolk yields fungi in great variety and abundance. This is due in part to the presence of extensive marshes, which conserve humid microclimates in their rank and matted vegetation. Sea mists add to precipitation in the coastal belt, while even in the comparatively parched Breckland region, moisture from the air is condensed nightly on the rapidly chilling sandy soil.

The diversity of the fungi present owes something to the fact that air-borne spores from a large tract of vegetated country are brought to East Anglia year after year on the prevailing south-westerly winds.

DUNES

Fungi characteristic of the unstable sands of yellow dunes include a deeply rooting agaric, *Psilocybe ammophila*, a sandy cup-fungus, *Peziza ammophila*, and the rare sand stink-horn, *Phallus hadriani*, appearing in late summer and autumn; the common stink-horn, *Ph. impudicus*, more usually associated with woodland soils, also occurs in this habitat.

On grey dunes, where there is more organic matter mixed with the sand and often a surface mat of lichens and mosses, many more species are represented. Among the more typical are an earth-tongue, *Geoglossum cookeianum*, a small stalked puffball, *Tulostoma brumale*, two sand puffballs, *Lycoperdon ericetorum* and *L. spadiceum* and among the agarics, several of the waxy and brightly coloured species of *Hygrophorus*, *Omphalina pyxidata*, *Stropharia coronilla* and a dune mushroom, *Agaricus devoniensis*.

Geastrum minimum, an earth-star found commonly on calcareous dunes in Sweden, was discovered recently on shelly sands at Holkham. Norfolk is rich in earth-stars,

many of which grow in conifer plantations on dunes, and on glacial sands inland.

Tussocks of marram grass harbour numerous saprophytic and parasitic micro-fungi. The rust *Puccinia ammophilina* and the ergot-forming *Claviceps purpurea* commonly attack this host. Sand-sedge has a rust, *Puccinia schoeleriana*, which bears yellow cluster-cups on common ragwort in late spring. Capsules of sea bindweed can often be found filled with spores of a smut, *Thecaphora seminis-convolvuli*. The sporangia of several kinds of myxomycetes (slime-fungi) are found maturing on dead remains of dune plants after showery weather in autumn.

SALTMARSHES

Coastal marshes inundated regularly by salt tides are devoid of agarics; but rusts of many species parasitize nearly all of the flowering plants and seem not to be harmed by periodic immersion in sea-water. The genus *Uromyces* is strongly represented in this zone, with species on thrift, sea-beet, annual sea-blite, common sea-lavender, sea-spurrey, sea-milkwort, and sea-glasswort.

THE BROADS

Reedswamps, fens, and carrs provide conditions highly favourable to the growth of a large number of moulds, cup-fungi, pyrenomycetes, rusts, and smuts. Few agarics tolerate very wet habitats and most of those found in marshes are comparatively small saprophytes of withered leaves and stems. A few larger forms develop on decaying wood of alders and willows and on slightly raised mossy soil round the bases of trees. The

E.A. ELLIS is Joint Botanical Recorder to the Norfolk and Norwich Naturalists Society

agaric flora includes a high proportion of ecologically specialized forms and recent studies of these at Wheatfen Broad, Surlingham, by P.D. Orton, have resulted in the discovery of a number of additions to the British list. The larger fungi become more numerous at higher levels in the oak-ash woodland merging with fen-carrs along valley margins.

Aquatic fungi in this area include most of the hyphomycetes discovered in recent years by C.T. Ingold on decaying leaves of trees in streams. Here they occur abundantly in dykes alongside carrs.

Sooty moulds (Dematiaceae) are plentiful in fens, on withering reeds, rushes, and sedges. The genus *Periconia* is represented here by numerous marsh species.

The fens and in particular, the *Glyceria maxima* beds of the Yare Broads have proved outstandingly rich in entomogenous fungi, of which some fifty species have been found here, attacking insects, spiders, and mites.

The marsh cup-fungi include several species of *Sclerotinia* parasitic on rushes, sedges, and various herbs, species of *Ciboria* developing on fallen catkins of alder, sallow, and sweet gale in spring, and two species of *Symphyosirinia* producing slimy, water-dispersed conidia and apothecia on fallen fruits of angelica and marsh bedstraw. One of the more noteworthy pyrenomycetes present in muddy interstices of marsh vegetation mats is *Tubeufia helicomyces*, accompanied by grey patches of its spirally coiled conidia on decaying grass culms.

Among rusts, mention should be made of *Puccinia opizii*, which has cluster-cups on cultivated lettuce and completes its life-cycle on sedges. This species was imported into Norfolk a few years ago and infected tussock sedges, whence it was able to maintain itself in the Broads area for several generations.

The smut *Ustilago grandis*, parasitic on the reed (*Phragmites*), is conspicuous in some places; although it causes very obvious disfigurement, the host plant is not killed. Fens and damp woods yield a wealth of myxomycetes.

BRECKLAND

The agarics of the open Breckland heaths are mostly of small size and seldom appear in any quantity until October. In very dry seasons, such as that of 1959, very few are to be seen. The genera most fully represented are *Mycena* and *Leptonia*, while *Galerina vittaeformis* is widespread. Some fungi present are equally typical of the coastal dunes: these include *Omphalina pyxidata* and *Geoglossum cookeianum*. A small pink encrusting fungus, *Corticium fuciforme*, is often conspicuous on the grasses.

Since much of the area has become afforested, many agarics and boleti typically associated with conifers have colonized ground under the trees, while fungus pathogens, notably *Fomes annosus*, have shown a corresponding increase.

Fig. 1 Symphyosirinia galii; *apothecia and secondary synnemata on mericarps of* Galium palustre, *Wheatfen Broad, Surlingham, Norfolk*

mammals   F. J. TAYLOR PAGE

DESPITE THE FACT that the land of this agricultural region is more intensively used than ever before, and that its mammalian fauna has been increasingly exposed to human interference, it is still possible to record the occurrence of thirty-eight different wild and feral land mammals. The total populations of some mammals have declined during the past fifty years, but there has been no reduction in the number of species found in the region. In fact, since the *Scientific Survey of 1935* was published, six hitherto unrecorded species have been added to the fauna list.

Fortunately there are certain large areas where mammals are relatively safeguarded against Man's intrusion. The Broadland, the Breckland, and the heathlands all provide food and shelter for certain species – particularly in those parts which are scheduled as Nature Reserves. The comparatively young forests are also important, although mammals are here more subject to controls. Thetford Chase, for example, is an important

British stronghold for the red squirrel (*Sciurus vulgaris leucorus*). In addition small numbers of red deer (*Cervus elaphus scoticus*), fallow deer (*Dama dama*), and roe deer (*Capreolus capreolus thotti*) are well established. A fourth species, the Chinese muntjac (*Muntiacus reevesi*) is an occasional vagrant from Bedfordshire, and is likely to increase within the next few years.

Even where one would expect more definite restraint, it is encouraging to find the hand of Man less rigorous than formerly, and a kindlier disposition exists towards species such as the badger (*Meles meles*) which, until recent years was rarely recorded. In 1959, more than ten new sets were known to be in use in Norfolk.

In 1927 the coypu (*Myocastor coypus*) was introduced in the south-eastern counties. Some escaped between 1934 and 1937 in central Norfolk, and in the last twenty-five years widespread dispersal has been occurring. About 1950, feral colonies of these large South American rodents were firmly established in many parts of the county, and a southward extension along the Suffolk coast had begun. Intensive trapping and shooting had, until then, kept numbers under control, and it had been generally conceded that these animals threatened no danger to crops or menace to river banks. In the absence of natural enemies, and with a decline in the market for nutria fur, the coypu population has unfortunately tended in the past five years to get out of hand. Increasing evidence of damage has led to reassessment of the position. The coypu is now being treated as a serious pest.

Modern control of rodents has been effectual almost everywhere, and with it has come the near extinction of

R. Gaze

Fig. 1   *Young coypu, Taverham, 1959*

F.J. TAYLOR PAGE is Recorder of Mammals to the Norfolk and Norwich Naturalists Society

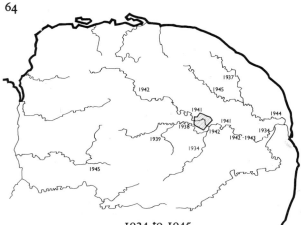

1934 to 1945
Establishment of colonies in the rivers of eastern and central Norfolk

1945 to 1950
Effects of control, particularly in the Yare valley. Nutria skins were worth £5
High mortality in the severe winter of 1947

1950 to 1955
Relaxation of control and decrease in value of Nutria fur

1955 to 1960
Widespread outward movement from large colonies in the river valleys into new areas in the south and west

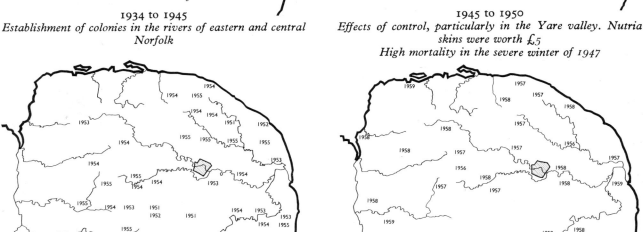

Fig. 2   *Distribution of Coypu from escape c. 1934 to 1960*

the black or ship rat (*Rattus rattus*). Mechanized agriculture now virtually confines the harvest mouse (*Micromys minutus*) to its natural home in reedswamps. The yellow-necked field mouse (*Apodemus flavicollis wintoni*), well established in Suffolk, has only recently been identified in the south-eastern part of Norfolk. The dormouse (*Muscardinus avellanarius*), introduced in the same area about 1840, never seems to have survived, and it has not been seen during this century.

Disease has reduced the population of two species, the rabbit (*Oryctolagus cuniculus*) and the fox (*Vulpes vulpes*). On 17 May 1954, myxomatosis reached the south of the county of Norfolk and spread rapidly north and west. The mortality rate was up to 98 per cent, and in some places total extermination occurred. Correlated with this, though the exact significance is not understood, has been the astonishing increase in the population of the hare (*Lepus europaeus occidentalis*) and the migration of this species into areas where twenty years ago it was rarely seen. Deaths among foxes attributed to encephalitis may have been due to the use of certain types of seed-dressing by farmers. The effects of the poison can extend to foxes if they eat the carcasses of affected birds.

The study of East Anglian bats has been much neglected, but our records include the whiskered bat (*Myotis mystacinus*) in the underground workings of Grime's Graves, the serotine bat (*Eptesicus serotinus*) at Lowestoft, the Barbastelle bat (*Barbastella barbastellus*) in north Norfolk, Daubenton's bat (*Myotis daubentoni*) in the Yare valley, and most recently the lesser horse-shoe bat (*Rhinolophus hipposideros minutus*), in the chalk caves at Bury St Edmunds and at Geldeston, near Beccles.

Of our marine mammals, the most noteworthy in recent years is the grey seal (*Halichoerus grypus*) which appears to have bred spasmodically on the Wash sandbanks since about 1880. But in 1958, the regular breeding of a small grey seal colony among the native herd of common seals (*Phoca vitulina*) was confirmed for the first time on Scroby Sands off Great Yarmouth. A southward movement of the species from the Farne Islands is indicated by recovery of ringed specimens.

H. Auger

Fig. 3 (*above*)
Large herds of common seals frequent the Wash where they breed on the sandbanks. There are strong colonies too at Blakeney and Scroby

Fig. 4
Grey Seal pup, Scroby Sands, 1958, the year when breeding was confirmed

W. J. Woolston

birds M. J. SEAGO

THE OPENING months of the year see the arrival in Norfolk of great companies of wildfowl. At first they congregate on the Broads and flood waters, but in prolonged spells of Arctic weather, they are forced to seek tidal waters. From the Ouse Washes stretching south-west from Denver the hungry birds flight to the Wash. In the south-east corner of the county, Breydon Water attracts them from the frozen Broads.

The Washes may claim to be the most striking winter haunt of wildfowl in eastern England and in early 1956, a severe Continental winter resulted in exceptional gatherings there. The spectacle included over 700 Bewick's swans, 9,000 wigeon, and almost 2,000 pintail. Remarkable, too, were the flocks of red-breasted mergansers. Breydon held 3,000 wigeon during this cold

C.C. Doncaster

Fig. 1 *Gatherings of 100 and exceptionally 150 ruffs make prolonged stays in autumn at favoured localities*

spell, together with many scaup, golden-eye, goosanders, and smew. On the north coast, a peak of 3,000 brent geese congregated in the silted harbours at Blakeney and at Brancaster.

Pink-footed geese have unfortunately declined since the last war when a maximum of 2,000–3,000 regularly wintered on the marshland adjoining Breydon. White-fronted geese however still winter in this lonely area, regularly flighting to Scroby Sands off Yarmouth. One locality in the Yare valley regularly attracts a gathering of bean-geese. Single lesser white-fronts have been detected among the bean-geese on three occasions since 1956.

April and May sees the arrival of many exciting visitors. One, or rarely two, ospreys will spend perhaps a week fishing in the Broads area. Parties of up to ten non-breeding spoonbills, doubtless from Holland, regularly visit both the wader grounds at Hickling and Breydon mud-flats. Some years they are present for weeks at a time, leisurely travelling up and down the coast. The spring wader pageant is eagerly awaited with the prospect of godwits, spotted redshanks, grey plovers, ruffs, knot, and other northern nesters all in full breeding plumage. With winds in an easterly quarter, numbers of black terns pass through in May. Rockland Broad and the Norfolk Naturalists' Trust reserve at Cley are most favoured. In 1959, 120 appeared at the former locality; but this figure was eclipsed in 1960 when 350 passed Cley in a single day.

In high summer, the coastal reserves at Blakeney Point and Scolt Head are full of interest, with their nesting colonies of Sandwich, little and common terns;

M.J. SEAGO is Recorder of Birds to the Norfolk and Norwich Naturalists Society and Editor of the *Norfolk Bird Report*

C.C. Doncaster

Fig. 2   *Thousands of knot and hundreds of redshank frequent the Wash and silted north coast harbours*

oystercatchers and ringed plovers, redshanks and sheld-duck. Scroby Sands, too, has its ternery. As many as 1,900 pairs of Sandwich terns and 3,700 pairs of common terns nest at these stations in a good season. On the crumbling cliffs east of Weybourne brooding fulmars sit patiently: 1957 was a record year with over thirty chicks. The following season, kittiwakes attempted nesting among the Sandwich terns at Blakeney.

In Broadland, the reedbeds echo to the vibrant calls of bearded tits. These most attractive birds benefited greatly from the warm dry summer of 1959 when at least seventy pairs bred. Bitterns may be heard booming at all hours. Recent information suggests that there are at least sixty 'boomers' in the county.

The Broads are also the traditional home of the marsh harrier. Up to 1959, three to four pairs of marsh harriers bred regularly and one hopes that the lack of successful nests in 1960 is only a temporary setback. The apparent loss of breeding Montagu's harriers is very disappointing. None has nested in the Broads area since 1956. In the following two years nests were discovered in Breckland, but not subsequently.

In the Breck, many stone-curlew now nest in the forest rides and also on arable land which has to be disturbed by cultivation. On the remaining heathlands, the almost complete absence of rabbits leaves the grass too tall for these birds. Other areas have been ploughed in the hope that the stone-curlews will return. The Breck population of woodlarks, ringed plovers, and wheatears is similarly threatened.

One of the latest additions to the county list of breeding species is the collared dove. Breeding was first proved in 1955 and the birds have since spread from north Norfolk to Yarmouth where they nested successfully in 1960. There is yet to be a dramatic spread throughout the county, but a gathering of eighteen collared doves has been seen. Another comparative newcomer, the black redstart, first bred in the county, at Yarmouth in 1950. Breeding pairs have also appeared there in five

R. Jones

Fig. 3 *Bitterns are widespread in the Broads area and also breed at Cley. This nest was on the edge of Ormesby Broad*

subsequent years. A nest was found at Cromer in 1958 and two nests in Norwich in 1960.

Autumn migration begins as early as the first days of July, but it is during the second half of August that the wader passage reaches spectacular proportions. As many as seventeen species may be recorded in a single day. The marshes at Cley and Salthouse are watched daily, and in recent years the rarities there have included red-breasted snipe, Temminck's stint, white-rumped, pectoral, and solitary sandpipers, together with grey and red-necked phalaropes. Remarkable numbers of waders collect on the Wash. High-water counts at this season have included 6,000 oystercatchers, 500 turnstones, 50 greenshank, 8,000 curlew, 100 whimbrel, 100 little stints, and 50 curlew-sandpipers.

Under certain weather conditions, the suaeda bushes at Scolt Head and between Blakeney Point and Cley become resting-places for small north European drift-migrants. During one of these exciting periods in September, Cley Bird Observatory recorded 10–12 wrynecks, 10 bluethroats, 6–8 ortolan buntings, 4 each of icterine warbler and red-backed shrike, 3 barred warblers, together with single black redstart, wood warbler, red-breasted flycatcher, and rustic bunting.

October sees the arrival of countless numbers of thrushes, larks, finches, starlings, and other birds from northern Europe. These large-scale immigrations sometimes continue until well after nightfall. At this season light-vessel crews off the Norfolk coast co-operate by maintaining diaries and keeping a look-out for ringed birds which have struck the lanterns. Recent radar studies of migration have produced startling and hitherto unsuspected facts about the magnitude, direction, and altitude of movements affecting Norfolk.

The list of Norfolk birds is lengthy and at the time of writing totals 330 full species; 124 species have nested within the last decade, the most recent additions being the collared dove and little ringed plover.

freshwater fish QUINTON BITTON

UNTIL COMPARATIVELY recent geological times our Norfolk rivers, indeed probably many of the east coast streams, formed an outlying portion of a vast Continental river system, the lower portion of which is now engulfed by the North Sea. As a result, whereas the Rhine and other west European rivers flowing through a more varied terrain support a somewhat richer fauna, our smaller and now insular rivers, while prolific in actual numbers, hold comparatively few species of fish. None of these are endemic to the region.

The rivers Nene, Little Ouse, and Waveney form the landward boundaries of the maritime county which although it lies within a comparatively low rainfall area (25–27 inches per annum) is well watered by slow-moving and meandering streams, through areas of gentle gradient composed of gravels, chalk, boulder clay, and fenland. The waters throughout, where not adversely affected by pollution (fortunately rare), are organically rich, supporting a prolific and varied lower fauna and flora. The main watershed is a chalk ridge running in a south-easterly direction from Hunstanton to south of Watton. To the east of this flow the Yare, Wensum, Waveney, and their many tributaries, traversing in their lower tidal areas the unique region known as the Norfolk Broads. The shorter west-flowing rivers, the Nar, Wissey, Thet, and Little Ouse, together with the lower areas of the main river form a small part of the Great Ouse basin which extends far beyond the county boundaries. A second upland area known as the Holt–Cromer Ridge, an end moraine formed during the last Ice Age, runs eastwards at right angles to the main watershed and divides the waters of the small coastal streams Glaven and Stiffkey from the river Bure, a large tributary of the Yare.

Man has been responsible for making many varied and interesting artificial waters in the county, as instanced by the peat-digging of medieval times which activities were an important factor in the formation of the Broads. The ancient excavation of clay and more recently the continually increasing exploitation of the valley gravels, have also left their mark. In addition many lovely lakes on various estates have been created purely for their amenities and beauty.

Although the majority of our Norfolk fishes are native, Man has played a considerable part in their distribution and there are few, if any, of our rivers, lakes, and even isolated ponds, that have not been artificially stocked at some time or other. In medieval times there occurred the introduction of carp species into monastic stew ponds and manorial waters. Latterly there has been widespread stocking of rivers with trout species and to a lesser extent with grayling, both aliens to Norfolk waters. But perhaps the most interesting example of man's interference with nature is the recent successful introduction of chub into the Upper Yare and tributaries, a species which is widely found in the Great Ouse and Nene river systems. Similarly, the bleak which is prolific in parts of the western rivers does not occur naturally in the east of the county. With the phenomenal growth in popularity of angling, experimental introductions of large-mouthed bass, pike-perch, European catfish or wels, and barbel have been attempted, and whilst the first-named species has not established itself, it is at the moment premature to comment on the measure of success attending the other introductions.

E. QUINTON BITTON is Fisheries Superintendent to the East Suffolk and Norfolk River Board

SPECIES OF FRESHWATER FISHES AND ALLIED FORMS

CYCLOSTOMATA

Brook Lamprey, *Lampetra planeri* (Bloch). Common locally

River Lamprey, *Lampetra fluviatilis* (L.). Fairly common

Sea Lamprey, *Petromyzon marinus* L. Decreasing in numbers

PISCES

Sturgeon, *Acipenser sturio* L. Rare visitor

Allis Shad, *Alosa alosa* (L.). Rare visitor

Sprat, *Clupea sprattus* L. This species has been recorded in fresh water

Salmon, *Salmo salar* L. Rare visitor

Sea Trout, *Salmo trutta* (L.). The catadromous form occurs seasonally

Brown Trout, *Salmo trutta fario* (L.). Introduced

Rainbow Trout, *Salmo irideus* Gibbons. Introduced

Brook Trout, *Salvelinus fontinalis* (Mitchill). Introduced

Smelt, *Osmerus eperlanus* (L.). Seasonally common

Grayling, *Thymallus thymallus* (L.). Introduced

Bream, *Abramis brama* (L.). Common native

Bleak, *Alburnus* (L.). Restricted to west Norfolk

Barbel, *Barbus barbus* (L.). Introduced

White Bream, *Blicca bjorkna* (L.). Locally common

Crucian Carp, *Carassius carassius* (L.). Introduced

Carp, *Cyprinus carpio* (L.). Introduced

Gudgeon, *Gobio gobio* L. Locally common

Roach, *Rutilus rutilus* (L.). Abundant and widespread

Dace, *Leuciscus leuciscus* (L.). Common

Minnow, *Phoxinus phoxinus* (L.). Common

Rudd, *Scardinius erythrophthalmus* (L.). Locally abundant

Chub, *Squalius cephalus* (L.). Now relatively widespread

Tench, *Tinca tinca* (L.). Widespread

Stone Loach, *Nemacheilus barbatulus* (L.). Common

Spined Loach, *Cobitis taenia* L. Local

Catfish, *Silurus glanis* L. Introduced

Eel, *Anguilla anguilla* (L.). Ubiquitous

Pike, *Esox lucius* L. Common

Ruffe, *Acerina cernua* (L.). Abundant in suitable habitats

Pike-perch, *Lucioperca lucioperca* (L.). Introduced

Perch, *Perca fluviatilis* L. Common

Bullhead or Miller's Thumb, *Cottus gobio* L. Local

Three-Spined Stickleback, *Gasterosteus aculeatus* L. Abundant and widespread

Ten-Spined Stickleback, *Pygosteus pungitius* (L.). Local

Burbot, *Lota lota* (L.). Last recorded in 1945

Flounder, *Platichthys flesus* (L.). Widespread in tidal waters

It is difficult to state with any degree of accuracy the species of anadromous, marine, or partially marine fish that penetrate our extensive areas of fresh water accessible to the sea. In addition to species already listed, the Viviparous Blenny (*Zoarces viviparus*) and Common Goby (*Gobius minutus*) are resident in most brackish areas, which are also visited from time to time by large shoals of Grey Mullet (*Mugil* sp.) and to a degree by Whiting (*Gadus merlangus*), while odd species such as Conger Eels (*Conger vulgaris*), Ling (*Molva vulgaris*), and Saury Pike (*Scombresox Saurus*) have been taken at points several miles from the sea.

insects

E. T. DANIELS | K. C. DURRANT

THE VARIETY of habitats in Norfolk supports a corresponding wealth of insect species.

On the coastal dunes and associated marshes are well-established colonies of the Fritillaries, *Argynnis aglaja* (L.), *cydippe* (L.) and *selene* (Schiff.), and characteristic Diptera include *Philonicus albiceps* (Mg.), *Thereva annulata* (Fab.), and *bipunctata* Mg., as well as the smallest Bombyliid, *Phthiria pulicaria* (Mik.).

Predatory Dolichopodid flies occur on the surfaces of salt pools along with large populations of the springtail *Lipura maritima* Guerin. The extensive saltings produce specialized beetles in profusion. Among these are *Dicheirotrichus obsoletus* Dej., numerous species of *Bembidion* and the weevils *Apion limonii* Kirby and *Mecinus collaris* Germar. *Malachius barnevillei* Put. occurs in the dunes at Scolt Head and in no other county. Mention should be made too of the very local beetle *Nebria livida* L. which surprisingly succeeds on the eroding faces of the soft clay cliffs which are a feature of some parts of the coast.

The Broads area, with its extensive stretches of open water, its reedswamps, fens, and carrs, supports a unique insect fauna. Pride of place goes to the swallow-tail butterfly, *Papilio machaon* L. This magnificent species flourishes and is common in most years. The black form, ab. *niger*, is occasionally seen in the wild state and in 1933 the unique ab. *obscura* was bred from a caterpillar taken at Hickling. The fens and reedswamps sustain 'Wainscot' moths of various species, notably *Arenostola brevilinea* (Fenn) not known to occur elsewhere in the world. Among the orthoptera the great green grasshopper *Tettigonia viridissima* L. occurs but is restricted to one Yare valley area. The Odonata furnish much of interest. *Coenagrion armatum* (Charp.) was first discovered at Sutton in 1904. It still persists and is known in no other county. The dragonfly *Aeshna isosceles* (Mull.) has its headquarters in the Ant valley and is practically confined to Norfolk, while *Libellula fulva* Mull., another local insect, occurs commonly in places. Of the water bugs, *Hydrometra gracilenta* Horv. and the minute Veliid bug, *Microvelia umbricola* Wroblewski, are found in the vicinity of Barton and Sutton Broads lurking in tunnels formed by overhanging tussocks of *Carex paniculata*. Apart from the New Forest, no other stations are known for *H. gracilenta*, and *M. umbricola* is recorded elsewhere only at Wicken Fen. The Diptera are mainly represented by members of the *Sciomyzidae*, *Tabanidae*, *Tipulidae*, and the purely aquatic-breeding *Culicidae* and *Chironomidae*. At the same time the entomologist may regard the Broads as disappointing for two orders of aquatic insects. The trichopterist will not find a large range of caddis flies but mention may be made of the striking and local *Limnephilus xanthodes* McL. Similarly immense hatches of Ephemeroptera do not occur on a scale known elsewhere in the country and these insects are not abundant, although a species new to Britain, *Caenis robusta* Eaton, was discovered a few years ago.

Recently a severe falling-off in numbers of Zygopterid dragonflies has been reported. The reason for this is not clear but at Wheatfen, where *Corixae* used to swarm, they are virtually non-existent, and these corixid disappearances are correlated in time with the outpouring of detergents from Norwich.

In the south-west of the county the sandy Brecks, though greatly reduced in area, still produce specialities. Among the Lepidoptera the moths *Anepia irregularis*

E. T. DANIELS and K. C. DURRANT are Joint Recorders of Insects to the Norfolk and Norwich Naturalists Society

Fig. 1 *Characteristic Diptera of the coast*

1 Philonicus albiceps (Mg.)
2 Dysmachus trigonus (Mg.)
3 Eristalis aeneus Scop.
4 Thereva annulata (Fab.)
5 Thereva bipunctata Mg. ♀
6 Thereva bipunctata Mg. ♂

K.C. Durrant

(Huf.) and *Emmelia trabealis* (Scop.) are found. The Heteropteron *Chorosoma schillingi* (Schummel) is common in many places, as is also the Dipteron *Dysmachus trigonus* (Mg.). The two latter species illustrate one of the peculiarities of Breckland, they occur elsewhere only on coastal sandhills. The coniferous forests of recent origin contain both species of wood wasps *Urocerus gigas* (L.) and *Sirex juvencus* (L.) and the Ichneumonid parasite *Rhyssa persuasoria* (L.).

The environment in this mainly arable county is generally hostile to insects. However, it can be recorded that since the early 1930's the Comma butterfly, *Polygonia c-album* (L.), and the White Admiral, *Limenitis camilla* (L.), have established themselves and the Speckled Wood, *Pararge aegeria* (L.), hitherto restricted to two localities, now seems to be spreading. In isolated areas such species as the Chalk-hill Blue butterfly, *Lysandra coridon* (Poda), the Purple Emperor, *Apatura iris* (L.), and the Silver-washed Fritillary, *Argynnis paphia* (L.),

linger, as well as *Ceriagrion tenellum* (de Villiers) and *Orthetrum coerulescens* (Fabricius).

In addition, partly because of its long coastline the county receives a constant invasion of migrants, varying in intensity from year to year. In 1960 immense swarms of hover-flies (*Syrphidae*) and ladybirds (*Coccinellidae*) appeared. The butterflies, the Painted Lady, *Vanessa cardui* (L.), and the Clouded Yellow, *Colias croceus* (Fourcroy) are frequent, while occasionally the Camberwell Beauty, *Nymphalis antiopa* (L.), and recently even the Apollo, *Parnassius apollo* L., have been noted. Among the moths the Death's Head, *Acherontia astropos* (L.), the convolvulus hawk, *Herse convolvuli* (L.), the humming-bird hawk, *Macroglossa stellatarum* (L.), and sometimes the rarer *Sphingidae*, may be expected. These migrants often breed here, a notable instance being the migrant dragonfly, *Sympetrum flaveolum* (L.), which established itself as a resident for a few seasons on one of the Broads.

The Norfolk Aeschna, *Aeschna isosceles*. A striking
early summer dragonfly, extremely local and virtually
confined in the British Isles to the Norfolk Broads

R. Jones

The bearded tit population has steadily built up in recent years and in 1959 there was an exceptionally good breeding season. The stronghold is the Hickling, Heigham Sounds and Horsey area of the Broads. Smaller breeding colonies may be found at Barton, in the Waveney valley and on the north coast at Cley

R. Jones

The most recent county census of great crested grebes was undertaken in 1954 when 342 adults were counted. Forty-four waters were
occupied. In early autumn the majority desert their breeding
quarters and make for coastal waters. To the Wash it is then a
common visitor and considerable concentrations have been seen
there including sixty together at the end of August

The Swallow-tail Butterfly, *Papilio machaon*, probably
the most magnificent of British butterflies, is
common in most years around the Broads.

land and freshwater mollusca
A. E. ELLIS

NORFOLK, particularly the eastern part, is rich in non-marine Mollusca. All the British freshwater Gastropoda (except *Planorbis acronicus* Férussac), twenty out of twenty-seven species of freshwater Bivalvia, and about three-quarters of our native species of land Mollusca are recorded from the county. Species unrepresented are mainly those of a western or northern distribution, or those characteristic of primeval woodland, a type of habitat in which Norfolk is deficient. As would be expected from its extensive waterways and swamps, the county is exceptionally rich in freshwater Mollusca, the most favourable habitats being the rivers and dykes (drainage ditches) of the north-east.

Most of the British species of freshwater mussels (*Unionidae*) inhabit the rivers or Broads, including *Pseudanodonta complanata* (Rossmässler), which occurs in the river Yare below Norwich. The Zebra mussel, *Dreissena polymorpha* (Pallas), which is unique amongst freshwater Mollusca in having a veliger larval stage, lives in the Broadland rivers.

Of the freshwater Gastropoda, those which are rare or local in Norfolk include the following species: *Valvata macrostoma* Mörch, restricted to a few localities in south-east England; *Planorbis vorticulus* Troschel, recorded besides for Sussex and one pond in Middlesex; *P. laevis* Alder, recorded for the river Wensum; *Segmentina nitida* (Müller); *Lymnaea glabra* (Müller), recorded from Reffley, North Runcton, and North Tuddenham; *L. glutinosa* (Müller), from the rivers Wensum and Upper Yare and a ditch at Colney; and *Aplexa hypnorum* (L.) from Thorpe-next-Norwich and St Germans. The last two species are not only very local, but of sporadic occurrence.

The Broads district is especially favourable for eco-

Fig. 1 Pseudamnicola confusa (*left*) . Assiminea grayana (*right*) (× 5)

Fig. 2 Valvata macrostoma (× 5)

Photographs by the Rev. R.A. Ellis

Fig. 3 Planorbis vorticulus (× 5)

logical studies of freshwater Mollusca, as most types of habitat except rocky streams are represented, and the transition from aquatic to terrestrial habitats, via swamp and fen, is well exemplified.

Being deficient in extensive tracts of ancient woodland,

A.E. ELLIS is the author of *British Snails*

Photographs by the Rev. R.A. Ellis

Fig. 4 Succinea elegans (× 3)

which constitute a favourite habitat for many kinds of snails and slugs, Norfolk is not exceptionally rich in land Mollusca. Furthermore, considerable areas, such as the heaths or brecks and cultivated land, are unsuitable. The marshes and damp woods or carrs near the Broads offer congenial habitats for land snails. The very local *Vertigo moulinsiana* (Dupuy) is abundant on reeds and sedges by some of the Broads, and the rare *V. angustior* Jeffreys occurs at Royden Fen, Flordon Common, and Saxlingham Thorpe, but is more frequently taken in flood jetsam than alive. Two other uncommon species of *Vertigo*, which are amongst the smallest of snails, are recorded from Norfolk, namely *V. pusilla* Müller and *V. substriata* (Jeffreys). *Succinea elegans* Risso (*sensu stricto*) was first verified, by dissection, as a British species from Norfolk examples, and the marsh-dwelling slug, the true *Agriolimax agrestis* L., was first recorded from the Norfolk Broads. *Monacha granulata* (Alder), which occurs in a variety of habitats in the west, in this county appears to be confined to marshes and damp woodland. The minute land operculate snail, *Acicula fusca* (Montagu), has been recorded from Caistor Wood.

Brackish water and saltmarsh species are naturally well represented on the Norfolk coast. *Assiminea grayana* Fleming, at one time thought to be restricted to the Thames Estuary, is now known to extend around the coast to King's Lynn (and farther north to the Humber). The rare *Pseudamnicola confusa* (Frauenfeld) occurs near the Suffolk border, sometimes in association with fresh-water species. *Hydrobia ulvae* (Pennant) or *H. stagnalis* (Küster) is to be seen in countless myriads on the mud of saltmarshes.

REFERENCES

The following are some of the papers to which reference has been made in compiling these notes. Further references will be found in Ellis, A.E. 1941 and 1951, and in Mayfield 1909.

1. ELLIS, A.E. (1931). 'Notes on some Norfolk Mollusca.' *J. Conch.*, **19**, 177–8.
2. ELLIS, A.E. (1941). 'The Mollusca of a Norfolk Broad.' *J. Conch.*, **21**, 224–43.
3. ELLIS, A.E. (1941). 'Ecological Notes.' *J. Conch.*, **21**, 258 (*Lymnaea glutinosa*).
4. ELLIS, A.E. (1941). '*Anodonta minima* Millet in Norfolk.' *J. Conch.*, **21**, 280 (*Pseudanodonta complanata*).
5. ELLIS, A.E. (1949). 'A Broadland Slug.' *Trans. Nfk. & Norwich Nat. Soc.*, **16**, 388 (*Agriolimax agrestis*).
6. ELLIS, A.E. (1951). 'Census of the Distribution of British Non-marine Mollusca.' *J. Conch.*, **23**, 172–244.
7. ELLIS, E.A. (1945). 'The Rond Snail.' *Trans. Nfk. & Norwich Nat. Soc.*, **16**, 82–4 (*Assiminea grayana*).
8. ELLIS, E.A. and OLDHAM, C. (1934). 'Non-marine Mollusca of Scolt Head Island.' *Scolt Head Island*, 214–20.
9. MAYFIELD, A. (1909). 'Fauna and Flora of Norfolk: the Non-marine Mollusca of Norfolk.' *Trans. Nfk. & Norwich Nat. Soc.*, **8**, 783–808.
10. PEAKE, J.F. (1960). 'The Terrestrial Mollusca of the Island.' *Scolt Head Island*, Second Edition, 246–59.

marine fauna R. HAMOND

THE NORFOLK COAST, being unspectacular and often bitterly cold, provides very little shelter for marine animals. The fauna is further limited by the turbidity of the sea-water, the wide annual range in sea-temperature offshore, and the extraordinary extent of very shallow water near the coast, especially to the north.

In recent years various habitats have been investigated. These include the water of Blakeney Harbour for plankton and also the stony, sandy, and muddy shores; the 'Scaup' at Hunstanton, a long promontory fully exposed to the sea and covered with mussel-lays; the very sheltered quayside at Wells; the shore at West Runton, where boulders lie on hard chalk, with a rich fauna under the rocks and in little pools; and the dredging-grounds within a radius of six or seven miles of Blakeney Harbour entrance.

Plankton hauls taken at dusk on a flooding tide show a distinct seasonal pattern. In winter the macroplankton

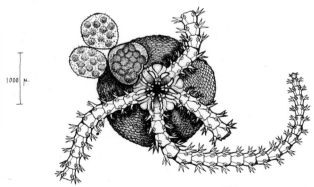

Drawn by R. Hamond

Fig. 1 Cancerilla Tubulata, ♀ *with ovisacs, on* Amphipholis Squamata *from among whelk pot rubbish from off Salthouse in 10 fathoms*

consists of large diatoms, *Sagitta setosa* (never *elegans*) and a few copepods, while the microplankton provides enough feed to ensure fattening of the mussels which constitute such an important local industry. In March there is a sudden increase in number of winkle eggs (*Littorina littorea*) and of larvae of other molluscs and worms, which persists until late May or early June when an outbreak of the gelatinous alga *Phaeocystis* renders hauling impossible for some weeks. When this outbreak is over the water becomes clear, large medusae (*Aequorea vitrina* and *Chrysaora hysoscella*) appear in numbers and huge shoals of whitebait enter the harbour with the tide. These are eagerly preyed upon by terns from the nesting-grounds on Blakeney Point. Mackerel appear offshore at this time, but vary greatly in abundance from year to year and rarely come into the harbour before late August. They leave in late September, after which the plankton finally dies down to its winter level. Interesting species taken include the medusae *Tima* (in March), *Staurophora* (April), *Eutima gracilis* and *Mitrocomella brownei* (September), the pteropod *Clione* (April), and the monstrillid *Cymbasoma zetlandicum* (September). The old larvae of the polychaete *Poecilochaetus* and the gastropod *Aporrhais* appear together constantly from July to September and that of the shrimp *Philocheras* in September. These three are as yet unknown off north Norfolk as adults, but *Philocheras fasciatus* (and possibly other species) is taken by the Yarmouth shrimpers.

The shores of Blakeney Harbour are of clean sand or mud (fig. 2). Burrowing amphipods are abundant but do not extend into Morston Creek whose lowest reaches are notable for sessile protozoa, diatoms, and hydroids

R. HAMOND is Recorder of Marine Biology to the Norfolk and Norwich Naturalists Society

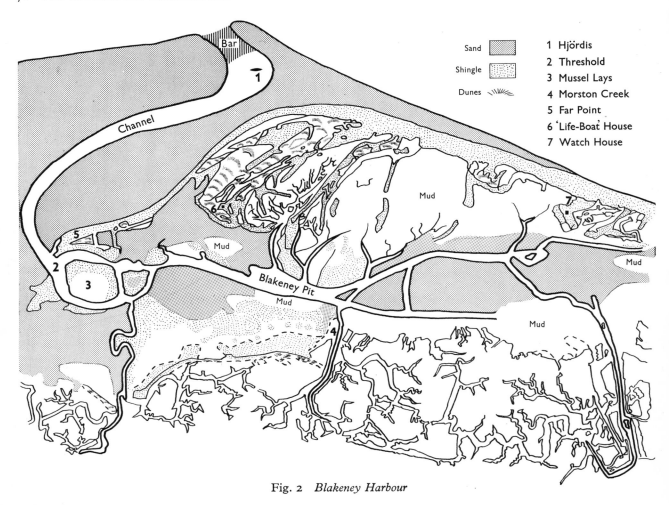

Sand	1 Hjördis
Shingle	2 Threshold
Dunes	3 Mussel Lays
	4 Morston Creek
	5 Far Point
	6 Life-Boat House
	7 Watch House

Fig. 2   *Blakeney Harbour*

such as *Laomedea* spp. Where the channel drains past the end of Blakeney Point there is a flat, stony threshold covered with *Laminaria saccharina*. The holdfasts of the *Laminaria* shelter a rich fauna of small arthropods. On the south shore opposite the Point are mussel-lays with many associated polychaetes, e.g. *Audouinia*, *Notomastus*. Athwart the middle of the channel as it turns to enter the sea the wreck of a coaster, the *Hjördis*, is full of sessile organisms.

The burrowing fauna of the Hunstanton 'Scaup' is very like that of the mussel-lays in Blakeney Harbour and masses of hydroids are cast ashore there by gales.

Wells Quay, although fully marine, is very sheltered and never dries out at low tide. The rocks downstream which are not exposed at low tide have thick tufts of the polyzoan *Bowerbankia* on the undersides, and a dense fauna of protozoa, nematodes, and small crustacea. The sponge *Halichondria* and the anemone *Metridium* dominate the fauna under the quay. They are less abundant among the rocks below, where rotting posts harbour great numbers of the isopod, *Limnoria*.

West Runton is a fully exposed rocky shore, with a fauna rich in polyclinid ascidians and other animals that rarely or never occur elsewhere. The coelenterates *Dynamena pumila* and *Actinia equina*, common species,

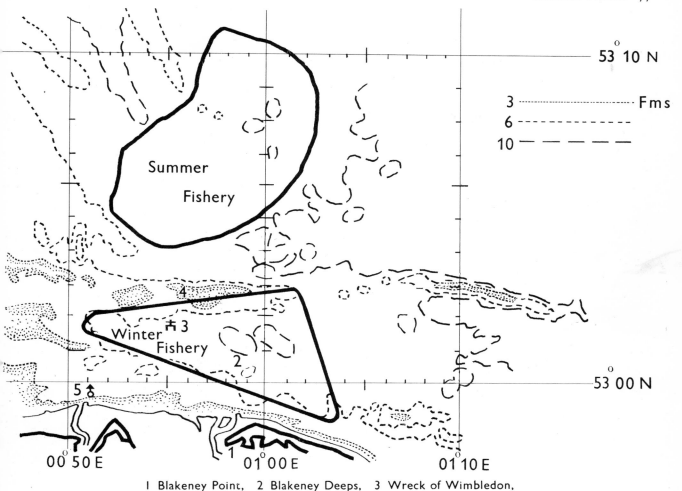

1 Blakeney Point, 2 Blakeney Deeps, 3 Wreck of Wimbledon,
4 Blakeney Overfalls, 5 Wells Bar.

Fig. 3 *The offshore grounds north of Blakeney Harbour*

do not appear at any other point on the Norfolk coast. Extremely rare forms which are found include *Pista maculata* and *Zeppelinia monostyla*. There is no *Laminaria* but myriads of crustaceans live in *Corallina*, while the chalk is bored by great numbers of *Zirfaea*.

Off Blakeney Harbour lies Blakeney Deeps, the floor being a strip of waterworn dead shells grading into muddy sand and the far boundary formed by Blakeney Overfalls (fig. 3). This is a submarine bank covered with gravel and empty bivalves. On the seaward side there are reefs of *Sabellaria* and thickets of hydroids and polyzoans, while slightly to the west are forests of *Flustra*. In addition there are rich grounds off Stiffkey with an abundance of *Lanice* and *Ampelisca* and to the north of the wreck of the *Wimbledon* is a vast expanse of clayey mud covered by pebbles and shells. In summer this is the site of an important whelk fishery. The winter fishing is in the Deeps. The average depth is between 6 and 10 fathoms, the greatest being 12 fathoms north-east of Blakeney Overfalls Buoy.

nature conservation
ERIC DUFFEY

Unless one thinks man was intended to be an all-conquering and sterilizing power in the world, there must be some general basis for understanding what it is best to do. This means looking for some wise principle of co-existence between man and nature, even if it has to be a modified kind of man and a modified kind of nature. This is what I understand by conservation.

CHARLES S. ELTON

THE COUNTY of Norfolk has long been recognized by research workers and naturalists as a unique area in lowland England for the variety and richness of its wild life. It also has a remarkable record as a pioneer in Nature conservation in this country. The basis of this work was laid in 1869, when the Norfolk and Norwich Naturalists' Society was founded. The first practical move to establish a Nature Reserve was in 1912, when a public fund was raised to purchase Blakeney Point, which was presented to the National Trust. This was followed by the purchase in 1923 of Scolt Head Island. In 1926 Dr Sidney Long, a member of the Naturalists' Society, founded the Norfolk Naturalists' Trust, the first of its kind in the country. This important event was reported to the British Association meeting in Leeds in September 1927 by Professor F.W. Oliver, who commented at the time that if the Norfolk Trust was successful 'one would look forward to the time when every county would have its County Trust'. He would have been disappointed if he had known that no other County Trusts would be formed for nearly twenty years. From 1926, the Norfolk Naturalists' Trust laid the foundation of a Nature Reserve system which is still unrivalled in any other British county. The Nature Conservancy was incorporated by Royal Charter in 1949, and although one of its principal tasks is to establish and manage National

Nature Reserves, its resources are limited and because of the urgency of the tasks ahead County Naturalists' Trusts are needed as much now as ever.

Norfolk has four main types of country which are of great biological interest and where most of the Nature Reserves have been established. These are: the coastline with its extensive sand dunes and saltmarshes; the Norfolk Broads and valley fens; the sandy soils of Breckland; and fourthly the relics of heaths and fens all over the county, many of which have survived to the present day by virtue of their status as common land.

THE COASTLINE

The Norfolk coastline of wide, sandy beaches, extensive sand dunes and saltmarshes, and low cliffs of sand, clay and gravel, is one of the most important in eastern England. It provides amenities and enjoyment for many thousands of holidaymakers each year, and has areas of unique interest to the ornithologist, botanist, zoologist, and geologist. The steady development which has spread along all our coasts, especially along the south of England, during the last thirty years has also affected the Norfolk coast but to a lesser extent. Nevertheless, of Norfolk's 87 miles of coastline, over a third (31 miles) is affected by some form of building development. Along a 65-mile stretch of the Hampshire coast the built-up proportion has increased from 4.5 per cent in 1948 to 36 per cent in 1959. In Sussex 80–90 per cent of the coast has been built on.

The first Norfolk Nature Reserve, Blakeney Point, consists of 1,335 acres of saltmarsh, shingle beach, and sand dune, and adjacent on the east side are the 780

E. DUFFEY is the East Anglian Regional Officer of the Nature Conservancy

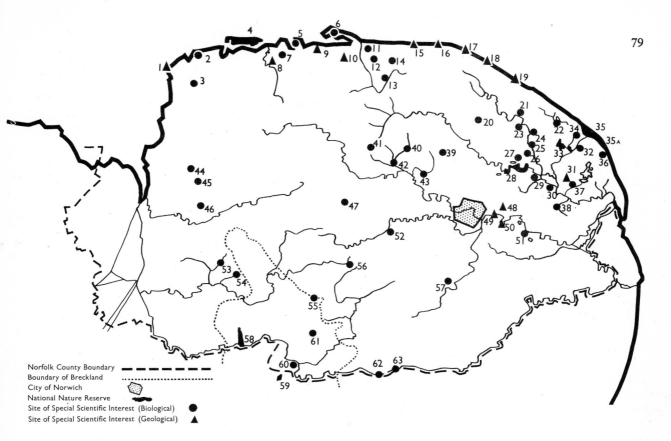

Norfolk County Boundary — — — —
Boundary of Breckland ··················
City of Norwich
National Nature Reserve
Site of Special Scientific Interest (Biological) ●
Site of Special Scientific Interest (Geological) ▲

list of sites

S.S.S.I. managed as Nature Reserves are in the
Nature Reserves List and are marked ●

N.N.R. *National Nature Reserve*
N.T. *National Trust*
N.N.T. *Norfolk Naturalists' Trust*

NATURE RESERVES
WITH OWNERSHIP DETAILS

26 Alderfen Broad (N.N.T.)
25 Barton Broad (N.N.T.)
6 Blakeney Point (N.T.)
28 Bure Marshes (N.N.T., N.N.R.)
11 Cley and Salthouse Marshes (N.T., N.N.T.)
61 East Wretham Heath (N.N.T.)
33 Hickling Broad and Heigham Sounds (N.N.T., N.N.R.)
34 Horsey Mere (N.T.)
32 Martham Broad (including Starch Grass – N.N.T.)
47 Potter and Scarning Fens (N.N.T.)
4 Scolt Head (N.T., N.N.T., N.N.R.)
51 Surlingham and Rockland Broads (N.N.R.)
59 Thetford Heath (N.N.T., N.N.R.)
58 Weeting Heath (N.N.T., N.N.R.)
35 Winterton Dunes (N.N.R.)

SITES OF SPECIAL SCIENTIFIC
INTEREST (BIOLOGICAL) ●

60 Barnhamcross Common
62 Blo Norton Fen, with Thelnetham and Hinderclay Fens
40 Booton Common
23 Broad Fen
39 Buxton Heath
37 Burgh Common
27 Burntfen Broad
53 Caldecote Valley
22 Calthorpe Broad
38 Decoy Carr
30 The Doles
21 East Ruston Common
46 East Winch Common
57 Flordon Common
54 Foulden Common
41 Foxley Wood
7 Holkham Lake
13 Holt Lowes
35a Horsey Warren
14 Kelling Heath
45 Leziate, Derby, and Sugar Fens
29 Ranworth Marshes
63 Redgrave and Lopham Fens
3 Ringstead Downs
44 Roydon Common

52 Runhall Common
12 Salthouse Heath
56 Scoulton Mere
24 Sutton Broad
43 Swannington-Upgate Common
55 Thompson Water
2 Thornham West Island
5 Wells Dunes and Marshes
20 Westwick and Walsham Woods
42 Whitwell Common
36 Winterton Great Valley

SITES OF SPECIAL SCIENTIFIC
INTEREST (GEOLOGICAL) ▲

31 Billockby Sandpit
50 Bramerton Pits
49 Crown Point Pit
8 Holkham Brickpits
1 Hunstanton Cliffs
9 Morston Cliff
19 Mundesley Cliffs
17 Overstrand Cliffs
18 Sidestrand and Trimingham Cliffs
15 Skelding Hill Cliffs
48 Thorpe Pit
16 West Runton Cliffs
10 Wiveton Downs

Fig. 1 *Nature Reserves and S.S.S.I.*

acres of coastal marshes at Cley and Salthouse. In addition to its physiographical and vegetational interest the whole area is of national importance for its bird-life, both as a ringing station and for migrant and rare breeding birds.

Scolt Head Island (1,821 acres), which lies some ten miles west, is famous for its breeding colonies of sea-birds, the range of plant-life on the extensive dune and saltmarsh system, its invertebrate fauna, and for the physiographical studies. It is one of the best documented Nature Reserves in the country.

On the east coast of Norfolk there is a large and important area of dunes and sandy heath extending south from Horsey to Hemsby. Part of this area, known as the Winterton Dunes National Nature Reserve (259 acres) was established by agreement with the owner in 1956. Certain plants of very considerable interest, such as the grey hairgrass (*Corynephorus canescens*) and the hybrid marram grass (*Ammocalamagrostis baltica*), which are very rare in England, are found here.

Other interesting areas along the Norfolk coast which have been scheduled as Sites of Special Scientific Interest under Section 23 of the 1949 National Parks and Access to the Countryside Act are indicated on the map in fig. 1.

THE BROADS

This extremely interesting region with its waterways, lakes, and fens, is probably the richest area for aquatic and fenland wild-life which survives in this country. Two Broadland National Nature Reserves have been established in Norfolk: Hickling Broad and Heigham Sounds, in the Ant valley (1,204 acres), by agreement with the Norfolk Naturalists' Trust; and 1,019 acres of broad and fen in the Bure valley, by agreement with three landowners. A third area in the Yare valley, including Surlingham and Rockland Broads, is a proposed National Nature Reserve, and this will complete a carefully chosen series, each with its own biological peculiarities and interests. Up to about thirty years ago most of these extensive marshes were used for summer grazing, cutting litter, reed, and sedge, but today much of the open fen is rapidly disappearing under bush growth. The management policy must restore the habitat diversity, and much can be achieved in this way by redeveloping the reed

and sedge beds and mowing or grazing on the mixed fen which produced litter.

The future of Broadland as a whole is a very important problem concerning private landowners, naturalists, commercial boat interests, navigation authorities, angling societies, holidaymakers, shopkeepers, and hoteliers. Pollution of the Broadland rivers is also of vital interest to public authorities who control sewage disposal and who depend on the rivers for their supply of drinking-water. No generally accepted solution has yet been found to the problem of maintaining a fair balance between the various demands made on the Broads, and it may be that an impartial committee of inquiry will have to be appointed to examine every aspect of the matter. Meanwhile the Broads continue to attract more people and boats each year. The following figures record a 37.5 per cent increase in the number of boats licensed between 1955 and 1960:

	1955	1960
Motor-boats	2,906	4,412
Sailing-boats	1,676	2,360
Houseboats	121	80
Rowing-boats	1,583	1,796
Total	**6,286**	**8,648**

The greatest increase has been in powered craft: 51.7 per cent in five years.

BRECKLAND

In Breckland, where agricultural progress, forestry operations, and military requirements have reduced the former stretches of open rolling heaths to some 3,600 acres, only nine isolated areas of relatively unspoilt heath now remain, six of them in Suffolk. Two heaths, owned by the Norfolk Naturalists' Trust, are now National Nature Reserves: Weeting Heath (350 acres), and Thetford Heath (225 acres), the latter being just over the county boundary in West Suffolk. The Trust also owns East Wretham Heath, famous as the site of Ringmere and Langmere, but most of this Reserve has been compulsorily taken over as part of a military training area. Barnhamcross Common, a fourth unspoilt heath, is well known for rare Breckland plants and the very local orb-web spider, *Araneus adiantus*, which is found on gorse bushes.

In 1954 and 1955 myxomatosis virtually wiped out the immense rabbit population, and this provided a remarkable boost to the vegetation growth which had previously been severely suppressed by grazing. While some plants became scarce and one or two, such as *Veronica verna*, have not been seen for some years, other Breckland plants flowered and grew more vigorously than in living memory. This surge of vegetation growth appears to have made the heaths less favourable as breeding habitats for the stone curlew and ringed plover, which were so distinctive of Breckland, and the disappearance of rabbit burrows has resulted in a drastic fall in the numbers of breeding wheatears.

The revolution in change of land use in Breckland is probably nearly over and a pattern is emerging dominated by cultivated fields, 50,000 acres of forestry plantations, and training areas, with the few surviving heaths isolated one from another. In spite of the great changes to Breckland we may perhaps look forward optimistically, providing conservation does not lose any further ground. The stone curlews are fewer in number but appear to be adapting themselves to the new environment provided by the forestry fire-breaks and rides, where many now nest. Certain plants and probably insects also survive in such areas, and the amenity belts of deciduous trees which fringe many plantations encourage a richer variety of small birds. On balance Breckland probably has a richer fauna and flora because of the increased diversity of habitat, and few, if any, of the characteristic species have been lost. However, set against this we no longer have the wonderful open views over miles of rolling heathland – 'wild Breckland' as it was called has gone for ever.

OTHER AREAS OF SCIENTIFIC INTEREST

The Nature Reserves in Norfolk are either owned and/or managed by one or more of the following: Norfolk Naturalists' Trust, National Trust, and Nature Conservancy. There are many smaller areas, which are however valuable for conservation and other scientific purposes, and which have been notified as Sites of Special Scientific Interest (S.S.S.Is) under Section 23 of the 1949 Act. A total of fifty-seven have been scheduled in Norfolk, and eighteen of these have some sort of common land status, the rest being privately owned. Commons are of special interest to the conservationist because they constitute one of the few types of country which in many cases have probably never been cultivated and many plants and animals have been able to survive in such areas.

In 1910 W.G. Clarke estimated that the total acreage of Norfolk commons was 11,324, and in 1958 8,386 acres remained, although much of this consisted of village greens or other amenity areas, or else was let for cultivation. Nevertheless it is significant that 31 per cent of Norfolk S.S.S.Is are commons, and three of these, Roydon Common, Buxton Heath, and the Waveney Fens by South Lopham, are of exceptional interest.

Individually some S.S.S.Is may not be of special importance except from the local point of view, but collectively they have great habitat diversity and form an essential part of the national conservation requirements if our heritage of wild-life is to have space to survive in the twentieth century. The fifty-seven Norfolk S.S.S.Is are scattered all over the county (see map) ranging in size from 1 acre (a geological site) to 1,700 acres of coastal marshes, and the whole totalling 14,201 acres. In the following table sixty-two sites in Norfolk (five National Nature Reserves and fifty-seven S.S.S.Is) totalling 18,942 acres have been classified in the following habitats:

NATURE CONSERVATION

	Number of sites	Total acreage
Fen and open water	27	8,534
Dry and wet heaths	11	2,486
Dunes, shingle, saltings, and coastal marsh	8	6,505
Woodland (not fen woodland)	2	862
Geological sites	13	497
Chalk grassland	1	58

THE 'NEW OUTLOOK' IN CONSERVATION

The development and importance of nature conservation today can only be considered in relation to other forms of land use. In Norfolk the dominant activity is arable cultivation, and in recent years agricultural science has made such progress that important refuges for wild-life such as marginal land, hedgerows, and roadside verges, are being reduced at a rapid rate. Wild-life conservation cannot consist solely of establishing isolated pieces of land as Nature Reserves, because these widely scattered areas form such a small proportion of our land surface and because much of our wild-life has to live on territory exploited in some way by Man. The 'new outlook' is the acceptance by the public as well as the scientist and naturalist that conservation can only succeed if it forms a part of our land management everywhere in the country-side. It is becoming increasingly recognized that ecological knowledge derived from conservation studies can often be of considerable value in many problems concerned with land use. For example, invertebrate populations exist wherever vegetation cover is able to survive, and the influence of this biological potential, whose main reservoir is the hedgerow, verge, and roadside, in maintaining some sort of ecological balance between pest and non-pest species is not known. Charles Elton has described our roadsides as being the last really big nature reserve we have in Britain because they run for something like 190,000 miles amongst our cultivated land. In Breckland the verges are the only connecting link between the Nature Reserves, and function as refuges for plants and animals, enabling them to recolonize areas when circumstances permit. It is important that these 'links' are not sterilized by the use of herbicides or by other treatments which destroy the natural vegetation cover.

The rate of development in the use of toxic chemicals in agriculture has caused a great deal of concern among naturalists. In 1953 it was estimated that 2,500,000 acres of land in Britain was treated and in 1960 the figure was over 8,000,000 acres. This is of special importance in Norfolk because 62 per cent of the area of the county is under arable crops. The use of toxic chemicals is now an accepted and important part of scientific agriculture, but it is the responsibility of conservationists to study and make known every way in which their use has an impact on our wild-life.

Fig. 2 *Dunes and saltmarsh on Scolt Head, N.N.R.*

physical anthropology

CALVIN WELLS

*Who knows the fate of his bones, or how often he is to
be buried? Who hath the Oracle of his ashes, or whither
they are to be scattered?*

SIR THOMAS BROWNE: *Norwich, 1st May 1658*

TO RECORD the physical history of Man in East Anglia
is a task to vex a saint and distemper a scientist. Artefacts
of human endeavour abound. From the modern office
blocks of the Norwich Union we can tread a broad
droveway down the ages seeing on every side churches,
manors, and husbandry, Saxon earthworks and Roman
sherds, microliths of such fastidious delicacy that we are
haunted by dreams of some archaic Fabergé, hand-axes
as massive and uncompromising as a vision of Henry
Moore. Then, with the epochs slipping behind us, we can
follow the trail, if it is congenial to our temperament and
imagination, to a stony dawn below the Crag. Here,
amidst the ambiguous twilight of the eoliths, we step
out of the weave of human history and abandon our last
contact with the myriad restless hands that wrought, in
idle boredom or frenzied need, this long and prodigal
heritage.

In contrast to this *embarras de richesse* to which the
archaeologist is heir the student of Man's skeletal relics
is meagerly endowed. From many periods nothing
survives but a handful of bones warped by the pressure
and gnawed by the acids of unfriendly soils. Huge gaps
occur in the record, untenanted by any splinter of human
remains or filled only by elusive wisps of evidence and
hints of what-might-have-been. From other eras the
bones survive in plenty but only as a chaotic, perplexing
mass, ill documented and as yet unanalysed. A start has
lately been made, however, at the task of reviewing all
the surviving remains from this region, but the work has
been begun so recently that only its general outline and a
few hesitant conclusions are ready for presentation in
this survey. In a few more years the untangling of our
local problems will doubtless be much farther advanced.
Our knowledge of the types and connexions of former
dwellers here will break from the haze of conjecture
that now shrouds it, and will achieve a brightness of
pattern and perspective that need fear no scrutiny
however searching.

An account of the physical anthropology of the region
cannot yet provide the main dish in this symposium. It
may, nevertheless, supply an elegant garnish or add
piquancy to more substantial fare. In this hope there
follows a brief description and catalogue of human
skeletal remains from Norfolk and Suffolk. In the space
at our disposal there can be no attempt to make either the
catalogue complete or the description elaborate. Documentation is likewise reduced to a minimum.

PALAEOLITHIC

No East Anglian bone existing today can support a
claim to date from the Palaeolithic Age. This can be
categorically stated despite the fact that from time to
time various fragments have been ascribed to the
Pleistocene or even Tertiary eras. The evidence in
favour of these claims is far too thin to sustain critical
examination and we need not perpetuate here even the
site-names of the claimant bric-à-brac.

Only the Foxhall jaw needs to be considered. The
story of its discovery in 1855 in a Crag pit near Ipswich,
its acquisition by the American Dr Collyer, its examination by such authorities as Owen, Huxley, Falconer, and
Busk, and its later disappearance (now nearly a century

CALVIN WELLS is an anthropologist and palaeopathologist, and
is a contributor to *L'Anthropologie, Antiquity*, etc.

ago) is too well known to bear repetition. The arguments for and against its alleged antiquity have by now an antiquity of their own and probably few anthropologists could be found who would wish to keen for its passing. I mention it again only because some workers may feel that Loren Eiseley (1943) reopened a closed account when he first called attention to an apparently overlooked primitive feature which is shown in the one surviving drawing of the jaw: a clear triplication of the left mental foramen. Flimsy evidence, no doubt, in view of the fact that triple mental foramina do occur in modern mandibles! They are rare, however, and in general are a primitive character. This may give just enough ground for delaying a final verdict on the bone against the unlikely event of its rediscovery.

MESOLITHIC

No human bones can definitely be assigned to this period but one skull is worth describing here. It is a well-preserved adult calvarium which was recovered in 1954 from the bank of the river Yare at Strumpshaw, a few miles east of Norwich.

It is possible, of course, that it may have been re-deposited as a result of flooding or of disturbance to

CATALOGUE OF HUMAN REMAINS FROM NORFOLK AND SUFFOLK (A) INHUMATIONS
I SPECIMENS FIRMLY DATED BY ARCHAEOLOGICAL ASSOCIATIONS

Find site	Archaeological date	Location and registration	Brief description of main surviving remains
Grime's Graves, Weeting, Norfolk	Neolithic	B.M.(N.H.)R.C.S. 4.0051 B.M.(N.H.)R.C.S. 4.0052	I male calva: fair condition Fragments of an adolescent girl: very fragile
Bodney, Norfolk	Beaker period	N. 185.930	I male cranium; some post-cranial fragments: fair condition
Bury St Edmunds, Suffolk	Beaker period	B.E. F.84	10 small cranial fragments
Wherstead, Suffolk	Beaker period	I. 920/52.7	I adolescent skeleton: much warped
Barnham, Suffolk	Bronze Age	B.E. F.55	A few fragments of I young adult
Barton Bendish, Norfolk	Bronze Age	N. 169.953	Remains of 2 or 3 adults
Methwold, Norfolk	Bronze Age	N. 165.955	A damaged calva
Heacham, Norfolk	Iron Age	N. 208.954	Scanty remains of I adult and I child
Roudham, Norfolk	Iron Age	N. 204.956	I female skeleton: poor condition
Ellingham, Great, Norfolk	Romano-British	N. 241.957	I female skeleton: fair
Flitcham, Norfolk	Romano-British	N. 415.960	A few fragmentary remains
Burgh Castle, Suffolk	Early Saxon	M.O.W.	Remains of about 300 skeletons
Bury St Edmunds, Suffolk	Early Saxon	B.E. K.62	I cranium
Caister-by-Yarmouth, Norfolk	Early Saxon	B.M.(N.H.)R.C.S. 4.10.3	I calvarium
Caister-by-Yarmouth, Norfolk	Early Saxon	N. 343.957	About 125 individuals in excellent condition
Caister-by-Norwich, Norfolk	Early Saxon	N. 77.939	Poor remains of about 10 bodies
Eriswell, Suffolk	Early Saxon	M.O.W.	About 30 skeletons in fair condition
Foulden, Norfolk	Early Saxon	N. 224.954	I skeleton
Foulden, Norfolk	Early Saxon	N. 104.958	I skeleton in fair condition
Framlingham, Suffolk	Early Saxon	C.U.D.	About 48 bodies in bad condition
Hunstanton, Norfolk	Early Saxon	N. 13.2.950	Half a mandible; a fragment of clavicle
Ipswich (Hadleigh Road), Suffolk	Early Saxon	I.	I damaged cranium
Mildenhall (Holywell Row), Suffolk	Early Saxon	C.U.D. 1.2.207–209	23 individuals
Mundford, Norfolk	Early Saxon	N. 27.952	I male, I female skeleton: fair
Mundford, Norfolk	Early Saxon	N. 18.955	Remains of I skeleton: poor
Mundford, Norfolk	Early Saxon	N. 275.956	Small fragments from 3 or 4 bodies
Narford, Norfolk	Early Saxon	K.L. A.101	I adult male
Thetford (Bury Road), Norfolk	Early Saxon	T. A.2508	I cranium
Thetford (Bury Road), Norfolk	Early Saxon	T. A.2509	I cranium
Thetford (Bury Road), Norfolk	Early Saxon	T. A.2510	Parts of I skull
Thornham, Norfolk	Early Saxon	N. 49.953	Fragments of I skeleton
Thornham, Norfolk	Early Saxon	N. 166.955	5 skeletons: poor condition
Thornham, Norfolk	Early Saxon	N. 244.956	15 skeletons: fair condition
Thornham, Norfolk	Early Saxon	N. 391.960	5 skeletons: bad condition
Watton, Norfolk	Early Saxon	N. 142.952	I male skeleton: incomplete
Wretton, Norfolk	Early Saxon	N. 153.929	A few fragments of cranial vault: 2 femora
Sedgeford, Norfolk	Late Saxon	N. 106.953	Remains of about 20 individuals: bad condition
Sedgeford, Norfolk	Late Saxon	C.U.D.	About 80 skeletons
Thetford (St Mary), Norfolk	Late Saxon	N. 12.950	About 60 burials: very incomplete but good condition
Thorpe (St Andrew), Norfolk	Late Saxon	N. 15.953	About 50 burials: many incomplete but good condition
Creake, South, Norfolk	Medieval	N. 167.955	Remains of about 20 bodies: almost entirely cranial
Elmham, North, Norfolk	Medieval	N. 375.958	Cranial fragments of 5 or 6 individuals: bad condition
Shouldham, Norfolk	Medieval	N. 50.954	About 20 individuals: fair condition
Thetford (Priory), Norfolk	Medieval	M.O.W.	Parts of 7 burials
Warham, Norfolk	Medieval	N. 220.960	Fragments of 7 or 8 bodies: much broken
Worstead, Norfolk	Medieval	N. 227.955	Fragments of about 15 bodies: bad condition

2 SPECIMENS FOR WHICH A PROBABLE BUT NOT DEFINITE DATE CAN BE GIVEN

Find site	Archaeological date	Location and registration	Brief description
Feltwell, Norfolk	Romano-British	K.L. F.137	Scanty remains of 3 individuals
Ipswich (Dales Road), Suffolk	Romano-British	I.	I male cranium
Brandon, Suffolk	Anglo-Saxon	C.U.A. (see note, p. 86)*	About 220 skulls
Congham, Norfolk	Anglo-Saxon	N. 90.955	About 15 individuals
Fowlmere (Bran Ditch), Cambs.	Anglo-Saxon	C.U.	About 50 bodies: many decapitated
Grimston, Norfolk	Early Saxon	N. 61.955	Remains of 2 bodies
Norwich (Bishop's Palace)	Late Saxon	N. 392.960	Remains of about 8 bodies
Norwich (Palace Street)	Late Saxon	N. 156.952	I male skeleton
Pakenham, Suffolk	Early Saxon	I.	Remains of 3 burials
Stiffkey, Norfolk	Saxon	N. 36.955	Fragments of 2 adults and I child
Thetford (Bury Road), Norfolk	Saxon	N. 472.960	I damaged cranium
Thetford (Calverly site), Norfolk	Late Saxon	N. 158.953	
Thetford (Red Castle), Norfolk	Late Saxon	N. 167.957	About 85 burials: good condition
Thetford (St John's), Norfolk	Late Saxon	W.	Remains of 4 individuals: fair condition
Beachamwell, Norfolk	Medieval	N. 73.15	Remains of 5 bodies: fair condition
Burnham Market, Norfolk	Medieval	N. 470.959	Remains of 2 bodies: poor condition
Ellingham, Great, Norfolk	Medieval	N. 241.957	About 25 burials: fair condition
Elmham, North, Norfolk	Medieval	N. 255.958	I damaged calvarium
Ipswich (St James Leper House)	Medieval	I.	2 damaged calvae
Norwich (Trevor Page site)	Medieval	N. 225.955	I damaged cranium
Swaffham, Norfolk	Medieval	N. 135.959	Scanty remains of about 7 bodies
Thetford (Priory), Norfolk	Medieval	N. 117.960	Remains of 5 bodies: mostly cranial
Thetford, Norfolk	Medieval	N. 425.959	I calvarium: good. Fragments of I adult and I child

3 UNDATABLE SPECIMENS

(a) *In which the balance of probability is Iron Age or earlier*

Find site	Location and Registration	Brief description
Feltwell, Norfolk	N. 64.02	I mandible
Foulden, Norfolk	N. 321.956	I calvarium: good, but lacks R. maxilla
Methwold, Norfolk	K.L. A.103	Fragments of 3 bodies: poor condition
Strumpshaw, Norfolk	N. 65.954	I calvarium

(b) *In which the balance of probability is later than the Iron Age*

Find site	Location and Registration	Brief description
Bressingham, Norfolk	N. 376.958	I incomplete skeleton
Darmsden, Suffolk	I.	I calva
Feltwell, Norfolk	N. 469.959	A few cranial fragments
Haveringland, Norfolk	N. 417.960	I damaged calvarium
Hocheston, Suffolk	I.	2 or 3 bodies in poor condition
Hockwold, Norfolk	N. 160.952	Remains of I adult
Icklingham, Suffolk	C.U.A. 469 and 470	2 calvaria
Ipswich (Cheapside)	I.	Calvarium
Ipswich (Dale's Road)	I.	Calva
Ipswich (Orwell river bed)	I.	Calva
Ipswich (Orwell river bed)	I.	Calvarium
Lakenham, Norwich	N. 164.957	A few fragments from 2 or 3 bodies
Norwich (Agricultural Hall)	N. 468.959	Remains of 3 bodies: poor condition
Norwich (Castle Mound)	N. 473.960	Fragmentary remains of 6 or 7 bodies
Norwich (Opie Street)	N. 256.958	A few cranial fragments from about 6 bodies
Peddar's Way, Norfolk	N. 30.346.958	A damaged calvarium
Postwick, Norfolk	N. 416.960	A damaged calvarium
Reedham, Norfolk	N. 254.958	A calvarium: a few post-cranial fragments
Runham, Norfolk	N. 148.954	I calvarium
Surlingham, Norfolk	N. 374.958	A very few post-cranial bones
Weeting, Norfolk	N. 97.960	A few cranial fragments of a child
Whitlingham, Norfolk	N. 50.955	A left parietal bone
Worthing, Norfolk	N. 153.947	A damaged calvarium
Wroxham, Norfolk	N. 473.959	I calvarium
Yarmouth (Marine Parade)	N. 467.959	A few much damaged fragments of I or 2 bodies
Yarmouth (Station Road)	N. 393.960	Remains, mostly cranial, of about 10 bodies

CATALOGUE OF HUMAN REMAINS FROM NORFOLK AND SUFFOLK (B) CREMATIONS

Find site	Archaeological date	Location and registration	Number present
Bealings, Little, Suffolk	Bronze Age	I.	About 20
Bury St Edmunds, Suffolk	Romano-British	B.E. H.181	2
Caistor-by-Norwich	Anglo-Saxon	N. 77.939	About 10
Cawston, Norfolk	Bronze Age	N. 400.960	1
Hollesley, Suffolk	Bronze Age	I. 956.128	2
Illington, Norfolk	Anglo-Saxon	N. 220.950	104
Narford, Norfolk	Bronze Age	K.L. A.102	1
Pakenham, Suffolk	Bronze Age	I.	1
Pakenham, Suffolk	Romano-British	I.	3
Risby, Suffolk	Bronze Age	B.E. F.112	1
Rockland All Saints, Norfolk	Anglo-Saxon	N. 13.950	1
Thetford (Red Castle), Norfolk	Anglo-Saxon	N. 167.957	1
Wolterton, Norfolk	Anglo-Saxon	N. 33.16	1
Worlington, Suffolk	Bronze Age	I.	2

ABBREVIATIONS USED

B.E.	Moyse's Hall Museum, Bury St Edmunds, Suffolk	N.	Castle Museum, Norwich, Norfolk
B.M.(N.H.)	British Museum (Natural History), London, S.W.7	T.	Thetford Museum, Norfolk
C.U.A.	Cambridge University (Anatomy Department)	W.	Remains at present held by Calvin Wells, Mulbarton, Norfolk for various owners
C.U.D.	Cambridge University (Duckworth Laboratory)		
I.	Borough Museum, Ipswich, Suffolk		*The Registration numbers of these crania are:
K.L.	King's Lynn Museum, Norfolk		C.U.A. 471–479, 635–638, 640, 668, 676–678, 684–714, 732–748, 755–767,
M.O.W.	Ministry of Works (Inspectorate of Ancient Monuments)		781–895, 1032, 2225, 2439, 3055–3067, 3072–3075, 4226–4231, and 5583

the bed and bank of the river, and no conclusion can be based on its stratigraphic level which remains uncertain. Its interest is in its appearance.

The most casual glance at once reveals its similarity to the Mesolithic population from Téviec, Brittany (Péquart, 1937). So striking is this likeness that I took it to Paris and, through the courtesy of Professor H.V. Vallois, compared it with the Téviec specimens.

The Strumpshaw skull is probably a male. It is robust in build with strongly developed attachments for the neck and other muscles and has temporal lines that are strikingly prominent. Viewed from above, it is ovoid in contour; from the side, the frontal bone is smoothly rounded over a moderate supra-orbital ridge, there is a trace of post-coronal sulcus, and the back of the skull falls rather steeply to a sharp turn below the superior nuchal line. When it is placed on a table it rests on the occipito-molar plane which the tips of the mastoid processes fail to reach by about 5 millimetres. There is slight upward keeling of the vault in the mid-parietal region. The eye-sockets are rectangular and set almost level. The palate is broad and the dental arcade U-shaped. Face, nose, and orbits are all low in proportion to their breadths, the eye-sockets exceptionally so. Its nearest neighbour amongst the Téviec series is No. 15, a female, to which it is extremely close both metrically and

morphologically though somewhat heavier in build. Dr K.P. Oakley has kindly supplied a phospho-fluorine and nitrogen analysis for it. The results are: $N = 2.94$ per cent, $F = 0.17$ per cent, $100(\text{per cent } F/\text{per cent } P_2O_5) = 0.7$. Unfortunately we lack sufficient comparable material to permit a confident interpretation of these findings. Dr Oakley says, 'on the limited data available it seems rather more probably post-Mesolithic than Mesolithic'.

Clearly, then, this skull cannot be firmly dated to the Middle Stone Age, but it is highly probable that it represents a relatively pure survival from that period to some later indefinite date.

NEOLITHIC

This is represented by the remains of two skeletons from the Grime's Graves flint-mines. One is a male skullcap, the other a broken lower jaw with some post-cranial fragments from a girl about twelve years old. The skullcap is in the low mesocranial range and is ovoid in contour, of average build and with moderately strong brow ridges. The damaged but well-domed frontal bone is of medium width, the highest point of the skull was probably unusually far behind the fronto-parietal junction, but there is no feature which makes this calva especially noteworthy: it has neither the marked narrowness nor light, gracile build that has sometimes been associated with skulls of this period. By contrast with this the remains of the girl are extremely slender and lightly built. They consist of the body of the lower jaw carrying all the permanent teeth except the third molars. Caries is absent and attrition slight. The mandible is shallow but moderately thick. Most long bones are also present but damaged. The clavicles are quite exceptionally slender but all are frail and delicate. The thigh bones are somewhat more bowed than the average, the shins are rounded with no sharp margins, the joint surfaces widely developed. If this girl is representative of the Norfolk Neolithics she invites us to think of them as being a people of uncommonly lithe and supple physique.

BEAKER PERIOD

Three inhumations of this date exist: one from Wherstead, Suffolk, one from Bury St Edmunds, and one from Bodney, Norfolk.

The Wherstead skeleton is that of a young adolescent male. The skull is severely warped and badly reconstructed so that no adequate description of it is possible at present. It is lightly built and probably just within the long-headed range. The eye-sockets are high, the dental arcade is overcrowded and ill-formed. Six vertebrae are present, also the damaged pelvis and fragments of long bones. These are small and slender but not markedly so.

The Bury St Edmunds specimen consists only of ten small fragments of cranial vault.

The Bodney skeleton is that of a middle-aged man. It comprises a damaged skull and a few dozen post-cranial fragments, mostly small and broken. The cranium was reconstructed by Keith (1932), and although much of it remains uncertain in detail the main pattern is clear enough. It is strongly dysharmonic, the broad vault contrasting with an apparently long face and an undoubtedly narrow mandible to give a form that is not easy to duplicate in later material. There is a temptation to see this individual as the product of racial mixture, his light narrow jaw and face retaining Neolithic features, his skull already influenced by the earliest pioneers of Bronze Age culture.

BRONZE AGE

Little survives that can be definitely assigned to this period. From Barton Bendish there are the remains of two, perhaps three, individuals. A fairly well-preserved cranial vault and a couple of dozen fragments of limb bones permit a glimpse of what their appearance may have been. The skull is heavily built with strong muscular attachments and firm brow ridges. Both broad and high it must have been a capacious head carried, if we can judge from the limb bones and other fragments, on a powerful thickset body. A few other remnants from Methwold heighten this dark picture of bulky, globular heads on sturdy torsos. The rest is veiled in the cobwebs of speculation.

IRON AGE

An incomplete female skeleton from Roudham gives the best indication of the local Iron Age pattern. This is yet another skull that is both warped and broken, and needs too much reconstruction to permit an accurate estimate of its original measurements. It is now considerably higher and shorter than the pattern of native Iron Age crania as identified by G.M. Morant from material in other parts of the country. In its original form the difference may have been less stark. It seems likely, however, that if this skull is at all representative of the average for the region then there was a local type of population here with some distinctive characteristics to set them apart from their contemporaries in other areas of the British Isles. It is regrettable that this suggestion is unsupported by stronger evidence: its clarification one way or the other would have interesting implications for the pre-history of the region.

ROMANO-BRITISH

Anthropologically the centuries of Roman occupation should be seen, perhaps, as merely the continuation of the Iron Age, profoundly altered culturally but at first hardly changed at the physical level apart from sporadic and scanty hybridization in the immediate neighbourhood of the major Roman settlements. No Roman cemetery has been excavated in this area and there is little that can safely be dated to the period.

A semi-metopic skull from Dales Road brickfield, Ipswich, has no firm associations but is probably Romano-British. It is a sturdy skull, asymmetrical in its development, with weak brow ridges and a bossy frontal bone.

A more interesting specimen comes from Great Elling-ham. Amongst a group of inhumations, discovered while a road was being widened, a skull was found with a small sliver of bronze in a matrix of soil adherent to the inferior surface of the basilar part of the occipital bone. This bronze, which was identifiable as a Roman coin of about A.D. 270, was precisely in the position at which it would have come to rest had it been dropped into the mouth of the corpse in accordance with the Roman rite of pro-viding the departed with 'Charon's fee' for the passage of the Styx. Later excavation produced the remains of about two dozen bodies consistently associated with medieval sherds and debris. Eventually a few pieces of Romano-British pottery were turned up on the site but not in direct conjunction with any bones. Although the bulk of the material is undoubtedly medieval it would seem perverse and graceless not to accept the 'passage penny' as denoting at least one Roman burial. If there were others their thrifty obsequies betray no clue to guide us to them. The body is that of a female about thirty years of age. The skull is low and very narrow in relation to its length; seen from above it is ellipsoid in contour. The brow ridges are insignificant and the fore-head steeply rising. The occiput is smoothly curved; the eye-sockets are small; the nose inclines to broadness and is *retroussé* at its root. The lower jaw is light and slender with a clean-cut prominent chin. The few sur-viving post-cranial bones reveal a slimness of body build and a stature near 5 feet 4 inches.

ANGLO-SAXON

This period provides us with more material than any other and enables us to form a good picture of the skeletal pattern whilst posing some tantalizing problems. The best assemblage is the series of about a hundred and twenty-five bodies from Caister-by-Yarmouth. Metrically and morphologically the skulls are very close to the well-known series from Burwell, Cambridgeshire, but the Caister population was lower in cranial height, longer and narrower in the face, and deeper in the mandible.

A group of fifteen individuals from Congham are even closer to the Burwell folk but they, too, have slightly lower heads. Unluckily the numerous remains from Framlingham, Suffolk, and Caistor-by-Norwich are too crumbled and time-worn to give a clear picture of the type present in these cemeteries. As far as it is possible to judge the Caistor people were very similar to those from Caister.

At Thornham the material is again disappointingly poor for most of the twenty-five skeletons, but two distinct types appear to be present. Most of the bodies resemble the local Anglo-Saxon variety as far as this is known. A smaller section is distinguished by having a lower skull with stronger brow ridges and a more sloping forehead: a skull that suggests the survival in the area of the old native Iron Age pattern. The fact that an apparent Iron Age survival occurs as a contemporary inhumation in a sixth to seventh–century burial-ground prompts several questions. To what extent were the earlier inhabitants still surviving at this period, perhaps as an under-privileged class relatively free from intermixture with the invading Saxon? Does the consistently low height-length ratio here, which is wholly due to the reduced height, as compared with the Burwell or Bidford-on-Avon populations imply that Saxon overlords were interbreeding more extensively with their immediate precursors in this part of the country? (The crania from Melbourn, Cambridgeshire are intermediate in head height between those of Burwell and Caister-by-Yarmouth.) A further point worth noting is that this characteristic shallowness of the head in Norfolk Saxons is mostly due to a flattening of the cranial base; the supra-auricular heights are little different from those of the more southern and westerly populations.

What, too, is the significance of the Eriswell community which appears to be metrically similar to their Caister-by-Yarmouth contemporaries but distinctly more spare in build? Does this indicate merely a difference in diet and living conditions or is it another hint that hybridiza-tion varied significantly from place to place?

These are all Early Saxon peoples. As we move into the Late Saxon period some very definite trends are found. At Thorpe St Andrew a drift towards brachy-cranialization, or widening of the skull, has shifted the cranial index well into the mesocranial range whilst the height-length ratio still remains low. The population here is less uniform than the Caister dwellers, an expression, no doubt, of the increasingly diverse elements that were gradually being added to these later Saxons.

At Thetford St Mary we have an interesting situation. Here, in a muster of about sixty burials, the contrast between the sexes is much more marked than is usual amongst Anglo-Saxons. About 68 per cent of the males are long-headed, 26 per cent intermediate, and 6 per cent round-headed. Of the females only 13 per cent are long-headed, 62 per cent intermediate, and 25 per cent round-headed. In height-breadth ratio 70 per cent of the males are intermediate and 30 per cent have a low ratio whereas for the females only 20 per cent are in the intermediate class and 73 per cent are low. Other measurements and characteristics reinforce a strong hint that these men were in fact getting their women from some other enclave with different traits from their own. For the historian as for the archaeologist this suggestion poses some alluring problems, not the least of which is the possible location of such an assembly. Now it happens that the Thetford Red Castle site, which huddles tree-girt less than a mile from the St Mary settlement, was at about that time occupied by people who differed greatly from any of the other Anglo-Saxons we have mentioned. This series of eighty-five inhumations is a round-headed community with an intermediate height-length ratio (fig. 1). It has many other distinctive characters and although the St Mary women are not identical with the Red Castle population they appear to be closer to them than are the St Mary males. We may wonder what was the nature of the intercourse, if any, between the two groups. Unfortunately the exact date of the Thetford Red Castle burials remains obscure. It is a compact cemetery in one corner of a mound that is surrounded by a substantial ditch and bank. There is no evidence that these people were Danes of the Great Army that wintered in the town in 869–70; its encampment has never been found but these folk probably lived well after that event. Equally they seem to be much too early to have any direct connexion with the Hythe or Rothwell brachycranials. Their origin eludes our scrutiny: perhaps we should seek their closest affinities among the terp dwellers of Westergo and other Friesian sites.

A further perplexing curiosity at Red Castle is the presence of two decapitated heads of the dolichocranial Saxon type which had been buried along with the brachycranials but in scooped-out hollows neatly lined with flint and chalk blocks. What connexion these two

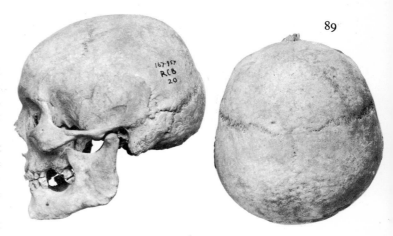

Fig. 1   *Thetford Red Castle cranium No. 20*

skulls had with the main band must remain wholly conjectural. All that can be said of them is that their deep grey colour is quite different from the light sandy tint of the rest of the inhumations and suggests that they had previously been buried elsewhere before their careful re-interment among the settlers of Red Castle.

If, as some people believe, the Anglo-Saxon period was crucial for the introduction of blood group B into western Europe we may find that reliable determination of the blood groups of these various East Anglian populations will help to unravel the complexity of their relationship to one another. It seems likely that this may be effected in the not too distant future. Mrs Madeleine Smith has already accepted some of the material for testing.

It is not yet possible to say much about the series of over two hundred interments from Brandon. Through the courtesy of Professor J.D. Boyd I have made a preliminary survey of the material, and it appears to be chiefly composed of moderately homogeneous Saxons with uncommonly long faces, a tendency to crowding of the incisor teeth, and a somewhat 'pinched' anterior maxillary region. They are mostly males and almost no post-cranial bones survive. A few individuals of the residual Iron Age type occur here also.

I am indebted to Mr D.R. Brothwell for details of a series of over eighty inhumations from Sedgeford which he is examining. They are just dolichocranial but fail by a few points to fall within the low category of the height-length ratio. Their stature is close to 5 feet 9 inches for males and 5 feet $3\frac{1}{2}$ inches for females.

MEDIEVAL

As we enter this period the brief light of Saxon day fades; dusk falls again over the human remains.

No substantial series is yet available on which to base a firm description of the population then living here. Several small fraternities come from religious foundations: Cluniacs at Thetford, Carmelites in Norwich, Gilbertines at Shouldham. Each is inadequate but together they build up a picture of slowly increasing diversity that is more apparent in the general pattern of their skeletal architecture than in any specifically metrical features. Isolated details emerge from the small and damaged collections available. The earlier tendency towards brachycranialization develops no further; it may even regress. The predominantly edge-to-edge bite of Saxon teeth is giving way to an overlap of the upper incisors. There is no evidence of a later re-emergence of the old low-headed British Iron Age type that Morant found in seventeenth-century Londoners. Indeed, the Norwich Carmelites have consistently higher heads than their predecessors. Stature is becoming less, though not markedly so, whilst the expectation of life appears to be on the increase. This, however, may be related to the more sheltered existence led by men dwelling under a monastic rule.

PATHOLOGY

Many problems arise concerning the inter-relationships of the bands who roamed or settled in this region: problems that will only be resolved when further analysis of the material yields more evidence of genetic affinities, hybridization, territory of origin, and population movements. This will be for the future. Now we can best add a few more touches to the outline sketched here by harvesting some random straws from the field of pathology.

For earlier periods there is little to say. For the Anglo-Saxons we can hazard a few conjectures . . . or at least frame some provocative questions.

Why is it that the Thetford St Mary population can show ninety-eight teeth lost ante-mortem from 1,274 identifiable dental positions (7.6 per cent), whereas at Thetford Red Castle we find a 15 per cent loss and the Congham cluster has the high figure of 26 per cent? Compared with this a group of jaws from Caister-by-

Yarmouth gives 130 ante-mortem extractions from 2,167 positions – only 5.9 per cent. Were these a basically sea-roving people whose high fish diet gave them a degree of dental protection denied to the inland dwellers? Or should the question be rephrased in terms of a more starchy diet at Red Castle and Congham or even of an extraneous factor such as the mineral content of the local water?

The caries rate in surviving adult teeth is low: 2.1 per cent for Thetford St Mary, 1.5 per cent for Red Castle. This is very much less than is recorded for any present-day inhabitants of the district except for one small Order of nuns. For the combined early populations a rough calculation can be made of a mean annual caries rate, i.e. the percentage of all teeth becoming carious each year. It is estimated to be about 0.16 per cent. For the modern community of thirty nuns a similar rate has been computed after having discounted any caries developing within the first year of embracing the conventual régime. Their subsequent dental records reveal an annual caries rate close to 0.25 per cent which, although well above that of the Saxons, is a remarkably low figure. It is interesting to observe that their diet is habitually frugal. Little sugar is allowed them, sweets are forbidden, and cake permitted only rarely; whereas fruit and green vegetables are given a prominent place together with a moderate amount of meat and fish. Their bread is made from a coarse stone-ground flour. In some respects, notably in its low content of sugar and fine-textured carbohydrates and also, perhaps, its overall frugality, this diet may be nearer to that of the Anglo-Saxons than is usual in most dining-rooms today. Their well-water has 0.2 parts per million of fluorine.

In all the early groups, and independent of the caries rate, there is a high frequency of alveolar or paradontal abscesses around the roots of the teeth. These are presumably caused by sharp husks of grain and spicules of bone becoming wedged between tooth and jaw. A few seem to be produced by severe erosion of the teeth outstripping the rate of secondary dentine formation and opening up the roots, especially of the molars. In Saxon times most of the flour must have been extremely coarse as well as containing scobs of grit from the friable Niedermendig lava which was regularly imported for use as querns. Whatever the cause may have been gross attrition of the biting surface is the rule; milk-teeth are often heavily eroded before being shed, and the permanent molars commonly have their cusps worn flat within a year or two of eruption. There appears to be only moderate variation in the frequency of paradontal abscesses. Most groups have about a third of the population affected by them. An exception is the Caister-by-Yarmouth people who show well over half their number afflicted. In this maritime community, some of whom practised pseudo-ship burials, we are tempted to invoke fish-bones as the likely cause of the condition. The position is somewhat anomalous in view of the low rate of tooth loss but once resorption of the alveolus has occurred it is not always possible to be sure whether the shedding of a tooth was primarily due to paradontal abscess or not: in the majority of instances it probably was.

Apart from dental conditions, much the most frequent disease is osteo-arthritis. This is quite distinct from rheumatoid arthritis, and is commonly supposed to be due to injury, often of slight degree but constantly repeated. Almost any joint can be attacked but its site of election is the spinal column. This may well reflect occupational hazards such as long continued minor damage in a farming community obliged to carry heavy burdens over rough ploughland and broken stubble. Its predilection for the jaw reinforces the dental evidence of tough meat and crusty bannocks laboriously chewed; its appearance in thumb and fingers reveals a life of heavy manual work. Again there are curious differences in the incidence of the disease. At the Thetford Red Castle site almost every adult shows it; their St Mary neighbours (admittedly a defective series) have only four clear cases. About 15 per cent of the Shouldham Gilbertines have it.

A few cases of *cribrum orbitae*, a porous condition of the bone, are scattered throughout the material. Its cause is unknown but there is some slight evidence that it may be a deficiency process. No other disease occurs often enough for special mention although a wide variety is found. Fractures are common but their anatomical distribution is not unusual. The lower leg bones are most commonly affected and, together with the forearm, probably indicate accidental falls. Broken fingers and toes point rather to the buffeting of direct violence.

Almost all these fractures show patterns of healing that may be described as 'spontaneous and unaided'. Surgical treatment, if any, had no influence on the natural processes of repair. Occasionally, however, we meet a strong suggestion of competent surgical intervention as in an oblique tibial fracture from Grimston which has united without any of the shortening and angulation of the bone which is always found in the absence of treatment.

On the negative side we may note the total lack of evidence for rickets, leprosy, syphilis and, incidentally, trephination.

Extensions of the joint surface on the distal end of the shin bone and on the neck of the talus immediately below it are common in all material before the Late Saxon period. During and after this time they become more rare. These prolongations of the articular surface are known as 'squatting facets' and as their name implies indicate the frequent or habitual use of that posture amongst people unaccustomed to the use of chairs or benches. Occasional examples of marked bowing of the lateral metatarsal bones may hint at the use of a tight sandal thong or similar footwear. A salient character of all the Anglo-Saxon congeries is the delicacy of the small bones of the wrist and ankle joints. It is common to find men with powerful limbs, craggy with muscle ridges, whose wrists are as fine-spun as those of many a modern teenage girl.

STATURE

Far too little evidence is available here to give an estimate of the stature of pre-Saxon inhabitants. Most of the Saxons have an average height close to 5 feet 7½ inches for males and 5 feet 3 inches for females. The St Mary women are somewhat taller than this, 5 feet 4½ inches.

VITAL STATISTICS

With the high destruction of infant bones that must occur in this area we cannot compute reliable mortality rates but a few facts may be gleaned from the larger cemeteries. About a third of the burials are those of young people under eighteen years of age. Of these very few occur in the 10–17 range which emerges as the period of lowest mortality in each of these populations. The average age at death exclusively for those individuals aged 18 and over is about 36 ± 2 for the males,

29±2 for females. At Congham the mean male age is about 42, a fact which may explain their higher dental loss. The frequency of paradontal abscesses with their attendant oral and respiratory tract infections and systemic toxicity must have been a major cause in bringing about the rapid deterioration of health that began in early adult life. Profound general effects would also follow the gross osteophytosis of the vertebrae which in many cases was so severe that long sections of the column were fused into a solid rod, the so-called 'bamboo spine'.

Finally, it seems probable from the ages and distribution of deaths that these were stationary populations in which the death-rate was just about balanced by the birth-rate. No clearly expanding or declining group can be recognized in the region.

CREMATIONS

A number of cremations occur in the area. They range in date from Early Bronze Age to Anglo-Saxon but the best series is an Early Saxon one of 104 individuals from Illington, Norfolk. Throughout the region and for all periods a similar technique is employed and the end-results are much alike. The normal practice was to lay the body supine on the ground or in a shallow trough, to heap the pyre above it, burn it completely and collect the residual bones as far as possible free from ash. In Saxon burials the fragments were often artificially broken to get them into the urns. This was unnecessary, though it may sometimes have been done, when using the largest Bronze Age pots. In about 20 per cent of Saxon cremations we find domestic animals burnt with their dead and some differences according to age and sex occur. Evidence for the burning of animals in earlier periods is indeterminate.

It has been possible to estimate the temperature at which Saxon cremations were carried out by investigating the melting-point of semi-fused glass beads recovered from the remains. An average close to 900° C. was found. In contrast to what is seen in the Wessex barrows, multiple cremations are rare at all periods here. It would be interesting to know whether this difference stemmed from variations of ritual in the two areas or whether a need for economizing with fuel stimulated the western populations to dispose of several bodies in a single pyre whenever it was practicable. No artificial selection for age and sex can be recognized.

As an extensive study of cremation based on the Illington remains has recently been published (Wells 1960) no further elaboration of the material is presented here.

THE PRESENT

It would be satisfactory if this slight essay could end with a description of the modern population but little exists on which to base such a codicil. Blood groups are distinguished by having the highest incidence of A for any major division of the country. The group and gene frequencies were established some years ago by Dr Kopeć (1956) as being O 43.79, A 45.34, B 7.70, AB 3.16, and p 28.24, q 5.59, r 66.17. Dr A.E. Mourant tells me that despite the many more results now available the situation which she described still holds good and no significant heterogeneity has been found in Norfolk or Suffolk though some is present in Lincolnshire. The stature and weight records kept by the local School Medical Services are too limited and fallible to use. The dental records are better but they are not immediately available in any form acceptable for our present purpose. The most that can profitably be done here is to give a few details about the regional incidence of disease.

The sporadic occurrence of *cribrum orbitae* was noted above; as with the rest of the country, it is now never seen. The widespread osteo-arthritis of earlier times still occurs but in general both its onset and peak are delayed until a later period of life. From the seventeenth to the nineteenth century stone in the bladder was pre-eminently the Norfolk disease and East Anglian surgeons were second-to-none in cutting for it. Gutteridge, the surgeon, removed a 34-ounce one from the wife of Thomas Raisin of Norwich and showed it to Charles II before giving it to Trinity College, Cambridge. It remains common but very much less so than it used to be; the reason for this is uncertain. Occupational diseases are few. Workers in the shoe factories contract allergic dermatitis from handling both leather itself and the dyes that stain it. Almost all other urban industrial diseases are relatively rare. Agricultural workers are especially liable to develop toxic symptoms from weed-killers such as DNOC; indeed, the first major group of cases of poisoning from this substance was recognized in Norfolk. Farm-workers are also prone to catch Weil's disease, or leptospirosis. This is a form of infective jaundice which is spread by rats and affects those who come in contact with them, as in threshing out stacks or disposing of carcasses. Sugar-beet lifting, a job which starts with the onset of the cold winter months, entails two common hazards. Firstly, deep cuts or even amputations of the fingers of the left hand as a result of slicing them whilst 'topping' the beet, a process which is done in all weathers often with numbed or half-frozen hands. Secondly, true frost-bite of the fingers, toes or, most typically, of the margins of the ears.

A few conditions are wholly or partly independent of occupation. Foremost is tetanus. This grim disease is much more prevalent here than elsewhere in the country, and though common on farms it often strikes people who have no connexion with agriculture. At least three species of mosquito (*Anopheles algeriensis*, *A. maculipennis atroparvus*, and *A. claviger* which breed respectively in the fens, brackish dykes, and woody carrs of Norfolk) are vectors of *Plasmodium* and cases of malaria are still sometimes seen, belated reminders of days when the marshes bred ague as well as will-o'-the-wisps.

Asthma is said to be unusually common here but comparative figures are difficult to obtain and some physicians deny this. However, a high local incidence of one specifically allergic form of it does occur as an occupational disease of corn millers. The pollens of timothy grass, sheep's fescue, and other Graminae are well known to cause hay-fever in most parts of England. Even among the urban dwellers of Norwich it becomes embarrassingly obtrusive in the months of May and June whenever a strong east wind is blowing. At these times the air over the city is highly charged with the pollens of *Carex riparia*, *C. acuta*, and many other sedges which grow abundantly along the banks of the Broads and of the Yare and Bure river systems. In villages where mains water is not available many of the wells contain a dangerously high amount of nitrites. If this water is drunk by infants *methaemoglobinaemia* may develop, a condition which produces one of the forms of 'blue babies'.

Two other diseases are relatively common. One of these, Huntington's chorea, is a rare hereditary condition in which neurological degenerations occur. Historically its introduction into the U.S.A. can be traced to three affected brothers from Suffolk who sailed with John Winthrop in 1630. By a curious coincidence another emigrant to travel with them was a Norwich merchant named Huntington, the great-great-great-grandfather of the man destined to give the classic description of this disease 250 years later. The other is *dystrophia myotonica*, again a hereditary disorder, in which specific muscular and hormonal defects are found in association with cataract. Finally, we may mention the greater and lesser weever fish (*Trachinus draco* and *T. vipera*) which together with sting-rays and a few other denizens of the shore waters inflict their searing wounds on the unwary bather, angler, or Peter Grimes, as old Sir Thomas Browne observed three centuries ago: 'a sting-fish, wiver, or kind of ophidion . . . which venomously pricketh the hands of fishermen'.

Here we end this brief account of Man's semblance in the Norwich region. Much is lacking, much is tentative – it is at best a silhouette, shadowy and remote. Writing from Oulton Broad in 1843 George Borrow said: 'My favourite, I might say, my only study, is man.' Now it is the task of anthropologists to echo his words, confident that in them lies the secret of one day transforming that evanescent silhouette into a portrait of enduring clarity and splendour.

REFERENCES

1. EISELEY, L.C. (1943). *Trans. Kansas Acad. Sci.*, **46**, 57–9.

2. KEITH, A. (1932). *Proc. Prehist. Soc. E. Anglia*, **7**, pt. I, 109–10.

3. KOPEĆ, A.C. (1956). *The Advancement of Science*, **13**, 51: 200–3.

4. PÉQUART, M. and ST J., BOULE, M., and VALLOIS, H.V. (1937). *Arch. de l'Institut de Paléontologie humaine*, Mem. 18.

5. WELLS, C. (1960). *Antiquity*, **34**, 133: 29–37.

My thanks are due to the Ministry of Works for permission to refer to the Caister-by-Yarmouth, Thetford Red Castle, and Thetford St Mary material.

archaeology

R. RAINBIRD CLARKE

THE PHYSIOGRAPHY of Norfolk forms the background for its human settlement in the post-glacial periods. An area of heavy soils, formerly supporting thick woodland, occupies the centre of the county and is flanked by loams, sands, and gravels on the east and by lighter sands and chalk on the west. These lighter soils, particularly in Breckland and west Norfolk, were easily worked by agriculturalists with primitive equipment, and the relatively open woodland which grew on them was gradually removed by the slash-and-burn technique. As the population increased, pioneer farmers encroached on the thicker woodland of the heavier soils and gradually utilized this land for agricultural purposes. The first recognizable inroads on the denser forests took place in the Roman period, but large-scale deforestation took place mainly in the Late Saxon and Early Middle Ages. These periods therefore saw a more even distribution of population than in the Neolithic and Early Bronze Ages, when peasant cultivators with their grain plots and nomadic pastoralists with their herds were largely concentrated in western and northern Norfolk, though a few patches of lighter soil in east Norfolk were also inhabited.

Geographically Norfolk is intimately linked with the surrounding areas of Suffolk and Cambridgeshire by narrow valleys or arbitrary modern boundaries, and cultural influences have been received by land in the county or have emanated from it through successive centuries. The natural route for this economic and cultural intercourse was through the relatively open chalkland of Cambridgeshire and north-west Suffolk leading into Breckland and west Norfolk, a route well-known as the Icknield Way, which ultimately linked East Anglia with Wessex. During the Roman Age military engineers constructed the first made-roads, some of which cut through the wooded areas, and thus improved the system of communications by land. Water transport for men and goods has been important in every period, for most of the Norfolk rivers are navigable and coastal navigation was often quicker and cheaper than transit overland. It was by sea too that many of the early invaders of East Anglia arrived, often as refugees, from the opposite shores of the North Sea only just over one hundred miles away, and the rivers draining into the Wash and into the North Sea near the site of modern Yarmouth provided convenient routes into the interior.

In a low-lying region such as Norfolk, where extensive tracts now lie at, or even below, modern sea-level, past changes of land and sea-levels have exercised a significant influence on the areas of human occupation. For instance, the marine transgression of Neolithic times covered an extensive tract of north-west Norfolk which had been habitable up to that time, and which now lies beneath the sea.

In the following paragraphs an attempt will be made to summarize the conclusions suggested by the available archaeological evidence for successive periods of human occupation in Norfolk. Space will not permit the inclusion of the detailed evidence, most of which is accessible in published form.

THE PALAEOLITHIC (*About* 400,000–8000 B.C.)

During the immensely long Palaeolithic period East Anglia was in the intermittent grip of an Ice Age. Warmer inter-glacial periods occurred between the principal ice advances named locally after Lowestoft,

R.R. CLARKE is Curator of the Norwich Museums

Fig. 1 *Some important visible monuments*

Neolithic long barrow	Roman road	Deserted medieval village site
Neolithic flint mine	Early Saxon linear earthwork	Medieval domestic building
Neolithic 'henge' monument	Late Saxon cathedral	Medieval moated site
Bronze Age round barrow group	Medieval monastery	Medieval guildhall
Iron Age fort	Early medieval church	Medieval street plan
Roman fortress	Late medieval church	Other medieval buildings
Roman town	Medieval castle	County boundary
Roman barrow	Medieval town walls	0 5 10 miles

the Gipping valley, and Hunstanton. It was during these inter-glacials that small groups of hunters penetrated into the area and established temporary camps near rivers and lakes while engaged in pursuit of the game on which they lived. The archaeological evidence for this consists of a number of flint tools mainly recovered from the sands, gravels, and clays laid down during the inter-glacials in Breckland, west Norfolk, the Cromer Ridge, the Norwich area, and the Waveney valley.

The identification of Man's earliest tools is bound to be controversial, and wide differences of opinion have been expressed as to the human or natural origin of the flaked flints discovered in the Norfolk Stone Bed. This deposit forms the base of the Norwich Crag which precedes the Cromer Inter-glacial, and the Lowestoft Glaciation. The acceptance or rejection of these flints depends on the personal opinion of the investigator, and in view of this lack of objective evidence judgement on this Sub-Crag industry must be suspended. The Cromerian flake industry found on the foreshore at Cromer and the Runtonian industry from the Runton Sands have also been regarded as of human origin, but it is difficult to substantiate this view. The earliest industry unquestionably of human origin is the Acheulian-Clactonian, which is represented in the area from the waning of the Lowestoft Glaciation, and which, in various forms, lasted through the ensuing Hoxne Inter-glacial and persisted into the Ipswich Inter-glacial, a span of about 200,000 years. Not unnaturally the industries at the best investigated sites – Whitlingham in Norfolk, Barnham, Hoxne, and High Lodge, Mildenhall, in Suffolk – which are not strictly contemporary,

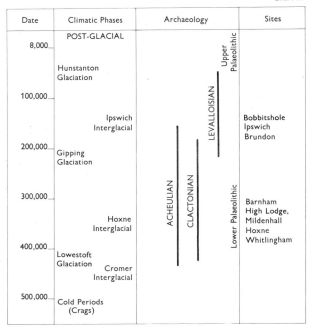

Chart A

Fig. 2   *The Palaeolithic*

display considerable variations. Core tools predominate at Whitlingham and developed flake tools at High Lodge. Another cultural group termed the Levalloisian is known in East Anglia from the Gipping Glaciation to the Hunstanton Glaciation but is not at present well represented in Norfolk. A flint industry, claimed to be contemporary with the brown boulder clay of the Hunstanton Glaciation, has been classified as of Upper Palaeolithic Age, but the form of these tools suggests that they are more likely to be of Mesolithic date. No human skeletal remains of Palaeolithic date are known from Norfolk, as those found at Hunstanton are clearly later.

THE MESOLITHIC (*About* 8000–3000 B.C.)

During the cold Pre-Boreal climatic phase, which lasted until about 7000 B.C., East Anglia was still joined to the Continent, and much of the present North Sea was fen and lagoon. It was thus possible for small groups of hunters to cross 'Northsealand' from what is now north-west Germany to Norfolk, and immigration from this direction is suggested by the discovery of a few tanged flint flakes. Apart from these, no other traces of human occupation during this phase of the Mesolithic have been recognized in the county.

During the ensuing Boreal phase, ending about 5000 B.C., the climate was of Continental type with an average summer temperature higher than today. At the beginning of the phase Norfolk was still linked to the Continent, but a rapid rise in sea-level created the North Sea and made Britain an island by about 6000 B.C. Two cultural groups – the Maglemosian and the Sauveterrian – have been detected at a number of sites. The former is represented by a flint industry of core axes, scrapers, and microliths with the resultant waste flakes, suitable for coping with a forest environment. Many are found on the seasonal camping-sites used by these hunters and fishers, of which the best known in Norfolk are on Kelling Heath and at Two Mile Bottom, Thetford. The barbed antler point from a fishing-spear found near the Leman and Ower Banks, some twenty-five miles north-east of Cromer, and dropped when the North Sea bed was still freshwater marsh, represents an important aspect of the material equipment of this culture. This organic equipment is ill-represented in England but much more adequately in the Baltic area. The material culture of the Sauveterrians is characterized by a flint industry of geometric microliths and by the absence of wood-cutting tools appropriate to tree-less localities such as sand dunes. It is on formations of this type bordering the Fens at Wangford and Peacock's Farm, Shippea Hill, just beyond the county boundary, that temporary camp-sites of this culture have been explored.

The final phase of the Mesolithic between about 5000 B.C. and 3000 B.C. coincided with the warm and moist conditions of the Atlantic phase, when the level of the North Sea was still rising, though slowly, and deciduous woodland was replacing the open pinewoods of the Boreal. The spread of woodland fostered the development of local cultural groups and the flint industries thus display regional peculiarities, as in some sites in the Wensum valley. Non-geometric microliths and core axes were still being made, though the latter were being increasingly supplemented by axes made from flakes. Groups of Maglemosians and Sauveterrians probably also survived into the early part of this phase, but the material collected from many sites is often too

Fig. 3 *Grime's Graves – air photograph of infilled Neolithic flint-mine shafts*

scanty in quantity for its cultural affinities to be closely defined.

THE NEOLITHIC (*About* 3000–1700 B.C.)

The Neolithic is characterized by farming, a revolutionary practice which had originated in the Middle East about 7000 B.C., and by the introduction of hand-made pottery and ground flint and stone tools. Until recently, 2500 B.C. has been accepted as a probable date for the arrival in southern England of the first farmers, but several radio-carbon dates now suggest this occurred at least as early as 3000 B.C. The Neolithic may be divided chronologically into three phases, the last of which ended about 1700 B.C.

During Phase I many survivors of the Mesolithic tradition lived alongside the new immigrant farmers, some of whom may have crossed the North Sea from the Low Countries, north-west Germany, or Denmark, while others may have reached west Norfolk by traversing the Icknield Way route from Wessex. Light woodland was cleared in Breckland, west, and north-east Norfolk by these pioneer farmers whose grain plots, cultivated by hoes, soon exhausted the soil, compelling their owners to move. The surviving archaeological evidence for these farmers of the Windmill Hill culture consists of fragments of plain bag-shaped pots, and a flint industry characterized by core axes for felling timber and leaf arrowheads for hunting game.

The second phase ended about 1900 B.C. when at least four cultures can be recognized in the area. There was a regional development of the Windmill Hill culture possibly under influences from Wessex and from across the North Sea. The pottery, termed Mildenhall ware, is distinctive in both form and decoration, and has been found in quantity at the settlement at Hurst Fen, Mildenhall, Suffolk, where the post-holes of temporary buildings and pits for grain storage have also been located. The speedy exhaustion of the soil by the earliest farmers led to further clearance of woodland by the slash-and-burn technique and so to an increased demand for flint axes met by extensive mining at Breckland sites, of which Grime's Graves is the largest and best explored. Little is known about the burial rites of the Windmill Hill people in Norfolk, apart from the three earthen long barrows at Ditchingham, Harpley, and West Rudham, of which only the last has been excavated, though Windmill Hill pottery has come from the others.

Besides this developed Windmill Hill culture, there were two other cultures, the Peterborough and Rinyo-Clacton, both with local Mesolithic antecedents and distinguished by their characteristic pottery and flint industries. The Peterborough folk were predominantly stock-raisers and hunters, but also grew a little grain, and contributed to the mining development at Grime's Graves where their artistic tradition is apparent in the scratchings on flint crust. In addition to these activities, it seems probable that these peoples traded to Norfolk some of the stone axes made in Cornwall, south-west Wales, and the Lake District. The tough igneous rocks of which these tools were made were more durable than the local flint.

Finally there are the Bell Beaker folk who came to East Anglia from Holland and the Middle Rhine about 2000 B.C. Archaeologically they are distinguished by their pottery beakers and by their flexed inhumation burials in small round barrows or flat graves. In addition to hunting, they lived on their flocks, roaming over the heaths of Breckland, along the west Norfolk ridge, and the heaths of north Norfolk.

The Peterborough, Rinyo-Clacton, and Bell Beaker cultures persisted into the last phase of the Neolithic from about 1900 to 1700 B.C., and were supplemented by the Necked Beaker culture, a British development influenced by additional foreign elements. In Norfolk the remains of the two Beaker cultures are distributed over much the same terrain, for the Necked Beaker folk were also nomadic herdsmen. Their sprawling temporary camp-sites are represented, as at Edingthorpe, by numerous hearths associated with distinctive decorated pottery, flint dagger blades, arrowheads and stone axe-hammers and polished flint knives, an East Anglian invention. Contracted inhumation under large round barrows or in isolated graves was the burial rite of the Necked Beaker culture. One of the religious centres of these people is indicated by the henge monument at Arminghall, just south of Norwich, where the open-air arena, with its horseshoe setting of eight huge oak posts, forms the focal point of a large barrow cemetery now only visible as crop marks from the air.

THE BRONZE AGE (*About* 1700–500 B.C.)

The first metal tools used in East Anglia were of bronze and were imported into the area mainly from Ireland, though some came from the Rhineland. The Bronze Age in East Anglia can be divided into two chronological phases, before and after about 1200 B.C.

During the first phase until about 1500 B.C. there was a substantial survival of the Necked Beaker culture, which influenced some groups of the Peterborough folk to evolve between about 1700 and 1400 into the Food Vessel culture. The main concentration of this was in northern England, and there may have been some small-scale emigration from there to East Anglia, but the pottery in Norfolk suggests a local development as well. These people were pastoralists and traders who assisted in the diffusion of the earliest bronze tools in the area, and imported luxuries like jet. From about 1500 B.C. there are indications in west Norfolk of the Wessex culture, an intrusive group of wealthy pastoralists from southern England who became overlords of the Food

Vessel people and of their successors, the Urn folk. As these Wessex chieftains were nomadic herdsmen they have left no permanent settlement sites, and their principal monuments are the imposing bell barrows at Rushford, Great Bircham, West Rudham, and Weasenham and the less conspicuous disc barrows. Their wealth and wide trading activities are well illustrated at Little Cressingham by a male burial in a barrow, accompanied by bronze daggers, a necklace of amber from the Baltic, and mountings of gold from Ireland. They were also probably responsible for the diffusion among their neighbours of gold objects and beads of blue faience ultimately derived from Egypt.

The culture of the Urn folk takes its name from the coarse ill-fired urn (containing the cremated remains of the dead) which had evolved from Peterborough wares by about 1400 B.C. These urns, often inverted, were placed in a new round barrow or inserted as a secondary burial in a pre-existing mound. About 250 round barrows, either isolated or in groups, are known to have existed mainly in west and north Norfolk, and the majority are probably due to the Urn folk. These people were principally nomadic pastoralists but supplemented this activity by hunting and hoe-agriculture.

A local bronze industry developed about 1300 B.C. when sufficient raw material in the form of obsolete tools became available. Its principal products were awls, rapiers, daggers, axes, and spearheads. These are sometimes found isolated but are best known from hoards or caches. Small groups, like the rapier, axe, and sickle found in the fen near Downham Market, are probably the possessions of one person, but it is likely that the seventy axes and spearheads found together at Stibbard formed the stock-in-trade of an itinerant metalsmith.

The Urn culture persisted in Norfolk during Phase II, from about 1200 B.C. onwards, and the remains of the cremated dead were still placed in urns or enclosed in bags before insertion in a barrow. Sometimes the barrow was freshly erected and often very small, as in a group on Salthouse Heath, but on other sites the urn was buried probably without a mound. Alongside the Urn folk at sites like Grime's Graves and in Mildenhall Fen, Suffolk, have been found traces of occupation by pastoralists and agriculturalists who were using pottery in the form of barrels and buckets. These pots are probably derived from the wares of the Rinyo-Clacton culture, which must therefore have survived in the area sufficiently long after 1500 B.C. to have given rise to this development. This pottery is similar to some of that discovered in Urnfield cemeteries which were established about this time in the Ipswich-Colchester region as a result of the fusion of the Rinyo-Clacton, Necked Beaker, and Urn cultures. In Norfolk, however, few traces of similar cremation cemeteries have yet been found, and the precise affinities of these Bucket and Barrel Urn folk in Norfolk are uncertain. Traces of pile dwellings alongside the meres of Breckland have also been found, but insufficient material has survived to date them accurately.

This phase of the Bronze Age witnessed an enormous development of the bronze industry, and many hoards survive to attest the activities of the metal-smiths. Continental craftsmen between about 1100 and 800 B.C. were responsible for such additions to the local equipment as socketed axeheads, leaf-shaped swords, and pegged spearheads, while British smiths often modified their traditional weapons and tools in imitation of these new fashions. From about 750 B.C. continental types like carp's tongue swords and winged axes were imported into the Lower Thames and the area of the Home Counties, from which a few were traded into East Anglia where they occur in such hoards as those found at Gorleston and Carleton Rode. Local imitations of these imports were again made. In addition to these continental imports, axes from other parts of Britain such as Yorkshire and south Wales reached East Anglia, and Irish gold can be recognized in the hoard of bracelets and cloak-fasteners from Caister-by-Yarmouth. To the last century of this period belong the distinctive chapes of swords left behind by small groups of warriors raiding East Anglia from Belgium.

THE IRON AGE (*About* 500 B.C.–A.D. 43)

A knowledge of iron working had been common in central Europe for some three centuries before it was brought to East Anglia about 500 B.C. by refugees from the Low Countries. Unfortunately, owing to soil conditions, very few iron objects of the Iron Age survive in East Anglia. It is convenient to describe the development of the Iron Age in this area in three chronological phases separated by the dates 300 and 150 B.C.

The presence of these immigrant peasant-farmers of the first phase of the Iron Age in Norfolk is indicated by their characteristic pottery or by the ditches, pits, or post-holes of their farmsteads, which lie in the valleys of Breckland, on the west Norfolk ridge, and along the north Norfolk coast. The best explored site is at West Harling in Breckland, where two circular timber-framed buildings provided accommodation for the farmer, his family, and his stock. He herded sheep and oxen and cultivated cereals, probably wheat, and supplemented these activities with some hunting. The grain was probably

stored in large pottery jars after parching in clay ovens to help its keeping qualities. Spindle-whorls and clay loomweights indicate the production of home-made textiles. Few burials of this phase are known from Norfolk, but what little evidence there is suggests that both inhumation and cremation were practised and some barrows may still have been built.

By the third century B.C. the culture of these Iron Age 'A' peasant-farmers had spread throughout the inhabited areas of Norfolk. Their numbers were increased by further immigrants, including some probably from Wessex, and this peasant stock formed the bulk of the local population until after the Roman Conquest. From

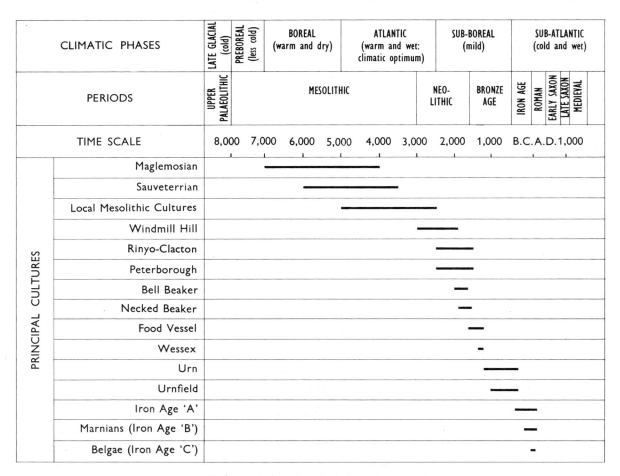

Fig. 4   *The later Archaeology of Norfolk*

J.K. St Joseph. Crown Copyright Reserved

Fig. 5 *Warham Camp – air photograph of Iron Age fort*

about 250 B.C. these peasants and their chieftains were harassed by military adventurers from the Marne area of France (Iron Age 'B') and by the end of the third century some of these had settled round the margins of Fenland to become overlords of the Iron Age 'A' population. Single bank and ditch fortifications like those at Narborough and South Creake may have been thrown up against these intruders, who introduced chariot warfare to the area. The arrival of this new aristocracy is witnessed archaeologically by pottery of imported types and by weapons, chariot and harness fittings. Some of this fine equipment, often of superb artistic quality, has been recovered from inhumation burials, and one of these found at Mildenhall, Suffolk, included two ponies and the chariot of the dead chieftain. This Marnian aristocracy and its subject population were collectively known as the Iceni by the end of the first century B.C., when the names of their rulers begin to appear on their coinage. It is likely that their Kingdom embraced two sub-groups centred respectively in Breckland and west Norfolk, and in the Norwich area.

About 100 B.C. south-eastern England was overrun by Belgic (Iron Age 'C') invaders from eastern France and Belgium, who rapidly established themselves in Kent and south Essex and spread into Hertfordshire. Economically these warlike farmers made considerable advances, as their more efficient equipment enabled them to convert dense woodland into arable fields, and they prospered sufficiently to substitute a monetary economy for barter. During the last few years of the first century B.C. the Belgic tribe of the Catuvellauni attempted to seize north Essex but, being repulsed, thrust northwards into Cambridgeshire. Then, during the next generation, they conquered the Iceni in north-west Suffolk, and by the eve of the Roman Conquest of A.D. 43 were threatening the Iceni in Norfolk. Fortifications such as the outworks of Thetford Castle, Holkham Camp, and Warham Camp may date from this period of warfare. This threat would probably explain the concealment of hoards of valuable equipment such as the harness fittings from Ringstead and the gold torcs, possibly regalia, and coins known as the Snettisham Treasure found near by in north-west Norfolk. Despite the hostility of the Iceni and their Belgic neighbours, the former were indebted to the latter for many cultural advances, paving the way for an eventual absorption which would doubtless have taken place soon after A.D. 43 but for the arrival of the Romans.

THE ROMAN AGE (A.D. 43–425)

At first the Iceni established friendly relations with the Roman invaders, but realizing their mistake revolted abortively in A.D. 47–8. Probably as a result of this a puppet king, Prasutagus, was set on the Icenian throne. During his prosperous reign, which lasted till about A.D. 60, Roman material culture and ideas began to penetrate the area. Roman greed and cruelty to his widow, Boudicca, provoked her formidable revolt in A.D. 60–1. After the defeat of the Iceni and their allies, Roman forces moved into East Anglia to pacify the survivors who hurriedly concealed hoards of metal-work and coins such as those from Santon, Westhall, and Honingham, and constructed a fortlet in the Roman manner at Thornham, in north-west Norfolk. It is likely that the Romans deported some of the rebels to the silt Fens to begin the drainage and settlement of that district.

The boundaries of the administrative areas in Roman East Anglia are unknown, but it is clear that the local cantonal capital was at Caistor-by-Norwich where unsubstantial huts were erected alongside gravelled streets about A.D. 70. Half a century later public buildings were erected in masonry, but wattle-and-daub timber-framed houses and shops were only replaced by masonry structures in the third century. About A.D. 200 imposing walls with rampart behind and ditch in front were erected to protect the inner core of the town, but the gatehouses were soon neglected as were some of the public buildings. During the fourth century the scale of occupation diminished further. The only other town in Norfolk was the fortified port at Caister-by-Yarmouth, which was founded about A.D. 125 as an *entrepôt* for the developing trade with the Rhineland.

In the countryside, the technique of farming and the dwellings of the farmers were in the Iron Age tradition for the first century of the Roman Age, but there was clearly an expansion of rural industry even before the end of this period. Local low-grade iron-ores were being

Norwich City Museums

Fig. 6   *Caistor-by-Norwich – masonry of Roman town wall*

smelted, local clay was being exploited for brick- and pottery-making, and salt was being distilled from saline water along the Fen edge. From about A.D. 125 timber-framed farmhouses in the Romanized manner were being built, and some were replaced by masonry structures later in the century. The more architecturally elaborate farmhouses and their farmlands are termed 'villas', and in Norfolk these are concentrated in west Norfolk though a few are found on the heavier soils of south Norfolk, indicating some clearance of woodland. Nothing is known of the field system associated with these villas, but aerial photography has revealed numerous groups of small rectangular fields associated with peasant steadings mainly in the silt areas of Fenland. Within the Norfolk boundary there are concentrations of this Fenland agriculture near Downham Market, at Welney and near Hockwold-cum-Wilton from which corn, went to the garrisons in the north. During the third century the bigger estates still prospered, but there is certain evidence to suggest that some of the smaller cultivators had been dispossessed and their lands converted to sheepwalk. The discovery of a number of weaving combs points to a local woollen industry. During the early fourth century some of the villa farmhouses were deserted, but their owners were not necessarily poverty-stricken to judge from the possession of pewter and silver table services like the Mildenhall Treasure.

Due to the harsh repression of the Boudiccan revolt, the Romanization of Norfolk was tardy and less intense than in other areas of lowland England. It was only in the early second century that importation of Samian ware from Gaul became normal, but from that time the area shared in the benefits of trade with other parts of Britain and abroad. From Dorset came shale table furnishings, from Somerset and Sussex the raw material for the tesserae of mosaic floors, from the east Midlands and south Yorkshire came quernstones for milling, and from the east Midlands, Durham, or Yorkshire coalfields came fuel for the Fens. Foreign objects of trade included pottery and lava millstones from the Rhineland, bronze paterae from Gaul, glassware from the east Mediterranean, marble for building from Italy and the Pyrenees, and a flood of coinage to facilitate this trade from the mints of Rome and Lyons.

From the middle of the third century the shores of East Anglia, in common with those of south-east England, were harassed by Saxon pirates, and a series of coastal forts was built close to suitable harbours which served as bases for naval squadrons. Fortresses were erected at Brancaster to guard the Wash and at Burgh Castle near Yarmouth to guard the estuary of the Yare. After the devastating attack of A.D. 367 when Saxons, Picts, and Scots all assaulted Roman Britain, the coastal defence was strengthened by the addition of signal stations. One of these was situated at Corton near Lowestoft and another may have been at Stiffkey in north Norfolk.

Distinctive pottery of Romanized technique, but decorated in Anglo-Saxon style and hence termed Romano-Saxon ware, was in use in East Anglia during the fourth century. It seems likely that this ware was produced to satisfy the Saxons or allied peoples resident in East Anglia, who were perhaps brought in as *foederati* or mercenaries early in the century. Whatever may be the explanation for this pottery, there is no doubt about the Germanic character of the cremation urn cemeteries established in the last few years of the fourth century at various sites, including two just outside the walls of Caistor-by-Norwich. These must contain the remains of *foederati* brought in by the Roman government to defend the area against barbarian attacks. But such expedients show that Roman society was itself becoming increasingly barbarized. After about A.D. 408 the forts were left unguarded and local defence rested in the hands of mercenaries.

THE EARLY SAXON AGE (A.D. 425–850)

The pottery and the grave goods in these cremation cemeteries show that the first of these *foederati* were principally Angles from Schleswig-Holstein together with some Saxons from the lands between the Elbe and the Weser in north-west Germany. During the fifth century these settlers were constantly being reinforced from their original homelands and adjacent territories. By A.D. 500 there was substantial Anglo-Saxon occupation in the Norwich area, in north and west Norfolk, in Breckland, and around the margins of Fenland. Survivors of the older peasantry dwelt adjacent to the newcomers, but their degree of Romanization steadily declined. In the early fifth century Roman coins were still being copied and remained in use until the latter part of the century. Little is known of fifth-century dwellings, but humble peasants probably lived in one-roomed huts, while affluent farmers may have shared timber-framed long houses with their stock, though no evidence for these has yet been recognized in East Anglia. The most impressive monuments of the period are the linear earthworks – long banks and ditches – which stretch between natural obstacles and normally lie athwart important lines of communication. The Bichamdich, for instance, and the Launditch bar progress along the Roman road running east and west across the county, while the Fossditch was built across the prehistoric Drove Road. The precise date or dates of construction of these politico-military barriers is uncertain, although two of them have been shown by excavation to be post-Roman and pre-seventh century. They are perhaps more likely to belong to an early phase of the Anglo-Saxon settlement and represent temporary frontiers between hostile groups.

During the early years of the sixth century further invaders arrived in East Anglia particularly in the Ipswich Region, and from a characterstic cemetery in that town have been termed the 'Ipswich People'. Their burial rite was inhumation and their dead were often buried in clothing fastened by a large square-headed brooch of gilded bronze. They probably came

Fig. 7 *Burgh Castle, Suffolk – bastion and walls of Roman fortress*

from Scandinavia as did their monarchs, the Wuffings, who, from their base in the Ipswich area, conquered the rest of East Anglia by about A.D. 550 and welded its heterogeneous population into a small but powerful Kingdom. This reached its apogee about A.D. 590 under King Raedwald, whose effective power reached to the Nene valley, and who was acknowledged overlord of southern England until his death in A.D. 624–5. Though some of the population of East Anglia had been Christian in the Late Roman Age, they had relapsed into paganism during the initial phase of the Early Saxon Age. It was during the reign of Raedwald that the re-conversion of the area began, and following a brief set-back, progressed steadily after about A.D. 630 when Bishop Felix established his missionary base at Dunwich or Felixstowe and Fursey built a monastery within the walls of the abandoned Roman coastal fortress at Burgh Castle.

The political power of the East Anglian Kingdom declined during the last phase of the Early Saxon Age between about A.D. 650 and A.D. 850, but there was considerable economic advance. Place-names indicate an expansion of settlement on to some of the heavier soils, and this must be correlated with a growth of population. Foreign products, particularly from the Rhineland, began to reach the area after about A.D. 600 and included the reintroduction of the potter's wheel. This trade

across the North Sea was one of the factors which led to the growth of town life in East Anglia in the eighth century. At present the only certain evidence for this comes from Ipswich, but it is likely that Norwich experienced a similar development. Some of the population of the Ipswich area may, in the middle of the seventh century, have migrated up the east coast to found new settlements like that at Caister-by-Yarmouth. Here huts were erected inside the Roman town walls, where their occupants used wheel-made Ipswich ware and buried their dead in the Christian manner, though about a dozen graves had been covered with boat timbers, a tradition derived from the aristocratic ship-burials found at Snape and Sutton Hoo in Suffolk.

During the seventh and eighth centuries Christianity extended its sway, and this is reflected in the division of the original diocese of St Felix with a new see established at North Elmham in A.D. 673. It is uncertain if any part of the cathedral now visible there dates from this phase, but it seems likely that the stone throne for the bishop, of which the remains are now in Norwich Cathedral, was originally set up in a cathedral at North Elmham in the eighth century.

THE LATE SAXON AGE (A.D. 850–1066)

Archaeological evidence alone would tell us little of the Danish raids and settlements in Norfolk which form an important feature of the period, and recourse must therefore be made to documentary sources. After some twenty years of sporadic raiding, the first large-scale landing of Danes in East Anglia took place in A.D. 865. They returned in A.D. 869 to spend the winter at Thetford, probably the earliest occupation over much of that site, burn Norwich, and slaughter the East Anglian king, Edmund. After several years of campaigning against Alfred's Wessex, a settlement was reached in A.D. 878 by which the Danish army retired to Guthrum's Kingdom of 'Greater East Anglia'. Norfolk remained part of this Danish Kingdom until the area was reconquered about A.D. 920 by the Anglo-Saxon monarchy. Further Danish raids took place in the late tenth century, and there were more serious attacks in A.D. 1004 when Norwich and Thetford were sacked by Swein Forkbeard's army and again in A.D. 1010, when the invaders won the battle of

'Hringmara Heath' near Thetford. For a generation Norfolk, in common with the rest of England, formed part of an Anglo-Danish Kingdom.

The surviving historical records devote much space to this intermittent warfare but fail to emphasize the considerable economic advances made during this period. It is likely that in A.D. 850 the population was relatively small and scattered. By A.D. 1066 East Anglia was the most densely populated area in England, and this increase was due both to the settlement of several thousand Danes and also to the growth of the earlier Anglo-Saxon communities, with the foundation of fresh villages. The Domesday Survey of A.D. 1086 records 726 separate places in Norfolk with a minimum population of 25,805, though the total figure was two or three times greater. The opening up of the richer soils of central and eastern Norfolk led to the economic advance of the Norwich zone, while after the Norman Conquest the economy of the Breckland zone remained static.

The earliest written evidence for the existence of Norwich comes from coins minted there about A.D. 930, though the evidence from the Morley St Peter coin hoard suggests the existence of a mint there a decade earlier. Both archaeological and historical evidence suggest an important riverine settlement by the middle of the ninth century, but the major expansion of its inhabited area took place between the arrival of Danish settlers at the end of the century and the Norman Conquest. This trading centre, market town, and port supported a population of about 5,000 by Domesday, being probably the largest town in East Anglia at that time, though Thetford was only slightly smaller.

Thetford owed its importance to its position on the Icknield Way at fords over the rivers Little Ouse and Thet. There had been a riverine settlement here in the Early Saxon Age, but its growth into a substantial town was a direct result of the settlement of Danes in the late ninth century. During the tenth and eleventh centuries houses of varied types were built alongside cobbled roadways, and no less than twelve churches existed by A.D. 1066. Some of its inhabitants were engaged in farming, while others were artisans working iron and copper or manufacturing wheel-made pottery – Thetford ware – on a considerable scale. This ware was supplemented by pottery from the east Midlands including the products

Norwich City Museums

Fig. 8   *North Elmham – Late Saxon cathedral converted into manor house in fourteenth century*

of the St Neots and Stamford kilns. Other imports included lava millstones from the Rhineland, and the growth of this trading centre is reflected in the establishment of a mint at Thetford about A.D. 960–70.

There are strong indications of a domestic woollen industry at Thetford, and the wool for this was probably from sheep grazing on the heaths of Breckland. Agriculture was, of course, of major importance over the whole of the county, but it was supplemented by other rural activities including fishing on the west Norfolk rivers, salt-making on the eastern shore of the Wash and around the 'Great Estuary' near Yarmouth, and the digging of peat as fuel for domestic purposes and for the salt industry.

Church life was disrupted by the Danish wars and most churches and monasteries were destroyed. Christianity took root again after the Anglo-Saxon reconquest of the area in the tenth century, when the see of Elmham was re-established for the counties of Norfolk and Suffolk and minsters were probably built in each hundred. A number of churches in which eleventh-century work survives show features inspired by contemporary building techniques in the Rhineland, while the outstanding ecclesiastical structure in the area, generally attributed to this age, is the small cathedral at North

Elmham. The round towers of many village churches of eleventh-century date are an architectural feature distinctive of East Anglia.

THE MIDDLE AGES (A.D. 1066–1550)

Medieval Norfolk was a rich county, and its wealth was created by the efficient system of agriculture inherited from Late Saxon times and augmented by industrial activities. In the countryside the density of population

Hallam Ashley

Fig. 9 *Baconsthorpe Castle – gatehouse of fifteenth-century fortified mansion*

is shown by the number of villages. The wealth of many of these is indicated by the rebuilding of their churches on a more lavish scale. New settlements were being established until the thirteenth century on freshly cleared land, but from the later Middle Ages unsuccessful farming on marginal lands caused the abandonment of many villages, especially in Breckland. These deserted villages are now often represented only by the ruins of a church, the outlines of houses and paddocks, faint indications of field systems, or by the mere survival of their names. Norwich, Yarmouth, and Lynn were the largest and wealthiest of the towns as is shown both by historical records and archaeological remains. Throughout medieval times Norwich was among the six largest provincial cities and by the early sixteenth century the circuit of its walls housed a population second only to that of London. Yarmouth and Lynn were among the leading English medieval ports, and for a time in the early fourteenth century the former was even larger than Norwich. Thetford, on the other hand, remained static as its economy was geared to that of Breckland, and by late medieval times it was in a state of decline. There were in addition several smaller towns, some with flourishing industries and all with a market. By the middle of the fourteenth century some 130 towns and villages in the county had the right to hold a market.

The principal industrial activity in the county during the Middle Ages was the manufacture of cloth, especially worsted. The existence of a domestic woollen industry in Late Saxon times has already been noted and this doubtless formed the basis of the medieval development. Some of the wool was woven locally in Norwich in the eleventh and twelfth centuries, but by 1300 much was exported to Flanders. During the fourteenth century the strength of the local weavers was augmented by the arrival of Flemish refugees, with a corresponding increase in the output of cloth and a decline in the export of raw wool. Most of the cloth was exported through Yarmouth, which handled more worsteds than any other English port. There were industrial activities too in the countryside. In the Early Middle Ages numerous salt-pans yielded salt for the preservation of meat. The local clays were utilized to make pottery and bricks, and, in the form of clay lump, used for building purposes.

Flint and chalk were also quarried on a large scale for building. Peat was still being dug for fuel during the first half of the Middle Ages.

The surviving archaeological monuments of medieval Norfolk are numerous and important. To the casual visitor the most obvious are the village churches and the less common late medieval houses in town and country, still often serving their original function. The deserted villages have already been mentioned. Scattered over the heavy soils of the county are numerous moats, often rectangular in plan, which drained the sites of farmsteads built mainly between the thirteenth and fifteenth centuries. There is often more than one of these to a parish and this indicates that the manor and the parish in Norfolk were rarely coincident. Castles were mainly built during the eleventh and fifteenth centuries. Among the numerous eleventh-century motte and bailey castles of earth and timber are those at Thetford and Horsford, while twelfth-century stone keeps can be seen at Castle Rising and Norwich. The fortified residences of the fifteenth century, such as those at Caister-by-Yarmouth and Baconsthorpe, reflect the unsettled conditions of the Wars of the Roses.

The monasteries of Norfolk survive only in a very ruinous state, for the lack of good building stone in the area has led to their utilization as quarries for later secular structures. Apart from hospitals and hermitages there were some seventy monasteries in the county, fairly evenly distributed. Among the more important were the Benedictine Priory of Norwich whose church was the Cathedral of the diocese from Norman times, the Cluniac house at Castle Acre, and the Augustinian Priory at Little Walsingham, a celebrated centre of pilgrimage.

The Middle Ages in Norfolk end in a welter of destruction. Civil strife exploded in Kett's formidable revolt of 1549, there was depression in the woollen industry and disturbance in the countryside with increasing rural depopulation. The great monastic estates were passing into private ownership and their vast buildings were being pillaged for timber, stone, and lead. In the new prosperity of the ensuing Elizabethan Age sensitive spirits could look back on typical destruction such as that at Walsingham:

> Bitter, bitter oh to behould the grasse to growe,
> Where the walls of Walsingam so stately did shew.
> Such were the works of Walsingam while shee did stand,
> Such are the wrackes as now do shewe of that holy land.
> Levell levell with the ground the towres doe lye,
> Which with their golden, glitteringe tops pearsed once to
> the skye.

> . . . .

> Weepe, weepe O Walsingam, whose dayes are nightes,
> Blessinge turned to blasphemies, holy deeds to dispites.
> Sinne is wher our Ladie sate, heaven turned is to hell,
> Sathan sittes where our Lord did swaye,
> Walsingam oh farewell.

REFERENCES

1. CLARKE, R.R. (1960). *East Anglia.* London. This is the most recent general work on the archaeology of the county up to Norman times, and the more important literature is listed on pp. 183–90. Distribution maps, correct to 1958, are included for each period up to A.D. 1200. Some papers of importance not included in the above are:

2. BARNES, H.D. and SIMPSON, W.D. (1952). 'Caister Castle.' *Ant. Journ.*, **32**, 35–51.

3. DICKINSON, R.E. (1934). 'The Town Plans of East Anglia: a study in Urban Morphology.' *Geography*, **19**, pt. 1, No. 103, 37–50.

4. DUNNING, G.C., HURST, J.G., MYRES, J.N.L., and TISCHLER, F. (1959). 'Anglo-Saxon Pottery: a Symposium.' *Med. Arch.*, **3**, 1–78.

5. GREEN, C. (1961). 'East Anglian Coastline Levels since Roman Times.' *Antiquity*, **35**, 21–8.

6. HOMANS, G.C. (1957). 'The Frisians in East Anglia.' *Econ. Hist. Rev.*, N.S. **10**, 189–206.

7. NORWICH MUSEUMS COMMITTEE (1960). *4,000 Years of Norfolk Farming*, handbook to exhibition.

8. RADFORD, C.A.R. (1961). 'The Bishop's Throne in Norwich Cathedral.' *Arch. Journ.*, **116**, 115–32.

9. RIGOLD, S.E. (1960). *North Elmham Saxon Cathedral.* M.O.W. Guide.

10. TYLECOTE, R.F. and OWLES, E. (1960). 'A Second-Century Iron-smelting site at Ashwicken, Norfolk.' *Norf. Arch.*, **32**, 142–62.

social, political, and religious

R. W. KETTON-CREMER

IT IS, of course, impossible to give more than the barest summary of four centuries of history in as many thousand words. There is room only for generalizations; and Norfolk has always been a county full of individualists, of men and women disinclined to fit into the accepted pattern. Nevertheless the broad outlines of a story emerge – the story of a community whose characteristics have not greatly altered in the course of 400 years.

The structure of the county has remained basically the same, with Norwich, its capital and cathedral city, a great manufacturing town; its two seaports, Great Yarmouth and King's Lynn; and its purely agricultural countryside. The manufactures of Norwich have changed. The ships from the ports are loaded with other cargoes and bound on other courses. The fields grow different crops and are cultivated by different methods. But fundamentally Norfolk has preserved its traditional aspect and its accustomed ways.

In 1550, when this survey begins, Norfolk was in a state of transition and disquiet. No man or class of men felt the ground secure beneath their feet. High and low were bewildered by the aftermath of the Reformation, the long-term effects of the Dissolution of the Monasteries, the enclosing of lands. Only a year before, Kett's rising had paralysed the life of the entire county. The accession of Mary only brought another perplexing turn of the wheel. The people of East Anglia in general had welcomed the Reformation. But during the last grim years of Mary's reign, the number of burnings for heresy in the diocese of Norwich was greater than in any other except those of Canterbury and London.

That nightmare passed, and the county found stability under the Elizabethan settlement. Civil administration was ably carried on by certain leading families – Bacons, Townshends, Calthorpes, L'Estranges, Pastons, Wodehouses – supported by the rank-and-file of the Justices of the Peace. Despite the drastic reductions to which Henry VIII had subjected the former power and revenues of the see of Norwich, a succession of capable Bishops brought their great diocese (which until the present century covered Suffolk as well as Norfolk) to a reasonable state of conformity.

There remained a widespread Catholic element amongst the gentry. For example the Walpole family, destined to rise to such power in the eighteenth century, was almost extinguished in the sixteenth by the enthusiasm of its young men for priestly or celibate ways of life. At least two Norfolk men, Henry Walpole and the poet Robert Southwell, suffered death for their faith. But the commonalty as a whole had decisively rejected Catholicism: indeed in matters of religion they tended to be drawn in the opposite direction. The Puritan movement struck early and tenacious roots in Norfolk; and the growth of more extreme sects, Brownists and Anabaptists, was watched with anxiety by those in authority.

During the 1560's Spanish policy in the Low Countries, and especially the religious persecutions towards the end of the decade, led to a huge influx of refugees into the eastern counties of England. They came mainly from the Flemish and Walloon provinces; but whatever their language and their place of origin, they were known collectively as 'the Dutch' or 'the Strangers'. They brought their families, their apprentices, their servants,

R.W. KETTON-CREMER is an historian and biographer, and author of *Thomas Gray*, *Horace Walpole*, and several books on the Norfolk past

and so far as was practicable they continued to ply their own crafts and trades. Their influence on the mercantile and social life of Norwich was far-reaching. By 1571 they may have numbered something like one-quarter of the entire population of the city. The textile industries, which had been drifting into stagnation, were revitalized by novel techniques and by the example of these industrious newcomers. In spite of some early difficulties, the assimilation of the Strangers was happily accomplished; and when the first Queen Elizabeth paid her famous and only visit to Norwich in 1578, the new community vied with their fellow-citizens in the warmth of their welcome, and staged their own special pageant in her honour. There can be few East Anglians today, now that four centuries of intermarriage have elapsed, without some admixture of Dutch, Flemish, or Walloon blood.

Throughout the later years of the sixteenth century and the opening decades of the seventeenth, Puritan opinions steadily gathered strength in Norfolk. The county as a whole was dourly opposed to anything that recalled the days of Popery. Widespread resentment was caused during the 1630's by the activities of three successive Bishops of Norwich, all strongly Laudian in their views, and one of them the particularly energetic and unpopular Matthew Wren. A good deal of Puritan emigration took place, some of it across the Atlantic Ocean, as many East Anglian place-names in New England bear witness. In general the people were more strongly moved by religious than by constitutional questions; but the educated minority, in most cases, regarded the disagreements between the Stuart monarchs and their Parliaments with deep misgiving. They believed, with the great Norfolk lawyer Edward Coke, that 'the privileges of this House are the nurse and life of all our laws, the subject's best inheritance'.

In the seventeenth century (and indeed until the Reform Act of 1832) Norfolk returned twelve members to Parliament – two Knights of the Shire, and two burgesses apiece for the five boroughs of Norwich, Great Yarmouth, King's Lynn, Thetford, and Castle Rising. Of the members elected to the Long Parliament in 1640, only two adhered to the King when the crisis came two years later. The remaining ten staunchly supported the Parliament throughout the ensuing war. The majority of the gentry in the countryside, and the merchants in the towns, were Parliamentarian in sympathy; and the scattered Royalist elements were easily overawed. Only once, during the whole of the Civil War, was there any fighting on Norfolk soil – when the town of King's Lynn declared for the King in 1643, and withstood a siege of five weeks before being reduced to submission. Throughout the war years the county, its own territory unravaged, provided an invaluable source of manpower and supplies for the Parliamentarian cause. The few active Royalist sympathizers, who took part in the rising at Lynn or had joined the King's forces elsewhere, were subjected to sequestration and heavy fines, from which several important estates never fully recovered. Norwich Cathedral suffered much desecration and damage, as did lesser churches throughout the county. The Bishop, Joseph Hall, despite his record of moderation, was deprived of his revenues and ejected from his palace. A great number of parochial clergy met with similar treatment; and their churches were given over to shameful iconoclasm.

The Commonwealth years passed uneventfully, though not without some stirrings of unrest. 'Pride's Purge' came as a rude shock to several local Members of Parliament who had played a leading part against the King in earlier years; and only one Norfolk man was actually among the regicides. On the other hand Cromwell's admirers and partisans, and those who for various reasons were content to uphold his authority, were strong enough to ensure a reasonable equilibrium until his death. Thereafter the argument for a restored monarchy found supporters everywhere; and in 1660 this once intransigent county swung over to the King with remarkable unanimity.

Its enthusiasm, however genuine, did not last long. Charles II, with his Queen and his brother, visited Norfolk in 1671, was charming to everyone, and knighted the most distinguished of Norwich's citizens at that time, the eminent man of science Dr Thomas Browne But the Country Party, spiritual successors of the old Parliamentarians, revived as the reign went on, and contested the three elections of 1679–81 against the Court with extreme bitterness. The parties took on the names of Whig and Tory; and although the Paston family, by now Earls of Yarmouth and coming fast to the close of their three centuries of active history, gallantly upheld the Tory cause, the tide was against them. The Catholics and a few Non-juring squires alone regretted the departure of James II. The Bishop of Norwich, William Lloyd, was a Non-juror, but for reasons of conscience and from no personal affection towards the exiled monarch. The reign of Queen Anne brought the Tories a gleam of deceptive sunshine; but a group of ambitious young Whigs, Townshends and Walpoles, had been steadily extending their influence in Norfolk. The accession of the Hanoverian line in 1714 was their opportunity, and they made full use of it.

Robert Walpole began life as a Norfolk squire of limited means and modest expectations. He was destined to control the affairs of the nation for twenty-one years, a considerably longer period than any other man has held the office of Prime Minister. He and his brother-in-law the second Viscount Townshend were the dominant figures in the government from 1721 until their quarrel in 1730, which led to Townshend's retirement. Thereafter Walpole, with the fullest confidence of George II and Queen Caroline, and greatly assisted in diplomatic affairs by his brother Horatio Walpole of Wolterton, remained the virtual ruler of Great Britain until his fall in 1742. The great mansion which he built at Houghton, to replace the 'plain homely dwelling' of his forefathers, still stands as his monument, although his magnificent collection of pictures was sold by his grandson to the Empress Catherine of Russia. Townshend's name is remembered with honour in the agricultural history of his native county.

It was the age of the 'Whig supremacy'. Some important families, such as the Bacons and Wodehouses, upheld the Tory interest; and they won the two county seats by a few votes in the hard-fought election of 1734, when the unpopularity of Walpole's excise measures was at its height. Thereafter, until the end of the century, the county usually accepted the blessings of compromise, and avoided the enormous cost of a contested election by returning one Whig and one Tory member. The Whig magnates as a rule managed to keep control of the boroughs.

Norwich continued to prosper through the eighteenth century. It was still in population the third city in the land. In 1701 it produced the first newspaper to be published outside London, the *Norwich Post*. In mid-century a group of excellent architects, of whom the best known is Thomas Ivory, designed such outstanding public buildings as the Assembly House and the Octagon Chapel, as well as many fine private houses. Yarmouth prospered too, as the port of Norwich and by virtue of its own rich harvest of herrings. The great days of King's Lynn, with its wine trade and its connexions by water far into the Midlands, had been in the later seventeenth century and during the rule of Walpole, who sat as one of its members almost throughout his life. In the latter half of the eighteenth century it began to decline.

The lesser seaports, strung all along the Norfolk coast, had declined likewise. It is hard to realize today that in the sixteenth and seventeenth centuries such places as the Burnhams, Stiffkey, Weybourne, Sheringham, and Cromer had an active maritime trade: that in 1580 there were eleven ships apiece belonging to Blakeney and Cley, thirteen to Wiveton, and nineteen to Wells. But gradually the harbours silted up, and the piers of the cliff-top towns were scoured away. Of all these little ports between Lynn and Yarmouth, Wells alone now retains any mercantile connexion with the open sea.

The agriculture of the countryside flourished abundantly. This was due primarily to the general establishment of the four-course rotation of crops, and to the widespread practice of enclosure, economically so necessary despite its injustices and abuses. The development of the agricultural industry is fully discussed by Dr Allison; and I need only draw attention here to the quality of the buildings – mansions, farmhouses, cottages, barns – which date from this era, and may be seen all over the Norfolk landscape. They bear witness to the progress in comfort and amenity which accompanied the improving agriculture of the age. As for the larger country houses, their decoration, furnishings, and contents reached during this century a standard unsurpassed before or since. Quite apart from such superb collections as those at Houghton and Holkham, works of art of high quality – paintings, sculpture, books, furniture, ceramics, bronzes – were acquired with enthusiasm by many squires in the countryside and many merchants in the towns.

The shortcomings of the Church of England in the eighteenth century are often exaggerated. A more authentic picture of clerical life is given in the diary of a Norfolk rector, the Rev. James Woodforde – not perhaps a man of great spiritual gifts, but conscientious, charitable, and kindly. Ever since their release from most of their disabilities by the Toleration Act, the Dissenting bodies had grown in respectability and opulence. In Norwich they were able to erect such admirable buildings as the Old Meeting House and the Octagon Chapel. John Wesley regarded the latter as a great deal too luxurious. 'How can it be thought', he wrote in his journal, 'that the old, coarse Gospel should find admission here?'

Towards the close of the century new figures appeared on the political scene, and the thunders of the French Revolution shook the land. William Windham, hitherto an ardent Whig, crossed the floor and took office in Pitt's coalition government. His friend Thomas William Coke, the famous agriculturist and the richest man in the county, adhered to the make-believe Radicalism of Fox. A more convincing exponent of Radicalism was Thomas Paine, who was born at Thetford and educated at the grammar school in that town. His extraordinary career ran most of its course in America and France; but *The Rights of Man* brought him many admirers in his native county, and his revolutionary ideas were studied with enthusiasm in Norwich, where the local branch of the Corresponding Society was exceptionally strong.

The most illustrious Norfolk figure of this time, however, was not a politician but a sailor. Horatio Nelson was the son of the rector of Burnham Thorpe. He went to school in the county, and spent there his brief periods of leave and his longer period of half-pay during the peaceful 1780's. No man, perhaps, has so effectively captured the imagination of his contemporaries; and even now there are public-house signs which bear not his name, but merely his portrait and the simple legend 'The Norfolk Hero'.

The threats of revolution and invasion passed away. And neither the menaces of Bonaparte nor the vociferations of Tom Paine had prevented a good deal of peaceable activity during those anxious years. Humphry Repton was laying out the grounds and 'improving' the parks of Norfolk landowners. Jane Austen was causing her characters in *Emma* to debate the advantages of Cromer as a watering-place in comparison with Southend. During the opening decades of the nineteenth century the city of Norwich became something of an intellectual centre, conscious of its reputation for progressive thinking and serious discussion, and proud of such luminaries as William Taylor, Amelia Opie, Sarah Austin, and the various Gurneys and Aldersons. Amongst the younger writers encouraged by this group may be numbered Harriet Martineau and George Borrow. Meanwhile the painters who came to be known as 'the Norwich School', Crome and Cotman and their disciples, were rendering the landscapes and skies of East Anglia with a new vision.

The Reform Act of 1832 removed some, though by no means all, of the anomalies of Norfolk's representation in Parliament. The pocket-borough of Castle Rising disappeared. The county was divided into two constituencies, east and west, with two members apiece. In the election of 1832 the Whigs harvested the fruits of the reforms they had so long advocated, and won a sweeping victory. Thomas William Coke took the opportunity to retire, after having represented Norfolk in every Parliament (except for one intermission of six years) since 1776. Further alterations in constituency boundaries, and wider extensions of the franchise, continued to be made throughout the nineteenth century. It is impossible to pursue here in detail the fluctuating politics of that age; but it may be observed that Norfolk on the whole maintained its traditional Whig and Radical bias, and usually tended to favour the parties and policies of the Left. Towards the end of the century Trade Unionism established a firm foothold in the rural areas as well as in the towns, and nowhere in the English countryside has the influence of the Agricultural Workers' Union been more marked.

Religious Dissent continued to flourish, and the Nonconformist vote was of great assistance to the Liberal Party during the nineteenth century, particularly in the rural areas. Nevertheless the Established Church held its ground. In the opening decades the Bishop of Norwich, Henry Bathurst, was notable as being the solitary Whig on the episcopal bench; but he sadly outlived his powers, and by the time of his death in 1837, at the age of ninety-three, his diocese had become 'a byword for laxity and irregularity'. It was known, as other dioceses have been known from time to time, as 'the dead see'. His successor was the energetic and capable Edward Stanley; and ever since, throughout the long episcopates of such Bishops as Pelham and Sheep-shanks, Pollock and Herbert, the see of Norwich has remained very far from dead.

Dr Allison has traced the industrial changes of the nineteenth century: the coming of the railways, the decline of Norwich as a great textile centre, and the establishment of other industries – footwear, agricultural machinery, heavy engineering, mustard and its allied products. Similarly he has described the fluctuations of agriculture, its alternations of depression and prosperity, the introduction of new crops and new techniques, down to recent times. The greatest social change, perhaps – apart from the impact of the two world wars of the present century – has been the rise of the holiday industry. For centuries the Broads were waste spaces of water, used for fishing, wildfowling, reed-cutting and nothing more. During the nineteenth century their immense possibilities for sailing and cruising gradually came to be realized; and now far too many people have realized them. For centuries the long coastline with its cliffs and beaches lay unregarded. Sea-bathing was undertaken strictly on medical advice; it had not occurred to anyone that there is enjoyment in swimming through the surf, or basking in the sun within sound of the waves. The nineteenth century saw the development of Hunstanton, Cromer, Sheringham, and many other places – large hotels, piers, promenades, golf links. The present century has brought the motor-car, the caravan, the organized holiday-camp, the Surrealist fantasy of the front at Yarmouth.

But the holiday industry, vitally important though it is to many thousands of people, affects only a few months of the year. Basically Norfolk remains as it was 400 years ago – the great city of Norwich; the two seaports, Yarmouth and Lynn; and everywhere else the market towns and villages, the farms and farm-buildings, the arable fields, the pastures, the small-holdings and gardens, the woodlands, the commons, the still intractable stretches of heath, that make up its rich and varied countryside.

the care of the sick and poor

M. W. BULMAN

THE AREA covered by this Survey, which has its focus in the present city of Norwich, has for many centuries been an important centre of population which, largely for geographic reasons, has been to some extent cut off from the rest of the country. It has therefore developed in an individual manner, relying on its own resources and creating its own culture until modern transport and communications, the inflow of a new population, and the requirements of industry brought about an inevitable change in the former mode of life of the inhabitants.

In such an area it is not surprising that from an early date the needs of the sick and the poor have been a matter of concern to those responsible for their care and that the relief of sickness and suffering by various forms of social service, appropriate to the times in which they originated, has in this area a long and interesting history.

As in other localities, the first efforts made in Norwich to relieve the sick and necessitous were made by the Church and this city owes to Walter de Suffield, then Bishop of Norwich, the foundation in the year 1249 of a hospital in what is now Bishopsgate, and which must be one of the oldest establishments of its kind in the country.

This hospital, which continues its valuable work today and where original buildings can still be seen, has been known at different times as St Giles' Hospital, St Helen's Hospital (not to be confused with St Helen's House Nursing Home which is situated next door), God's House, The Old Men's Hospital, and The Great Hospital.

In early days a hospital was essentially a church, the nave of which provided shelter for the infirm and services for their benefit and that of other parishioners were held in the choir. This arrangement can still be seen in the Hospice de Beaune, France, but in the case of The Great Hospital, which incorporates St Helen's Church, the choir provided wards for women, the nave for men, and the central part and transept were used for worship. The hospital as founded by Walter de Suffield was intended to shelter all poor and decrepit chaplains of the Norwich diocese who had not wherewith to maintain themselves. There were to be thirty beds or more if funds permitted. In addition to the chaplains, thirteen poor people were to have one meal a day and liberty to refresh themselves at the fire in winter. Furthermore, any poor man coming to the hospital infirm or ill was to be taken care of until he recovered. A master, four chaplains, four sisters of a minimum age of fifty, and other officers were appointed. The hospital was well endowed by its founder and by many subsequent benefactions and maintained its services to the community substantially unchanged until the Dissolution of the Monasteries. In 1535 and again later the hospital stood in danger of dissolution, but in 1547, responsibility for the work of the hospital passed by Indenture from the King to the Mayor, Sheriffs, and citizens of the city of Norwich by whom it was managed with few changes until 1858 when all property of the hospital was vested in twenty-one trustees. In an institution devoted for over 700 years to the care of the sick and infirm it is inevitable that there have been many changes in the customs of the times but it is a little surprising to read that in 1550 the chaplain brought a list of complaints to the Mayor of the city stating that 'there is picking and stealing, going brawling to bed, brawling at table, drunkenness and fighting' and he asks for powers of punishment, particularly that when 'two men or two women or one of each

M. W. BULMAN is Consulting Gynaecologist to the Norfolk and Norwich Hospital

sex fall afighting both should be laid in the stocks until they are appeased'. This is no doubt a sidelight on the disturbances of those days, this event taking place in the year after Kett's Rebellion.

A hospital of comparable type was founded in 1687 by William Doughty, who left £6,000 to trustees to erect and endow a hospital for twenty-four poor men and eight poor women. The trust provided for the appointment of a master who would be responsible for feeding the inmates of the hospital, for providing clothing, the type of which was specified both for men and for women, and for ensuring an adequate supply of coals. Each inmate was provided with two shillings weekly pocket-money.

The trust also laid down rules of conduct with which the inmates must comply and the trustees were empowered 'to turne out either ye Master or poore if they observe not ye orders of this place.'

The poor were told that they 'must live peaceably with ye Master and with one another as becomes Christians, neither cursing, swearing, keeping bad houres nor being drunk'.

This hospital, situated in Calvert Street, continues its valuable work and under the present trustees is being extensively modernized to ensure that the occupants are housed according to present-day standards.

In the thirteenth century barber surgeons were practising in Norwich, and at least three of them occupied at various times the house on Elm Hill now used as a restaurant and known as the Briton Arms. By the sixteenth century the Physicians and Barber Surgeons of the City of Norwich were a well-established and influential group, but it seems clear that medical practice in those days was by no means as well ordered or organized as it has become since. Thus there is a record of a petition presented in 1561 by the Company of Physicians and Barber Surgeons of Norwich to the Mayor of the city praying that certain orders and rules might be kept to remedy the great disorder in the practice of physic and surgery, the petition stating the need for such regulations by complaining that 'for as much as there be divers citizens and many others . . . that do take upon them to be physicians and surgeons and exercise and use the same, having neither experience or learning, as shoemakers, hatmakers, Dornick weavers, smiths and Worstead weavers with others and also divers and sundry

women. . . .' Appropriate regulations appear to have been drawn up.

Those who have considered the entry of women into medical practice to be a modern development may be surprised to see the reference to 'divers and sundry women', albeit unqualified even by the standards of those days, becoming medical practitioners. There are however records of a number of women who engaged in practice under licence. For example, in 1568 the Bishop of Norwich licensed Cecily Baldrye of Great Yarmouth to practise the art of chirurgery and in 1596 the widow of Nicholas Colman was licensed by the Privy Council. In 1666 the Mayor of Norwich paid to 'Mrs Scarfe for setting of Mary Usher, her leg, 10/-.'

In the sixteenth century the outstanding medical personality of Norwich was John Kaye, or Keys, better known as Caius. He studied at Gonville Hall, Cambridge, and later in Italy, specially at Padua. He returned to practice in Norwich, subsequently going to London as physician to Edward VI, Mary, and Elizabeth I. He was described as the prime glory among physicians in the reign of Queen Elizabeth. He passed through all the offices of the Royal College of Physicians and was president for seven years. A prolific author, he was also a well-known naturalist, though today he may be best remembered for his aid to Gonville Hall. As a result of this it was advanced to the status of a college with which his name has ever since been associated.

There appears to be no record of any physician or surgeon of consequence in Norwich at the end of the sixteenth or commencement of the seventeenth century, and indeed as late as 1679 Sir Thomas Browne writes to his son 'The ignorance of chirurgeons as to chirurgical operations creates so many mountebanks and stage quacksalvers. Here hath been a mountebank these two months who cutts for wrye necks, coucheth cataracts, cures hare lipps, etc., wherein no chirurgeon of this place be versed, he hath a great deal of employment to the shame of our chirurgeons.'

In 1655 a boy suffering from stone was sent to Bury to a Mr Gutteridge or Goodrick. It seems probable that at the time there was no capable surgeon in Norwich, a situation which would support the complaint from Sir Thomas Browne just quoted.

During the seventeenth century stone was a well

recognized and prevalent disorder in the whole of East Anglia. No satisfactory explanation of the frequency of this ailment has been found, though it has attracted the attention of the medical profession in all countries. The earliest known stone was found at Litlington, Cambs., in a Roman cemetery, where a large oxalate calculus was discovered in the bony pelvis of a skeleton. The largest stone taken from the human subject was claimed by Dr Heberden in 1750 to be one removed by Gutteridge in 1662. This stone weighed $33\frac{1}{2}$ ounces and was taken post-mortem from a woman who died after a journey on horseback.

At this period there were no general hospitals in the provinces, the hospitals in existence being for the support and care of the indigent, incurable, aged, and infirm and for that reason were known as infirmaries. In all in the Norwich diocese there were seventy-four such institutions together with six leper hospitals outside the walls of Norwich. During the seventeenth century sufferers from stone presented themselves before the Mayor and Aldermen to obtain help in getting surgical assistance. There remain many records of sums disbursed to cover not only the surgeon's fee but also to support the patient and relatives during the time of the illness. The necessary funds were raised by the Aldermen from the parish in which the patient lived, and in this system may perhaps be seen the germ of the present Welfare State.

In 1711 a Court of Guardians was formed by Act of Parliament to erect a workhouse in Norwich and to make provision for the sick. The responsibilities of the Mayor and Aldermen then ceased. As a result of the experience they gained in workhouse practice John Harmer and Benjamin Gooch became famous as operators for stone.

The state of medical practice at this time is well illustrated by an advertisement which appeared in *Cosgrave's Magazine* in 1732. 'Dr. Palmer of Loddon being lately deceased, who used the art of midwifery having served his apprenticeship some years since with the late famous Dr. Havers of Stoke Holy Cross near Norwich, well known by his skill in that practice, I Daniel Nelson, surgeon in Loddon aforesaid, having faithfully served as an apprentice with the said Dr. Havers and having by pains and study as well as anatomical courses made himself master of the said art so necessary for all

women labouring under any difficulties in child bearing he advertises this that he is ready at any time when wanted at the most reasonable charges.

'N.B. He undertakes to cure all lunaticks if curable.'

The Dr Havers mentioned was the Rev. Thomas Havers, better known by the former title. There is a monument to him on the outside of the south wall of Stoke Holy Cross Church on which he is described as being learned in theology, physic, surgery, and lithotomy. He occupied the living of Framingham Earl from 1683 to 1701 when he went to Stoke to devote his time to medicine and surgery. He died in 1719, leaving his instruments to his nephew Robert Bransby. Bransby moved from Hapton to Shotesham where he died in 1748. His daughter Elizabeth married Benjamin Gooch who later became the first surgeon to the Norfolk and Norwich Hospital. Sarah, daughter of Benjamin Gooch, ultimately married Dr D'Urban who succeeded Gooch in Shotesham and she became the mother of General Sir William D'Urban, founder of Durban, South Africa.

The absence of general hospitals in the provinces has already been noted but towards the middle of the eighteenth century those concerned with the care of the sick poor began to appreciate that more good could be done by working in co-operation than by individual efforts and as a result several hospitals were established in different parts of England about this time.

In Norfolk the first hospital established in this century was the Bethel Hospital, founded in 1713, to which reference will be made later, but the first hospital which can be considered as a forerunner of the modern general hospital was a cottage hospital erected in Shotesham, Norfolk, by Mr William Fellowes, squire of Shotesham, who was also a well-known philanthropist, and for many years a magistrate. This cottage hospital was provided for the treatment of the sick poor of the neighbourhood and was by many years the first cottage hospital established in England. The original building remains today, now occupied as a private residence.

Mr Benjamin Gooch, of Shotesham, already mentioned as a noted surgeon of his day, was surgeon to this cottage hospital before his appointment as the first surgeon to the Norfolk and Norwich Hospital.

In passing it may be mentioned that among his many benefactions Mr Fellowes also provided a bath-house for the use of poor people at the foot of Skeet's Hill, between Shotesham and Stoke Holy Cross. This building no longer exists.

The cottage hospital at Shotesham was, of course, never intended to be a county hospital but the need for a general hospital serving the county was becoming increasingly apparent.

In 1744 'an unknown wellwisher' wrote to the local Press suggesting that a county hospital be established and in 1758 Bishop Hayter, then Bishop of Norwich, who had consulted Mr Gooch on the matter, also tried to rouse public interest in this proposal.

For various reasons, however, no action was taken until 1770 when William Fellowes and Benjamin Gooch, who are by now well known to readers of this article, called a public meeting in Norwich. At this meeting a committee was formed, charged with the responsibility to erect a general hospital and in due course funds were raised, a suitable plot of land was purchased, and plans were approved. On 5 March 1771, the foundation-stone was laid and on 11 July 1772, the hospital was opened for the treatment of out-patients. Three patients were treated on that day, compared with 355 on the corresponding day in 1960. For some reason not recorded the hospital was not opened to in-patients until several months later, and even then only one-half of the intended 120 beds were available as the cost of the building had greatly exceeded the estimate, a state of affairs not unknown today, and money for the maintenance of the full number of beds was not available. Little of the original building now remains as the hospital was rebuilt in 1879 after a severe outbreak of infection which had caused great concern. The new hospital, which was designed for 220 beds, was built in accordance with what were then the most advanced ideas, and with certain modifications and many additions is in use at the present time with a bed complement of 443.

The reputation of the hospital has always been high, largely as a result of the progressive policies pursued by successive boards of management, with whom the medical staffs have worked in close association. As early as 1787 an electrical machine was ordered for use in the hospital. It was provided 'that the patients are not to be electrified in their beds and the Apothecary's time be not taken up for the purpose'.

In 1845 it was ordered that a register be kept by the house surgeon of all patients admitted on account of accidents on railways, a sidelight on conditions of those times, but a strangely modern note was struck at a rather earlier date by the concern expressed at the number of cases of serious injury admitted after road accidents. In those days the speed of traffic was not blamed but attention was drawn to the dangerous habit of many carters who returning from Norwich market the worse for drink rode upon the wagon shafts and, falling off, were crushed by the wheels.

Among many famous members of the medical staff special mention may be given to Edward Rigby (appointed 1772), the first to introduce vaccination into Norwich, John Greene Crosse (appointed 1823), a prolific medical writer, Edward Copeman (appointed 1851), Sir Peter Eade (appointed 1858), both of whom left among many other writings a history of this hospital, and William Cadge (appointed 1854), who was almost certainly the most famous lithotomist of his day and who enjoyed a European reputation. Benjamin Gooch (appointed 1771), the first surgeon to the hospital, was the inventor of 'Gooch's splinting' which remained in common use till the 1920's when it was replaced by plaster of paris.

The nineteenth century saw a widespread development of social services of all kinds.

In 1804 the Norwich Dispensary was founded as a charitable institution, the benefits of which were made available to patients by a subscriber's recommendation. This system was followed by most similar institutions and continued well into the present century.

Physicians were attached to the Norwich Dispensary in an honorary capacity and attended the dispensary to see patients. Those patients who needed attention at home were visited by the apothecary. This dispensary continued its work for over 100 years but records of it appear to end in 1916. Similar dispensaries were founded in King's Lynn and in 1828 in Bungay.

The year 1805 saw the foundation of the Norwich School for the Blind by a Norwich man, Thos Tawell, who had himself been blind for many years. This school continues to this day its valuable work and still occupies the original site in Magdalen Street.

The Norfolk and Norwich Eye Infirmary was founded

in 1821 and was amalgamated with the Norfolk and Norwich Hospital in 1925 partly as a result of shortage of nursing staff and partly to secure better co-ordination of the work of both hospitals.

The Norwich Lying-in Charity was established in 1832 'to provide skilful midwives and medical attendants for delivering poor married women in their own dwellings'. For some reason not explained it was laid down that 'No woman be admitted to receive the benefit of the Charity who has not one living child.' This proviso seems quite out of keeping with the present-day stress on the importance of skilled care in the first pregnancy and labour. This charity still existed in 1892.

The General Hospital in Great Yarmouth was founded in 1838 and the Thetford Cottage Hospital in 1898.

The famous singer, Jenny Lind, visited Norwich on several occasions as the guest of Bishop Stanley, Bishop of Norwich, and early in 1849 she came again to this city to give two concerts for the benefit of the poor. These concerts brought in £1,253, this sum being placed in the hands of trustees pending a decision as to its best use. Eventually, in 1853, it was decided to found a children's hospital, to be known as the Jenny Lind Infirmary for Sick Children. This hospital had high standards for the time of its foundation, and one rule provided that no nurse was to be engaged who could not read or write. In the course of time the hospital greatly extended its work and moved from its original premises to those now in use. The changes in medical and nursing requirements which came about after the First World War made it increasingly difficult for smaller hospitals to remain independent and at the same time maintain their standards. Furthermore, at that time co-operative working between hospitals was becoming recognized as essential for economy in a time of financial stringency and for the most effective use of staff. These considerations led to negotiations between the boards of management of the Jenny Lind and Norfolk and Norwich Hospitals over a period of several years which in 1929 resulted in an agreement which amounted virtually to an amalgamation between the two institutions and has been to their mutual advantage.

So far the account given of the development of the social services has been concerned with the physical ailments of the poor in this area. The needs of the mentally afflicted were not, however, overlooked for as early as 1713 the Bethel Hospital, Norwich, was founded by Mary, third daughter of John Mann, of that city. Mary, who was born in 1647, married Samuel Chapman, Rector of Thorpe-next-Norwich in 1682. She built the Bethel Hospital 'by the desire and advice of my late husband' on a site of some historic importance to the west of what was then the most populous part of the city. The foundress opened the hospital and later lived there up to the time of her death. She settled all her estates on trustees who were responsible for the management of the house. Many later bequests and donations were made to the hospital which continued in the same type of management until the commencement of the National Health Service.

In 1808, nearly a century later than the foundation of the Bethel Hospital, an Act of Parliament was passed 'for the better care of lunatics being paupers'. Prior to this time lunatics were, if maniacal or dangerous, confined to gaols or houses of correction, or if harmless in poorhouses or houses of industry. Some were boarded out or roamed the countryside. Advantage of this Act was taken to build the Norfolk County Asylum which was opened in 1814. At that time the only other hospitals built under this Act were in London, Nottingham, Leicester, and Northampton, so that in the provision of this hospital Norfolk was one of the leading areas in the treatment of mental disease, while the foundress of the Bethel Hospital was far in advance of her time.

The original Norfolk County Asylum has since been described as a gloomy and horrible place. When it was built the window tax was still in force with the result that the fewest possible windows were provided and those were guarded by iron bars. The bedding consisted of straw on which the inmates were chained.

Further facilities for the treatment of mental disorder were provided by the opening in 1859 of the Eastern Counties Asylum at Colchester and of the Norwich City Asylum in 1880. The latter replaced the older Norwich Pauper Lunatic Asylum situated at St Augustine's Gate.

The year 1851 saw the opening of the Norwich Waterworks, an important social service of quite a different character. In the previous year a company had been formed for this purpose, despite opposition by certain individuals who considered the scheme itself too expensive and the cost of water supplied to householders to be beyond the means of many of them.

The first Medical Officer of Health to the city of Norwich was appointed in 1873, Mr T.W. Crosse being elected at a salary of £200 per annum. A further addition to the services provided by the city of Norwich was made in 1890 by the opening of the Norwich Isolation Hospital.

The end of the nineteenth century saw, in 1898, the formation of the Norwich Diocesan Church Mission to the Deaf and Dumb, with its associations throughout the county.

Early in the twentieth century, in 1902, one of the most recent, if not the last of the important voluntary services was inaugurated. This was Kelling Sanatorium, where treatment was given to those suffering from tuberculosis who were unable to afford fees in private sanatoria. The late Dr Burton Fanning, physician to the Norfolk and Norwich Hospital, played a leading part in the establishment of this sanatorium and was prominently associated with it until his death.

From the foregoing summary it will be seen that the social services of this area have been developed in three main stages.

In the first stage, approximately from the thirteenth to the seventeenth century, such provision as was made for those unable to care for themselves was a matter of private charity and that provision consisted in the main of shelter, food, and clothing. Of treatment of diseases as understood today there can have been but little and such as has survived in the records appears to have been mainly bone-setting and cutting for stone. The purpose of such hospitals as then existed to all appearances corresponds to that of old people's homes and chronic sick institutions today.

In the second stage, during the eighteenth and nineteenth centuries, an expansion of hospitals and other charitable institutions took place to an increasing extent. Hospitals became recognizable as institutions in which treatment as distinct from simple shelter was evidently of greater importance, and for which progressively increasing knowledge had become available. In this era the charitable inclinations of individuals gained added value through co-operation of groups of people in larger enterprises. In addition, and particularly in the latter part of the nineteenth century one can discern the beginning of specialization in the establishment of hospitals, and charities for special purposes, such as maternity, blindness, deafness, and for the treatment of infectious diseases. The growth of population during this period also made it necessary to extend the buildings of the institutions concerned, and the various local authorities increasingly provided municipal services parallel to those of the many voluntary bodies. These municipal services filled in a number of gaps in the services provided by voluntary sources but ultimately, specially during the second and third decades of the present century, tended to produce wasteful competition with existing voluntary bodies which came to an end only with the start of the Second World War.

The third stage, that of the present century to date, has seen an unprecedented advance in medical knowledge which has led to a great increase in the cost and complexity of the treatment of disease. During the first three decades of this century all charitable institutions concerned with the treatment of illness faced progressively rising costs in every aspect of their work and found ever-increasing difficulty in raising the increasing income they required. Broadly speaking the nineteenth century made available a great number of new medical and charitable services while the twentieth century has greatly expanded those already available. To finance such an expansion under modern conditions became an impossibility for voluntary organizations, and in addition some co-ordination of the available services and in certain directions an improvement of standards had become highly desirable.

Thus, over a period of 700 years, we have passed from individual charity, through organized charity, to a National Service.

industrial and agricultural
K. J. ALLISON

TUDOR NORWICH, no less than the modern city, was the focal centre of industry in a predominantly agricultural county. Of the two great ports, King's Lynn flourished on its commerce rather than its industry, but Great Yarmouth was renowned for its fishing as well as its trade. In the countryside, the only industry of more than local note was that which weavers in the towns and villages of east Norfolk shared with those in Norwich – the manufacture of worsteds. Norwich, indeed, stood beside the West Country, Suffolk and Essex, and the West Riding as one of the chief textile centres of England. With no other occupation of a truly industrial character, worsted-weaving was the basis of the city's prosperity, and during the seventeenth century the proportion of the working population employed in the textile industry rose to nearly a half.

In the Middle Ages Norwich had built up a large export market in southern Europe for these fine, light-weight cloths that were made nowhere else in England. By the fifteenth century, however, worsteds were being made – and of a far higher quality – in the Netherlands, and the Norfolk industry gradually declined. It was revived by the bold enterprise of the Corporation which induced about 300 refugees from the Netherlands to settle in Norwich in 1565. Mr Ketton-Cremer has already remarked upon the far-reaching influence of 'the Strangers'. Their new draperies were imitated by Norfolk weavers, and by the turn of the century many new varieties of cloth had been devised. These became known as 'Norwich stuffs' and they regained for the city its old reputation in the markets of Europe.

Not until the early eighteenth century did serious difficulties again intervene. Norwich was faced by mounting competition from foreign and home-made cloths, above all from West Riding worsteds. The lower-grade types were soon extensively made in Yorkshire, and it was only the finest stuffs which enabled Norfolk to compete with considerable success for so long (fig. 1). The West Riding's advantages are well known. It was Yorkshire sheep and Yorkshire spinners that provided Norwich with much of its wool and its yarn. It was Leeds and Bradford, not Norwich, that had local water-power, coal, and iron with which to share in the Industrial Revolution. It was Yorkshiremen, not Norfolkmen, who adventurously experimented with machinery. By the middle of the nineteenth century the Norfolk industry was almost dead: it employed only about 800 people in Norwich in 1851, fewer than 200 in 1871, only about 80 in 1891.

The collapse of the worsted industry threatened the city with permanent economic decline. But it brought an unrivalled opportunity for new enterprise, and Norwich was not found lacking in men with the initiative to provide employment for skilled but idle hands. The railways, moreover, had linked Norwich with London and the Midlands in the mid-1840's: too late to offer much comfort to the worsted industry, but ready to bring in the raw materials and carry away the products of new industries. Many now well-known firms appeared on the scene, and a diverse industrial structure replaced the dangerous monopoly of a single staple industry. Some of the more spectacular changes in employment are shown in fig. 2.

One branch of the textile industry, emphasizing skill and quality, survived the struggle with Yorkshire –

K. J. ALLISON is Assistant to the General Editor of the Victoria County Histories

Fig. 1 *Sample Book with patterns of Norwich-made textiles, 1769. The patterns shown are glazed worsteds with brocaded designs for the Italian market*

silk-weaving. A few types of stuff had long been made of both wool and silk, but in the nineteenth century silk crapes and shawls came into their own. By 1851 probably about 4,000 people in Norwich worked on silk fabrics; there were still well over 1,000 in 1871 and only slightly fewer than 1,000 in 1891. A number of new firms were established and several continued working into the twentieth century, but in 1939 Francis Hinde & Sons Ltd bought out their last rival. Hindes' were established in 1810 and had built their second factory in the city in 1927.

Most prominent among the rising industries of the early nineteenth century was boot- and shoe-making. Before 1800 the local market had been served by many small master craftsmen, but shoe-making was well suited to succeed worsted-weaving as a major industry. It required abundant manual skill, and it could be readily carried on in the home rather than the factory. It is tempting, indeed, to see the 'garret-master' who distributed leather and shoes to be worked upon in employees' houses as the direct successor of the master weaver, putting out wool and yarn to be spun and woven. The total number of men and women employed rose rapidly: from 1,700 in 1841 to 4,000 in 1851 and 5,300 in 1861.

Machinery was introduced into the industry in the 1850's and by the early twentieth century most of the workers had moved from home to factory. In 1901, 7,500 were employed. The importance of skilled crafts-manship had from the first led Norwich to concentrate on women's and children's shoes (fig. 3), and new methods and designs have constantly been introduced to meet the demand for high-quality shoes. By 1931 there were 10,800 employees and in 1935 more than 6,000,000 pairs of shoes were made – over 16 per cent of the total British output. There were then twenty-six firms, the five largest and oldest employing over half of the total number of workers: James Southall & Co. Ltd, established in 1792 and said to be the oldest shoe-making concern in the country; Bally & Haldinstein Ltd (1799); the Norvic Shoe Co. Ltd (As Howlett & White Ltd, 1846); Sexton, Son & Everard Ltd (about 1886); and Edwards and Holmes Ltd (1891).

Another trade requiring manual skill and allowing home working was the manufacture of clothing. Its expansion was assisted by the introduction of sewing machines in the 1850's and at the same time a factory was built by F.W. Harmer, whose grandfather had established a draper's business in 1825. The decline of home working was probably responsible for the con-siderable fall in employment between 1891 and 1931 (fig. 2). Harmers', however, had built a large new factory in 1891 and they continued to make an important contri-bution to the city's industrial employment.

The expansion of two other industries in Norwich in the nineteenth century reflected the resources and the requirements of the surrounding countryside: the manufacture of food and drink, and the production of equipment in wood and metal. A leading role in these developments was played by the milling firm of J. and J. Colman Ltd. Established in about 1804 at near-by Stoke Holy Cross, Colmans' moved to Carrow Works in Norwich in 1856, attracted by the supply of labour and the railways. By 1900 they had about 2,200 employees. With an expanding production of mustard and starch, and a wide variety of patent foods and drinks, they have remained one of the largest firms in the city. This was not their only contribution. Colmans' helped William Scott to establish his engineering business, and both F.W. Harmer and the engineer Dawson Paul were relatives of theirs.

The removal of Colmans' to Norwich was closely followed by the establishment – as a chemist's – of A.J. Caley & Son Ltd in 1860. Mineral water was later made and in the 1880's Caleys' began to produce cocoa, chocolate, and Christmas crackers. By 1918, when a new factory was built, about 2,800 people were employed, and the firm has remained a leading employer. It was bought by J. Mackintosh & Sons Ltd in 1932. Among other manufacturers of food and drink were several large flour-millers and brewers, the vinegar-makers Hills & Underwood (established 1762), and Colemans', who began making tonic wine in the 1880's.

Of the wood- and metal-workers, the earliest well-known name in the field was Boulton & Paul Ltd. Established as an ironmonger's in 1797, the firm was joined by William Boulton in 1844 and Dawson Paul in 1853. A wide variety of agricultural, horticultural, and household goods was made, and by 1880 there were about 350 employees. Boulton & Paul's contribution to the First World War included aeroplanes, and these continued to be made in Norwich until 1934. By 1920 the firm had completed its move to the present large riverside site and nearly 3,000 people were employed. There, structural steel work was to become the leading product. Barnards Ltd began their manufacture of a similar range of goods in 1826; they made a notable contribution with the invention of a machine for weaving wire-netting, and both firms have retained netting as one of their specialities.

The city's second great engineering firm, Laurence, Scott and Electromotors Ltd, developed from the ambitions of a young engineer, William Scott. In 1883,

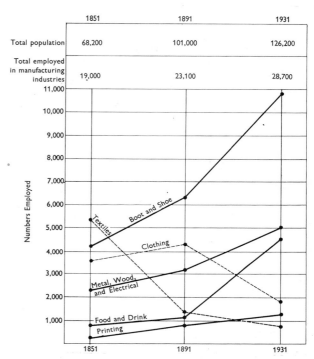

	1851	1891	1931
Total population	68,200	101,000	126,200
Total employed in manufacturing industries	19,000	23,100	28,700

Fig. 2 *Employment in manufacturing industries in Norwich, 1851–1931. (From the census reports. Figures are to the nearest 100)*

encouraged and backed by Colmans', he began to make his own dynamos, and he was joined in 1888 by Reginald Laurence. New works were built for the firm in 1896, and a second factory added in 1900. At about this time the installation side of the business was sold to an independent firm which later developed into Mann Egerton & Co. Ltd, the motor engineers. Laurence & Scott concentrated on the manufacture of electrical machinery, and before the First World War had begun their all-important manufacture of machinery for ships. The firm amalgamated with Electromotors Ltd of Manchester in 1927. A second electrical engineering firm, Heatrae Ltd, was established in 1920 and has manufactured heating apparatus on a large scale.

One other manufacturing industry – printing, bookbinding, and photography – has notably prospered in the nineteenth and twentieth centuries. Outstanding among the city's printing firms is Jarrold & Sons Ltd which moved to Norwich from Suffolk in 1823.

There is no space to mention other industries and smaller firms, but some account must be given of the vigorous growth of banking and insurance, which greatly assisted industrial expansion. Members of the Gurney family had long carried on banking transactions as a complement to their business as merchants before, in 1775, John and Henry Gurney established a bank in Norwich, with four branches in the eastern counties. Several local banks were acquired by the Gurneys during the nineteenth century, and three new branches opened in Norwich in 1893. In 1896 twenty private banks agreed to amalgamate, the largest of these being Gurney & Co. of Norwich, Barclay & Co. of London, and Backhouse & Co. of Darlington. Barclay's Bank, as it was later known, retained the former partners of the old private firms on local boards of directors to keep local connexions and members of the Gurney family are still local directors at Norwich.

In insurance, the Bignold family has been outstanding in the affairs of the Norwich Union Societies. Thomas Bignold founded the Norwich Union Fire Insurance Society in 1797, and the Life Insurance Society in 1808. The Norwich General Assurance Office (founded in 1792) was absorbed by the Norwich Union in 1821, and in 1864 the Union secured the amalgamation of the Amicable Society which, founded in 1706, was the oldest life insurance society in the world. The rapid growth of the Union's business may be illustrated by the increase of the total funds of the life office alone: from over £1,000,000 in 1830, to nearly £2,000,000 in 1890, nearly £9,000,000 in 1910, and nearly £34,000,000 in 1930. By the 1930's the Norwich Union Societies were employing about 1,300 people in the city.

The Second World War wrought many changes on the face of Norwich, not least to its factories. Much of the city's industrial capacity was diverted to military requirements: some a natural extension of the work of the engineering firms, some – such as munitions – a complete departure from normal production. Many employees were, of course, called to the Armed Services, the boot and shoe industry alone losing about 3,000 workers. Many factories, moreover, were destroyed or damaged during air-raids. Three shoe factories were completely destroyed, others damaged; one of Harmers' factories was destroyed; Mackintoshs', Boulton & Paul's, and Colmans' were all extensively damaged. Hasty reconstruction and the improvisation of makeshift premises enabled production to continue, and all the existing industries recovered after the war. The further diversification of the city's industries in the post-war period is discussed in a later section.

Until the early twentieth century, the prosperity of Great Yarmouth depended primarily upon its commerce and its share of the herring fishing industry. Other industries were on a small scale: for example, the manufacture of equipment for boats and clothing for fishermen, the preparation of imported corn and timber, and the manufacture of silk stuffs, introduced by a Norwich firm in 1818. Yarmouth's industry was dominated by the herring fishery from the sixteenth century, when Dutch boats outnumbered all others at the quays, until the First World War, when Scottish boats and Scottish fisher-girls thronged the port. The fishery was at its height in the first decade of the present century. Nearly 1,000 boats – a quarter of them from Yarmouth itself – landed

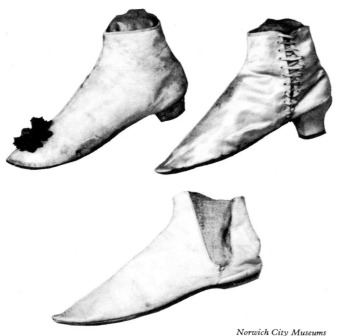

Norwich City Museums

Fig. 3 *Nineteenth-century ladies' shoes made in Norwich.*
(Bridewell Museum, Norwich)

their catches there during the season and in 1911 over 1,000 Yarmouth men were employed. The subsequent story of the fishery, which is told in a later chapter, is one of continuous decline. The holiday industry had by that time come to provide considerable employment, but its seasonal nature further emphasized Yarmouth's need to extend the range of its employment. Several new industries, such as the manufacture of potato crisps, had in fact been introduced before the Second World War, and rapid development was to take place after 1945.

King's Lynn's fishing industry never rivalled that of Great Yarmouth, and by the nineteenth century the heyday of its commerce was past. As in Yarmouth, minor industries served the needs of ships and processed their cargoes, but Lynn also catered for the farmers of west Norfolk in a way that Yarmouth did not in the east. Two engineering firms, for example, were established about 1850, fertilizers have been made since the late nineteenth century, and in the twentieth, fruit and vegetables have been canned and sugar refined from local beet.

In the small towns of Norfolk, industrial employment was considerably extended in the nineteenth and twentieth centuries. Most was dependent on the products and requirements of agriculture, but there were exceptions – printing at Fakenham, for instance. Engineering, moreover, gradually expanded to serve more distant and varied markets. By 1946 nearly 4,000 people were employed in these towns, with engineering, food and drink, and woodworking as the leading industries. East Dereham, with firms in all three groups, was perhaps outstanding. By the twentieth century fishing employed few men outside the two main ports, but the holiday industry had become important to many coastal towns and villages as well as to those of Broadland.

Our survey of industry began in 1550 with the worsted weavers of Norwich anxiously watching their dwindling trade. In the countryside, too, there was anxiety, for the peasantry, oppressed by their landlords, had been unsuccessful in their rising under Kett. But as 'the Strangers' revived the worsted industry, so did new methods of husbandry from the Continent gradually transform the old open-field farming of the countryside.

That transformation must figure prominently in this account, but old ways were slow to change and cannot be ignored.

The open-field area of Norfolk, where the most celebrated developments were to take place, was not the whole of the county. A substantial part of the Fenland lies in west Norfolk and was a world apart from the 'upland'. Much unimproved ground remained in the sixteenth-century Fenland, but extensive reclamation had already taken place: marsh on the seaward side and fen on the landward had been drained for both arable and pasture. Even in 'upland' Norfolk, the open fields did not everywhere dominate the scene. The heavy soils of mid and south Norfolk supported good pasture and did not need intensive dunging for the growth of corn; small enclosed fields were consequently predominant and dairying played an important part in a mixed-farming economy. This contemporaries called the Wood-Pasture Region. The remainder of 'upland' Norfolk comprised the Sheep-Corn Region, stretching in an arc from Breckland, through the west and north of the county, to the Loam Region in the north-east. This was open-field country *par excellence*. The light and medium soils yielded good corn only if heavily manured by sheep, and large flocks moved freely over the open fields whenever they were unsown. On these soils, too, heathland and commons were extensive and provided additional feed for the flocks.

The open-field husbandry of Norfolk was very different from that practised in other parts of the country. It cannot be described here but an outstanding feature was the dunging of the hungry soils by large flocks of sheep. Most of the sheep belonged to lords of the manor, but they fed over the small, unfenced strips of land which the lords' tenants held scattered in the open fields. In order to ensure that large and compact areas of the fields were available for the sheep, either as summer fallow or after harvest, complicated arrangements were necessary to ensure that compact areas were treated in the same way – left fallow, or sown with winter corn, or spring corn. Thus this, like all other forms of open-field farming, called for the subordination of personal freedom and convenience to a common routine. It was against this background that new crops and methods were gradually introduced in the seventeenth century, and in

Photographed from Print in possession of The Norfolk Club, Norwich, 1960. By courtesy of the Norwich City Museums

Fig. 4   *Thomas William Coke inspecting Southdown sheep with Mr Walton and the Holkham shepherds (1808)*

many villages individual initiative inevitably clashed with communal restriction.

The inconvenience of the open-field system was in itself an incentive to the progressive landlord or the self-improving tenant. But the seventeenth-century farmer had the added incentive of rapidly expanding markets. The Norfolk economy had perhaps never been entirely one of subsistence farming, and corn had long been sent to local markets or shipped from local ports. After 1600, however, the demand for food-supplies was greatly increased. Norwich had recovered its industrial prosperity and was growing fast, and the London octopus was reaching out to Norfolk for its corn, butter, and mutton.

If the improvement of husbandry was encouraged by these demands, it was made possible to a large extent by the introduction of new ideas from the Netherlands. Soldiers, travellers, fishermen, merchants, and not least 'the Strangers' who sought refuge in Norwich, all may have contributed to this import of new crops and methods. These innovations, moreover, had been tried and tested in conditions similar to those found on the light soils of Norfolk.

Improvement did not fit easily into the routine of open-field farming. The improving tenant wanted to consolidate and enclose his holding and to be freed from communal restrictions. He wanted, above all, to escape the annual incursion of his landlord's sheep, for new rotations and crops broke the old dependence on sheep dunging to restore fertility to the soil. The landlord found his sheep impeded by enclosures and by crops growing where custom dictated that none should be. Most friction was caused by the turnip. Brought in by 'the Strangers' as a garden crop, it was being grown in the open fields by at least the mid seventeenth century, and because it was sown as soon as corn was harvested, it occupied land traditionally available as winter sheep pasturage.

While some landlords opposed the innovations of their tenants, however, others were themselves anxious to break with old methods. On some of the largest estates, especially in the Good Sands Region of north-west Norfolk, open fields and heaths were completely enclosed. Large compact farms were created and leased to tenant-farmers, and the way was clear for improvement. Sheep were fed on turnips, clover, and sown grasses, all introduced from the Continent, and Scottish cattle were brought in to be fattened. New rotations were developed and marling was systematically practised. By the end of the seventeenth century, landlords were beginning to grant long leases to their tenants and to insist on the husbandlike cultivation of the soil.

Most of the practices which formed part of the celebrated Norfolk Husbandry had in this way been gradually introduced in the seventeenth century, and it is no longer possible to think of an 'Agrarian Revolution' in the eighteenth. 'Turnip' Townshend did not retire to his estates until 1730, and he did not introduce the turnip; Thomas William Coke did not inherit his estates until 1776, and he did not introduce wheat to a sandy waste. If they were not innovators or workers of miracles, their efforts were nevertheless of outstanding importance. They developed and systematized the improvements, and spread their knowledge among fellow-landlords as well as their own tenants. Coke's sheep-shearings at Holkham were notable gatherings at which ideas were exchanged, and his leases to tenants insisted on careful attention to the rotation of crops. Rotations varied with soil conditions, but it was the Norfolk Four-Course of turnips, barley, clover, and wheat which became the best-known feature of the new husbandry. Coke also popularized new breeds of sheep (fig. 4) and cattle,

methods of irrigation and under-draining, techniques of cultivation, and new fertilizing agents.

While the Norfolk Husbandry was being developed on the 'upland', improvements were also taking place in the Fenland. Large areas of marshland were embanked and reclaimed from the sea, and to the south the Fens were being drained by 'undertakers' and Dutch engineers. Throughout Norfolk, indeed, the seventeenth and eighteenth centuries witnessed a striking transformation of the landscape. Much remained to be done, but when the Parliamentary Enclosure Commissioners came to Norfolk they found few areas where the attack on open fields, heaths, and marshes had not already begun, and many where it had been completed.

During the final years of the eighteenth century and the first half of the nineteenth a great many Acts were passed to deal with the remaining unenclosed land in the county. Parliamentary enclosure enabled much existing arable land to be cultivated in accordance with the new methods, but it also greatly extended the cultivated area. Not only upland heaths, but also much marsh and fen, were brought under the plough for the first time. The development of chemical fertilizers and machinery assisted reclamation, and in the early years of the nineteenth century improvement was also stimulated by the high corn prices which followed the Napoleonic Wars. By mid-century there was more land in cultivation than at any subsequent time until the Second World War. The prolonged slump beginning in the 1870's discouraged corn-growing, and the spread of built-up areas, the growing demand for milk, and the reversion of poor land to heath, all contributed to a decline in the arable acreage. In Breckland, where marginal land has been used by the Forestry Commission and the War Department, the decrease was over 50 per cent. Only in the Fenland did the arable acreage increase as drainage was improved and the cultivation of fruit and vegetables extended.

In the present century, nearly three-quarters of the farmed area of Norfolk has been under crops. There have been fluctuations of course: the arable acreage notably increased during the First World War, but post-war conditions, culminating in the agricultural depression of 1928–34, caused a steady decline. Over

50 per cent of the ploughed area has been under cereals, barley continuing to take first place, followed by wheat. The acreage of all roots combined often approached that of barley during the 1920's and 1930's, and the decline of most varieties was offset by a twelve-fold increase in the acreage of sugar-beet between 1924 and 1936. The first modern beet-sugar factory in Britain was opened at Cantley in 1912; the later success of beet-growing enabled it to be reopened in 1920 and two others were built in the county in 1925 and 1927. Among crops occupying smaller acreages, vegetables grown for human consumption greatly increased in importance. The introduction of new crops in the twentieth century has met with mixed success. Tobacco was experimentally grown in Breckland, but received inadequate official encouragement; the reintroduction of flax, grown for fibre, and the introduction of commercial lavender-growing in north-west Norfolk were both successful on a limited scale. Fruit-growing was encouraged by the slump which affected other branches of farming in the late nineteenth century. It began on a commercial scale in the 1890's, and the acreage of small fruit alone doubled between 1914 and 1935: only Kent and Cambridgeshire then had larger areas.

Pasture-farming has continued to occupy a relatively small acreage but several significant changes have taken place in the twentieth century. The import of New World beef and the increasing demand for milk between the wars encouraged the keeping of cows in milk. By 1936 these represented nearly one-third of the total number of cattle. Sugar-beet tops and pulp played a large part by providing additional fodder. Sheep at first remained important on the arable farms on the lighter soils, but the increased use of fertilizers and the import of Australasian mutton caused a considerable decline in their numbers in the 1930's; pigs were then almost as numerous as sheep. Poultry-farming became popular during the late-nineteenth-century depression, and ducks and turkeys also came to occupy an important place in the farming economy.

One other feature of the Norfolk landscape has greatly changed in recent years – the woodlands. The improvement of heathland, the need for shelter belts, private and Parliamentary enclosure, and the vogue for parkland, were all associated with the planting of woods and hedgerows in the eighteenth and nineteenth centuries. Large quantities of timber have been cut from these woodlands, especially during the First World War, but large-scale forestry operations did not begin until the 1920's. Much of the land abandoned by the plough, as well as much unimproved heathland, was then taken over by the Forestry Commission in Breckland. By 1934 the commission controlled about 44,000 acres, a large proportion of it already planted, and the area was considerably extended before the Second World War. The impact of wartime demands and the changes made since 1945 in forestry, as well as in farming, are described elsewhere.

education in the City of Norwich   J. W. BEESON

EDUCATION has always been vigorously pursued in Norwich and the hints provided by the rather scanty records which survive from the Middle Ages make it clear that even then the opportunity for schooling in the city did not lag behind that generally available in England.

The first known reference to a Norwich school is in the statutes of St Giles' Hospital in 1256. Mention is made of a school already existing, in which some seven poor scholars were at that time receiving free dinners.

In pre-Reformation days Norwich had a large number of religious houses and many had grammar schools or choir schools of their own. These were lost at the Reformation, and it is interesting to note that one act which helped to meet the loss was a condition made by Henry VIII in granting Blackfriars to the city that it should be used as a school. The gap left by the Reformation must have been a matter of concern to the city and its citizens, since we find that Thomas Anguish, Mayor of Norwich in 1611, founded in 1617 the Boys' and Girls' Hospital Schools which were in existence until quite recently. Indeed there still exists in the city a building known as Anguish Homes, nowadays occupied by the Education Committee as additional infant school accommodation, the rent being paid to the Anguish Charity.

With the coming of the eighteenth century the rate at which educational institutions were founded increased all over the country, and by 1708 there were in Norwich no less than nine schools associated with the Society for the Propagation of Christian Knowledge (a society which had been founded in 1698). Of these nine schools at least two were in being comparatively recently and premises which housed them still survive. Other schools not associated directly with the Established Church were founded not long after this. In 1710 came the Joanna Scott School, whose funds still exist as an educational charity. In 1720 Norman School was established, and its name is perpetuated in that of the Education Committee's Norman School. Its funds are now used to help the descendants of one John Norman and many persons in the city still seek a certificate to establish their relationship with him and hence to share in his benefaction.

With the coming of the nineteenth century Norwich was again not lagging in the national drive to secure mass education mainly through the National Society and the British and Foreign Schools Society.

The Norwich Diocesan National School Society was established in 1812, and Lancastrian Schools are recorded as opening, one in 1811 and another in 1840. The National Schools Society contributed annually towards the support of Church Schools in the city, and it is interesting to note that it also supported an institution for training mistresses to take charge of schools. This last institution was transferred from the Cathedral Close in 1853 to larger premises in St George's Plain, where it became known as the Norwich Training College. From thence it was removed in 1892 to another site in Norwich in College Road. On this site it suffered severe damage during air raids, and has since been transferred to more permanent and spacious accommodation at Keswick, just outside the city.

In addition to the work of the Lancastrian Society and the National Schools Society various other bodies established elementary schools in the city. The Presbyterian Church Schools in Calvert Street were established in connexion with the Octagon Chapel, and two

J.W. BEESON is Director of Education for the City of Norwich

Roman Catholic Schools were built in 1857. In the same year Messrs J. & J. Colman established a school for children of their work-people, which later grew into a school for 600 children in premises on Carrow Hill. These premises have ceased to be a school now, and form part of the laboratory accommodation of the Carrow Works.

By 1864 the Norwich Charity Schools were attended by well over 5,000 children and many were clothed as well as educated. Most, however, paid a penny or twopence a week towards the cost of books, slates, etc. By the standards of the times Norwich at this point was quite well supplied with schools.

The Education Act of 1870 had an immediate impact on the city, and after some initial discussion the first School Board election in Norwich took place in April 1871. The initial survey made by this School Board showed that the provision of elementary schools in the city in August of that year was as follows:

National Schools	19 with 32 departments	
British Schools	9 with 16 departments	
Roman Catholic Schools	2 with 4 departments	
Endowed Schools	3 with 4 departments	

with total accommodation for 8,259 children.

In October 1872 the ceremony of opening the first school built by the Norwich School Board, the Mariner's Lane School, was performed by the Chairman of the Board, the Rev. Canon Heavyside. Another indication that Norwich was well up to date is that in October 1889 the School Board made its first step towards providing education of a higher character, when it opened the Higher Grade School in Duke Street for 308 boys and 320 girls.

The Grammar School which had been in the Close since 1549 was not apparently founded by the Cathedral authorities or the religious establishment in the Close. It moved to the Close as the result of action by the City Corporation, and in 1858 it was reorganized by order of the Court of Chancery. At that point the admission of free scholars was discontinued and the school was divided into two departments, the grammar or upper school, and the commercial or middle school, the latter being housed in new buildings located in St George's in 1861–2. These buildings are still used for educational purposes by the Boot and Shoe Department of the City College.

The city still lacked grammar-school provision for girls. This, however, was in part met as the result of a meeting in the Guildhall in July 1874, when it was decided to establish a branch of the Girls' Public Day School Company. The High School for Girls was shortly afterwards opened in St Giles' Street, in premises now occupied by the City Public Health Department; in 1876 it moved to the Assembly House where it remained until 1933 when it took over its present buildings in Newmarket Road.

The demand for higher education was, however, quite clearly in excess of the provision which these schools made, and with the rapidly changing social and economic pattern it became essential that extra provision should be made, especially for those children who were passing through the city's elementary schools.

The first step in this direction was by the School Board in 1889, when the Higher Grade School was opened in Duke Street. Two years later the City Corporation, under powers conferred by the Technical Education Act of 1889, began evening classes in trade and technical subjects. This work expanded so rapidly that courses in science, art, and technological subjects were soon being held in a number of more or less suitable premises in different parts of the city. By 1901, however, these were brought together in a newly built technical institute in St George's alongside the commercial school.

With the passing of the 1902 Act and the establishment of a Norwich Education Committee in 1903, attention was quickly given to the improvement of secondary education. The Higher Grade School was transformed into a Municipal Secondary School with boys' and girls' departments. Then after considerable discussion there opened in 1910 the newly established City of Norwich School at Eaton, which took over the functions of the boys' department of the Municipal Secondary School and the old middle school which had earlier been separate from the grammar school.

For some years after this the Municipal Secondary School for Girls continued to occupy the buildings in Duke Street until it was transferred to its present premises as the Blyth School in 1929.

A feature of the Acts passed by Parliament between

1902 and 1944 was that Local Education Authorities were given certain permissive powers by which they could take steps to improve and extend their education services in a variety of ways without being compelled to do so. Certain things they had to do – others they might do if they chose. During these years the city of Norwich became one of the leading authorities in the country in making extensive use of its permissive powers. A School Meals Service began as long ago as 1906, the School Medical Service followed in the succeeding year, while 1908 saw the opening of the first school to cater for physically handicapped children. The Education Act of 1918 gave even greater opportunities to progressive authorities. It enabled the school-leaving age to be raised to fourteen, and directed attention to the necessity of providing education particularly suited to the needs of adolescents. The Hadow Report in 1926 recommended the provision of separate schools for children over the age of eleven who did not go forward to grammar schools, and by 1939 the city was one of the limited number of authorities which had brought into being a coherent system of primary and post-primary schools by which all children over the age of eleven were taught in separate schools providing special opportunities for the children in them.

The end of the war found the system of schools in Norwich sadly damaged, and the Development Plan prepared in 1946 defined in detail the considerable problem which faced the city. It was, however, realized at that time that the city's problem was very much less than it otherwise might have been by reason of the progress made before 1939. With this in mind, therefore, the Development Plan aimed to effect the reorganization required by the 1944 Act in twelve years, a period very considerably shorter than that which many other authorities had to face at the time.

With the major exception of the scheme for the provision of nation-wide nursery schools, the provision envisaged in the 1946 Development Plan for Norwich was almost completely carried out within the period set by the Plan, i.e. by 1958. As with other authorities, however, the scheme of 1946 was radically modified as the years went by to take account of the immense flood of post-war building which occurred in Norwich. This post-war council house building, together with some private building, mostly occurred on the south, south-western, and western sides of the city, and opportunity was taken on these new estates to provide large playing-fields associated with the schools. Playing-field accommodation in the city has risen during post-war years from about 38 acres to a total of about 280 acres.

In making this post-war provision the ideal was set by the Education Committee that the schools for secondary modern children should equal in their facilities and amenities any provision which could be made for a similar number of secondary grammar school pupils. How this was effected can be seen very clearly in at least three places in the city. On the Gurney and Henderson site there are boys' and girls' secondary modern schools of three streams each, together with junior and infant schools in another corner of the site, while over 30 acres of the site are first-class playing-fields, and the area also includes a quarter mile four-lane cinder running-track. At West Earlham are the Earlham and Bluebell secondary modern schools, and a 62-acre site adjoining Earlham Park. This 62-acre site has well over 40 acres of playing-field and an all-the-year-round covered teaching swimming-pool, and in one corner a two-form entry junior school. On the third site at Lakenham, where the whole site is some 56 acres, there are two secondary modern schools for boys and girls, the Lakenham Secondary Modern Schools, together with a selective secondary school, the Hewett School, which is a four-stream mixed school intended to have a technical bias.

In the north of the city secondary provision remains in outline what it was before 1939, although even here substantial additional playing facilities have been provided and additional accommodation at each school helps to bring them up to the standard set by new schools on the southern outskirts of the city. The illustration in fig. 1 is an aerial photograph of the Gurney and Henderson site showing the secondary modern, the junior, and infant schools with the associated cinder running-track and playing-fields.

With the new housing estates and the gaps left by war-time bombing, much of the junior and infant provision in the city has had to be replaced in the last fifteen years. Here an attempt has been made to arrange that junior and infant schools are, where possible, associated together (on the view that a parent who wishes

Fig. 1 *Aerial View of the Gurney and Henderson site*

to accompany an infant to school often has junior children to deal with at the same time). The infant schools have in the main been provided as two-stream schools with some accommodation for under-five-year-olds where possible, and in each case associated with these infant schools there is the possibility of providing a nursery school when times permit.

Nursery schools themselves were fully planned at the time of the 1946 Development Plan, but throughout England their provision has not been approved in general by the Ministry of Education. Some nursery provision will probably appear as the press of children in the infant schools shrinks, and indeed in Norwich the present practice is to permit the admission of children as far as accommodation and staff allow down to the age of four years.

The infant schools have been planned to certain common ideas. Basically the classrooms are paired and each pair has its own cloakroom, washing and lavatory facilities, arrangements being such that children cannot get to and from the lavatory without passing the washing facilities. At the same time the unit is arranged so that one of the two teachers can, if need be, command both classrooms and both sets of ancillary accommodation if the second teacher is otherwise occupied. The junior schools too have been planned to match the infant accommodation, and in every case have been associated with adequate playing-fields, so that under-eleven-year-old pupils shall have an opportunity to begin games playing before they actually get to the secondary schools with their ample provision for this purpose.

With the post-war planning which has occurred, and its associated reorganization of pre-war accommodation, the position in 1961 is that quite 70 per cent of Norwich children are in schools which were not built before the war or which have been so completely modified since, that the provision is now of an entirely new character. The new schools built in the city since the war total twenty-one of which nine are infant, seven are junior and five are secondary schools. During the past fifteen years one of the great handicaps to an orderly provision of new schools has been the abnormal birth-rate in the two or three years after the end of the war, the so-called 'Bulge'. In earlier years this caused severe pressure on the infant schools, but by contriving the maximum use of those resources which could be found, there were at no time grossly overcrowded classes in the Norwich infant schools. Indeed the accommodation now available is such that classes of around thirty children are the rule rather than the exception. Various extra accommodation was brought into use to help deal with the 'Bulge' situation, but at no time was extensive use made of temporary hutted accommodation. As far as possible the great majority of schools provided since the war have been in permanent construction, and are in consequence more comfortably suited to their purpose. In some cases temporary accommodation has been brought into use by the adaptation of existing buildings. Two places brought into commission as temporary schools are noteworthy. One is the building of the old foundation of the Thomas Anguish Charity (mentioned earlier), and the other is Earlham Hall, the former home of the Gurney family, a house associated with the childhood of Elizabeth Fry. The latter is especially interesting since during the war it was used as a maternity hospital and, later, was converted into an infant school. Then as the number of infants diminished and other schools were built, it was transformed into junior accommodation until a new large junior school was completed near at hand. It is now additional accommodation for the near-by Bluebell Secondary Modern Girls' School. It is said that there are children who were born in the maternity home, and who have passed through the various schools which the building has since housed.

The city has adequate provision for selective secondary education. There are six schools to which over 25 per cent of the school population can go, mostly by selection at the age of eleven, but to some extent by fee-paying. These are:

(1) The City of Norwich School for boys (five streams)
(2) The Blyth School for girls (five streams)
(3) The Hewett School for boys and girls (four streams co-educational)

and three Direct Grant schools:

(4) The Edward VI School for boys (three streams)
(5) The G.P.D.S.T. High School for girls (two to three streams)
(6) Notre Dame Roman Catholic School for girls (three streams).

In addition to city children these schools provide about a thousand places for children living in the administrative County of Norfolk on the fringes of Norwich.

Further education in the city is conducted at the large Technical College, five departments of which are now housed in new buildings in Ipswich Road. As the result of their planning before the war, and the pre-war provision of the structural steel skeleton which was left unfinished during the war years, these buildings were the first of their kind erected after the war. The City College has in it some 7,000 full-time and part-time students, many of whom again come from beyond the city, mostly from the administrative County of Norfolk, but some from Yarmouth, Lowestoft, and near-by parts of Suffolk. The work in the college ranges from preliminary craft courses up to Higher National Diploma courses for engineers and courses in preparation for the examinations of the various professional bodies. The population density in this predominantly agricultural area is quite low and this means that advanced classes, because of the limited numbers in the catchment area, have to be conducted with relatively small numbers. Besides its normal classes for examination purposes at all levels, the City College has, of recent years, made contact with the general body of citizens by arranging a series of popular and scientific lectures. For the last ten years

Fig. 2 *The Ipswich Road building of the City College and Art School – the centre for Further Education in Norwich*

or so there has been held every fortnight throughout the winter a lecture alternately scientific and alternately of more popular appeal. These have been much appreciated and are attended by large numbers of citizens throughout the year.

Associated with the City College for many years has been a large and flourishing Art School. Plans for its rebuilding were approved before the war, but present difficulties have had the result that it is still housed in accommodation which it has occupied since the early years of the century, although this has been enlarged by the use of space made available by the removal of five technical departments from the St George Street building to the new premises in Ipswich Road.

In addition to the normal provision for primary and secondary school courses of various kinds, ancillary remedial work is conducted in a number of directions. At the age of eight all children in the city are given two tests – one to determine their approximate intelligence quotient, and the second to determine their reading-level. Where these two tests show a considerable divergence, children are further examined, and where necessary sent to Remedial Reading Classes, where they attend for five out of ten sessions of each week, until their reading ability improves, and they can be discharged back to full-time attendance at their normal schools. On discharge each child is given a prize for successful completion of the course. Children who fall behind by reason of a moderate degree of deafness which does not justify their being sent off to boarding Deaf Schools, are given instruction in lip-reading and remedial instruction in basic subjects in a special class for partially deaf children. Here again they attend for half the periods of the week, and the object of the class is to discharge them back to their own schools when they have gained sufficient facility in lip-reading and general work to return to their places in a normal class without difficulty.

Norwich too was early in the field with child guidance work associated with the schools, and a large and active Child Guidance Clinic is held for several afternoons each week.

The city provides its own day Special Schools and is in process of building a new school for 180 educationally sub-normal children, and as a continuation of this scheme, turning the old combined Special School into a reason-ably spacious school for about 100 physically handicapped children. Both the educationally sub-normal and the physically handicapped are conveyed to school by bus unless they live near at hand.

The School Meals Service in Norwich is served from some nine kitchens, and food is distributed from these kitchens to fifty-two dining-rooms. The service is used by about 41 per cent of the children and about 8,800 meals are eaten each day in term time.

The provision of recreational youth work has followed a normal pattern since the war, a large number of groups being provided in Local Authority schools and assistance being given both in money and in kind to the voluntary youth organizations of the city. With the impetus of the new Albemarle Report considerable activity is now occurring in this field, and it is the intention to enlarge the provision for young people substantially in the next few years. The large playing-fields now under the control of the city will naturally facilitate this work, and with time it is hoped that there will be on these playing-fields buildings specially reserved for Youth Service purposes.

Norwich is large enough, with rather over 20,000 pupils, to be able to make provision for each of the ancillary services commonly associated with an Education Authority. It is, however, sufficiently small for these services not to be duplicated, and therefore to form a readily apprehended picture which can be worked out to a satisfactory level of efficiency. The development of the system of secondary education throughout the city is by now nearing its completion in the sense of the original 1944 Act, and attention is already turning to the provision of advanced classes in all the Secondary Modern Schools. These will induce at least the great majority of pupils to stay on at school until the age of sixteen for specialist and advanced courses, including G.C.E. work. For those who leave, the Youth Service will now more and more provide facilities for recreational and purposeful activities.

The general standard of the educational service in Norwich is now at a point when we can face with some confidence the new and very important adventure on which the city is about to embark – the provision of a new regional University in the outer part of the city.

education in the administrative County of Norfolk

F. LINCOLN RALPHS

OF ALL the counties of England, Norfolk has the highest proportion of its population resident in Rural District Council areas. This essentially rural character is at once the source of the county's most attractive and intractable features and largely determines its pattern of education. While 30 per cent of the county's population is concentrated into the areas administered by the City of Norwich and the County Borough of Great Yarmouth, 70 per cent is distributed throughout the large area for which the County Education Committee and its Divisional Executive at King's Lynn have responsibility; 85 per cent of the schools maintained by the three local education authorities of Great Yarmouth, Norwich, and Norfolk are administered by the county. The disproportionately high percentage reflects the large number of small schools which are inevitable in rural areas if the heavy expense of boarding is to be kept within manageable limits and if travelling is to be reasonably restricted. Even so, of the £7,847,460 which comprises the Norfolk Education Committee's budget for 1961-2, no less than £224,750 is the estimated cost of providing transport for schoolchildren.

The distance which cattle could be driven to and from market formerly played its part in determining the scatter of market towns. Today the distance which children can travel to schools tends to become the module for their distribution. The availability of a good school is an increasingly important factor in determining the sites of new houses. The independent schools, of which there are comparatively few for such a large county, are less influenced by this factor. Many attract pupils from wide areas, and some, as in the case of Gresham's, have traditional origins outside the county.

SECONDARY MODERN SCHOOLS

The Development Plan which the Norfolk Education Committee devised for its secondary schools was approved by the Ministry of Education in 1947. This divided the county into forty secondary modern school districts with an average area of 50 square miles, a few of the more urban having more than one school. These districts had between 50 and 150 pupils in each yearly age group and as subsequently revised, produced the pattern of schools shown in Table I:

TABLE I

SECONDARY MODERN SCHOOLS

	Co-education	Girls	Boys
Two-form entry	13	3	3
Three-form entry	16	1	1
Four-form entry	5	—	—
Five-form entry	1	1	1
Total	35	5	5

When the plan was prepared fifteen secondary modern schools were in existence but most were, and nine still are, substantially below the standards of accommodation regarded as adequate by the Ministry of Education. In Norfolk the reorganization recommended in the Hadow Report had been slow to start. The war interrupted the programme almost as soon as it had been begun. In the post-war years the Education Committee have been anxious and determined to make as rapid advances as the

F. LINCOLN RALPHS is Chief Education Officer for the County of Norfolk

TABLE II
SECONDARY MODERN SCHOOL DEVELOPMENT

		1947	1950	1951	1952	1953	1954	1955	1956	1957	1958	1959	1960
In use		15	16	16	16	17	19	22	24	29	34	37	39
In construction		—	—	2	4	7	5	11	10	8	4	2	2
	Total	15	16	18	20	24	24	33	34	37	38	39	41

Ministry's capital allocation would allow. The progress made is shown in Table II.

The Norfolk Education Committee is almost unique in having its own architects, and full advantage is taken of the favourable building costs of the district. On no occasion has the Education Committee failed to start work within the allocated year on all the projects included in its annual programmes; all have been built within the cost limits required by the Ministry of Education and with less difficulty than in many areas. At Aylsham a national record was attained with 100 square feet per pupil. At Thorpe, by economic planning, it was possible to include in the St Andrew's Secondary Modern School a heated swimming-pool 60 feet by 30 feet, the first such pool provided in any county school in East Anglia. This has provided an invaluable asset for children and adults who come from a wide area to enjoy an amenity which should obviously be more generally provided.

SECONDARY GRAMMAR SCHOOLS

The traditional pattern of secondary grammar schools has been maintained with the oustanding exception of the residential college at Wymondham. Post-war building activity has been largely in the direction of extending and improving the existing accommodation at the eleven long-established grammar schools of which four are for boys, four for girls, and three are co-educational. One new co-educational grammar school was opened in 1958 at Thorpe and this is in process of expansion to a four-form entry school. A second new grammar school is being formed in association with Wymondham College. The county is fortunate in being able to establish its new grammar schools in this way. At no time does the new school exist only as a small group or with a single year of pupils. They come as day pupils to Wymondham College until they are an established community. Then, after three years in the case of Thorpe Grammar School, they are transferred to a separate site in or near the locality from which the pupils have been or are to be recruited.

Wymondham College is housed in an American military hospital set up during the last war. It occupies a site of 93 acres midway between Attleborough and Wymondham. New permanent buildings are now replacing the old Nissen huts. The improvisation which characterized the early years of the college has, however, provided a challenge which in itself is a good feature of any educational enterprise.

The link with America has been retained and is shown in the opening of Lincoln Hall and Elizabeth Fry Hall by Dean Acheson and Janet Whitney. The halls are of unique pattern incorporating a 'family' element. Junior pupils have dormitories each with six or seven beds;

Fig. 1 *Heated swimming-pool in the Thorpe St Andrew's Secondary Modern School*

Fig. 2 'Elizabeth Fry Hall', Wymondham College

these adjoin the bedrooms for middle school pupils and the single study bedrooms for sixth form students. The new Physical Education block now in course of construction includes a swimming-pool similar to the one at Thorpe, and perhaps more interesting a sports hall of 6,600 square feet, large enough to house full-scale netball tournaments.

The students themselves have made substantial contributions to the furnishings of the college. With an attractive landscape and lay-out the college when finished will be a considerable adornment to the educational provision of the county. It already has over 700 pupils in residence of whom 140 are in the sixth form.

INDEPENDENT SCHOOLS

Norfolk, the fourth largest county in England, has surprisingly few independent schools with substantial reputation. Sixteen are recognized as efficient by the Ministry of Education. Gresham's School for boys is the largest and best known. It has long associations with the Fishmongers Company and a distinguished record of success. Of the smaller schools for boys and girls the majority have been recognized by the Ministry since the war. The county has a number of preparatory schools with day and boarding accommodation. While local scholarships and places are available – the Holt scholarships at Gresham's for example – the common practice has been for Norfolk parents to send their children to public schools outside the county.

SECONDARY SELECTION

The Education Committee are not unaware that a modest advance in educational attainment by some children may represent more praiseworthy progress than more outstanding achievements by others. They are also anxious that so far as is reasonably practicable the desires of parents in the choice of schools shall be given every consideration. Those whose children are suitably qualified, and who desire places in schools other than those provided by the committee may apply for some financial assistance. This is normally available on an income scale basis. The committee have been glad to avail themselves of places in grammar schools in the city of Norwich, in the borough of Great Yarmouth, and in independent schools for both girls and boys. They are no less concerned to provide or to secure places in suitable schools for children for whom normal school work is specially difficult.

With children of very varied ability some form of selection may seem inevitable, although none can ever be perfect. For many years selection at about the age of eleven has been broadly based. It takes in consideration not only the modern standardized tests with their result-ant quotients but also more traditional methods of testing and the record of school-work. The selection procedure is the subject of constant review by a special Board on which the teachers are strongly represented. The 'eleven-plus' is not allowed to be inflexibly the final verdict. Over-age candidates may be re-tested at the age of twelve.

The public school tradition of selection at thirteen is also available in Norfolk for children whose parents are ready to consider boarding education. Generous assist-ance is given to enable them to do this. Boys and girls selected at thirteen are admitted to Wymondham College where, together with children who at the age of eleven appeared to have special aptitude for practical and applied studies, they take courses leading to the General Certificate of Education in a range of twenty-two sub-jects at Ordinary Level and twenty-three subjects at Advanced Level.

As more secondary modern schools develop fifth form courses children may take the G.C.E. or other appro-priate examinations. The committee encourage those who are able and willing to continue their studies at technical colleges. The door to higher education, to the universi-ties, and to the professions is always open. Some children advance by the quick and traditional road of eleven-plus selection and grammar school training, others by the slower, but no less worthy, route of secondary modern school and technical college. Some go via Wymondham College and others by admission to the sixth form of grammar schools having obtained five 'O' Level passes elsewhere.

PRIMARY SCHOOLS

The Church played an important part in the establish-ment of schools in Norfolk. Of the 417 primary schools now in use 78 have 'aided' and 117 'controlled' status. This early initiative has unfortunately left a legacy of property now regarded as sub-standard and a burden of financial responsibility which is heavier than the Church can reasonably be expected to bear. The energies of dissension and the enthusiasm for particular forms of religious instruction no longer excite passion and less obviously inspire voluntary effort than was formerly the case. The improving standard of religious instruction in county schools and the current and predominant interest in secular education have paradoxically combined to remove the issue of school management from the realms of vital interest or violent controversy. In the extension of school education into the secondary stage the Church has played a less obvious role. Of the forty-five secondary modern schools only one is aided and one of controlled status. At the primary level, however, the tradition of Church interest in management continues. The diocese shows an increasing concern that its schools should not lag behind those for which the Education Committee is more directly responsible.

The post-war priority given nationally to secondary school development has prevented much improvement to primary schools of all kinds. In Norfolk nearly half the primary schools are pre-1870; little more than 10 per cent have been built in this century. Most are, therefore, inadequate in some particular, although the transfer of children over the age of eleven to new secondary schools has reduced the overcrowded conditions of many small schools, and left a substantial proportion with an embarrassingly small number of pupils as is shown in Table III.

There was much that was attractive about the old village school with its school-master or mistress taking a leading part in the life of the community, and making the school no less than the church and the inn a centre of village interest and activity. There must, therefore, inevitably be some regret when the small all-age school is divided and the older children go to the seemingly remote secondary school. Often a remnant of youngsters is left behind as a handful too small to justify continued existence. None the less, apart from education re-organization, the rural population seems destined to concentrate into larger villages and towns. The scattered

TABLE III
PRIMARY SCHOOLS

No. of Schools	County	Voluntary		Total
		Aided	Controlled	
Less than 30 pupils	28	21	28	77
30–59	85	38	44	167
60–89	34	11	20	65
90–119	20	4	13	37
120–149	14	2	6	22
150 or over	41	2	6	49
Total	222	78	117	417

villages are tending to disappear and the educational needs of teenage children require the larger opportunities which the secondary schools now provide. The ultimate pattern of primary schools will be a two-teacher minimum and a reduction in the total number of primary schools from the present 417 to 270 as shown in Table IV. The immediate but temporary effect of building new secondary schools before it has been possible to deal with primary schools has been an increase rather than a decrease in the number with only one or two teachers.

The county has been fortunate in being able to attract to its service the full allocation of 2,346 teachers which the Ministry of Education currently makes. There is, however, less inclination for teachers to accept the inadequate standards of housing and school accommodation which persist. The need for improvement in primary school conditions becomes, therefore, ever more pressing. The Education Committee maintains a constant appeal to the Ministry for more capital for building and for improvements that are long overdue. Despite the inadequate accommodation available, new approaches to the instruction and development of young children, more cheerful decorations, the emancipation of walls

from the chocolate brown and olive green that sought to hide what was thought to be inevitable dirt, have combined to make primary school education in the county more attractive. Where it has been possible to build new schools and new houses for teachers the response leaves little room for doubt that even in a very rural county like Norfolk, primary education can overcome the difficulties of isolation and achieve a high standard of efficiency. The children come with eagerness and determination.

A survey of the education of young children in the administrative county would be incomplete without reference to the Education Committee's three nursery schools and the many private schools for young children varying in size from single classes to schools with several classes. Nursery school building is nationally at a standstill at present, but the new school at Emneth indicates their attractive potential in an area where mothers are often by long tradition employed on the land. The smaller private schools have tended to find favour with parents who dislike the prospect of their children being at any time far from home, or committed to a full day's schooling from the age of five.

TABLE IV

Primary Schools	1950	1955	1960	No. proposed in 1947 Development Plan
With one teacher	9	8	17	—
With two teachers	203	173	199	26
With three teachers	113	112	93	114
With four or more	124	144	108	130
Total	449	437	417	270

FURTHER EDUCATION

In common with most areas in England the post-war development of Further Education in Norfolk has been most marked. It is seen in the growing number of boys and girls going to universities, and the consequential increase in the number of major awards which have increased from 143 in 1950 to 469 in 1960. It may be of interest to note that of the current 469 awards, 40 were gained by county students attending the Norwich

City College and County Technical College at King's Lynn. The remaining 429 awards were gained by pupils from schools as shown in Table V.

This table illustrates the happy and effective co-operation of the three local education authorities in Norfolk, the success of county children in city schools, and the wide range of opportunity whether children are sent to school either in Norfolk or outside the county.

TABLE V

COUNTY MAJOR AWARDS HELD IN 1960

	Boys	Girls	Total
County pupils from Norfolk Grammar Schools	147	54	**201**
County pupils from Norfolk Independent Schools	18	2	**20**
County pupils from schools in Norwich	67	30	**97**
County pupils from schools in the borough of Gt Yarmouth	10	8	**18**
County pupils from schools outside Norfolk	59	34	**93**
Total	**301**	**128**	**429**

Within Norfolk the main developments of Further Education have been associated with the City College and Art School in Norwich to which reference is made in the preceding section on Education in the city of Norwich. Suffice it to say that of the city and county students attending the College in the Session 1959–60, 43 per cent came from the county and were responsible for 57 per cent of the student hours of instruction given to city and county students. A similarly happy association exists between Norfolk Education Committee and the enterprising and co-operative committee of Great Yarmouth. The Norfolk Education Committee's own major enterprise has been the County Technical College at King's Lynn. The new buildings occupied this year are already inadequate to accommodate the students now enrolled. The increase in numbers over the past ten years given in Table VI shows the development from the appointment of one Organizing Master for Further Education in King's Lynn in 1946 to the present staff of

sixty full-time teachers and a much larger and growing number of part-time staff.

The college provides general courses leading to the General Certificate of Education at 'O' and 'A' Levels, to the City and Guilds Certificates, Examinations of the Royal Society of Arts, Ordinary National Certificates, and Higher National Certificates. The college is recognized for Higher National Certificate Courses in Electrical and Mechanical Engineering, and has a creditable record of success. In the past few years it has gained each year a Technical State Scholarship from the 225 awarded for the country as a whole. For more advanced work the pupils transfer to the City College and Art School or to other technical colleges or institutions and colleges of advanced technology.

The special vocational interests of Norfolk are agriculture and horticulture, and these are dealt with in Section IV, 2 and 3 of this Survey. Suffice it to say that the Norfolk Education Committee in establishing the School of Agriculture on its 703-acre farm at Easton, and the Horticultural Station of 50 acres at Burlingham is rendering a service which is increasingly appreciated by the farming community. There is a happy association with the Norfolk Agricultural Advisory Service and with the Research Station at Sprowston. The desire to ensure that up-to-date scientific information is readily available for the actual workers encouraged Norfolk to pioneer the Stockmen's Clubs and the Farm Machinery Clubs

TABLE VI

COUNTY TECHNICAL COLLEGE

	Session 1949–50	Session 1954–55	Session 1959–60
No. of full-time students	40	234	535
No. of student hours	170,044	348,138	683,380

which are now being introduced in other counties. Young people interested in opportunities in agriculture, or indeed in any local or specialized employment, have the services of the Youth Employment Officers for which the county has for the past ten years accepted responsibility.

Also included in Further Education is the important task of teacher training. The Norwich Training College is a Church Training College founded in 1939, and originally situated in the City of Norwich. It now occupies a most attractive site at Keswick three miles to the southwest of Norwich. It is now being extended to take in 150 men, the first group being admitted in September 1961. This, in addition to the 187 women students now in college, will go a long way towards the ultimate aim of a total of 400 students. Norwich is the first of the ten teacher training colleges associated with the Cambridge Institute of Education to become co-educational. In common with all other establishments of Further Education it anticipates with pleasure the founding of the University of East Anglia which should provide a new incentive and encouragement to the development of education in the region.

SPECIAL EDUCATION ACTIVITIES

A lively education authority is always concerned to experiment with new ideas. The value of residential courses in a rural area is obvious and its advantages apply to all, however gifted. Everyone is agreed that the new University of East Anglia should be largely if not wholly residential. The County Education Committee has organized residential courses of all kinds. One deserving special mention is the course for fourteen-year-old pupils at Holt Hall. This was originally started as a termly course for boys and girls from the smallest all-age village schools for whom the raising of the school-leaving age brought little advantage. With the increasing availability of secondary schools the courses still have value for children from the remoter parts of the county. Now for a full year they are given a less formal but more demanding programme of activities. The emphasis is on individual initiative and endeavour. More than 1,000 pupils have been trained at Holt Hall, and there are few who do not, in the jobs they now do, and in their general attitude, reflect the influence of their stay in this delightful 87-acre site in north Norfolk. The grounds of Holt Hall are used for camping courses attended by young persons from all parts of the county.

At near-by Kelling the committee runs a hospital school and at Eden Hall, twenty miles to the east on the coast at Bacton, a school for delicate children. The county has two hostels for maladjusted children, and Sidestrand Hall, which caters for the needs of those with special education difficulties, has made good use of the old home of the late Sir Samuel Hoare (later Lord Templewood). The committee makes extensive use of the special facilities provided by the Great Yarmouth Authority at the East Anglian School for Deaf and Partially Sighted children; there is accommodation for approximately 180 children handicapped in this way, and of these approximately one-sixth are Norfolk children.

Also situated in Norfolk, although not the concern of the Education Committee, are the Bramerton Remand Home and the Red House Farm School. The former is administered by the Children's Committee of the Norfolk County Council jointly with five other authorities. Accommodation is provided for some twenty-five boys and girls on remand; children in care can temporarily be housed there, and Bramerton can also be used as a place of safety for a child waiting to appear before the Court. A teaching staff is provided to deal with the education and training of the children as far as possible on normal school lines. The Red House Farm School, Buxton, is an Approved School run by voluntary managers, the Home Office giving a certificate of approval. Ninety boys in the thirteen to fifteen age range are catered for and the training provided includes farming, gardening, and woodwork. The school is inspected periodically by officers of the Ministry of Education and the Home Office.

To deal with the special needs of backward or difficult children the committee maintains a school psychological service. This service, under the guidance of the educational psychologist who, with assistant and psychiatric social workers, carries out a county-wide service of diagnosis and treatment without undue concern for the 'abnormalities' which are normal in the average child. Also with a particular emphasis on health rather than disease, the Principal School Medical Officer and his staff provide a service of regular medical inspection and treatment. Well-equipped clinics with dental facilities are a feature of most new secondary schools. The health of children is undoubtedly improved by the supply of milk and meals which is an important service provided by the Education Committee. Norfolk schoolchildren consume over 300,000 gallons of milk each year supplied in one-third of a pint bottles each day. Teenage pupils, especially girls, are, however, increasingly reluctant to drink milk in this way. The 7,000,000 meals annually provided elevates the Education Committee to the status of one of the county's major feeding organizations. The percentage of children taking school meals in Norfolk is much higher than the average for English counties, and is likely to increase with the development of larger primary schools some distance from the children's homes.

The county has a number of mobile film units, and its visual aids service both makes and exhibits visual material and maintains the visual and audio-aid apparatus in the schools.

The schools of the county have the services of specialist organizers for Light and Heavy Crafts, for Domestic Science, for Physical Education. Two recent and somewhat unusual appointments are Senior Organizers for Science and Religious Instruction.

The County Music Committee and the County Drama Committee, like the Young Farmers' Clubs are closely linked with the Education Committee who pay the officers and provide specialist professional staff. This policy of linking the resources of the committee to the enthusiasm of specialist voluntary enterprise serves to emphasize not only the imaginative insight and potential opportunities of Section 53 of the 1944 Education Act, but also the status of the elected members of the County Council and Education Committee as voluntary representatives able to speak clearly for the people they represent.

Nowhere is this better illustrated than in the record of village halls and community centres. Direct contact between the Education Committee and local voluntary committees, and particularly through the county organizer, has led, during the past ten years, to the building of 135 new village halls, extensions and major improvements to 100 existing village halls, and to the completion of 150 new playing-fields.

No direct service to the public is more appreciated than that of the County Library. The committee's policy is to establish branches in all the main centres and to maintain a mobile library service in the more remote parts. Table VII indicates that in Norfolk the County Library is providing a service of education no less than of entertainment. The County Library is associated with the National Library system, and in this way books required for special study can be obtained for Norfolk readers from all parts of the country, while some are obtained from abroad. Each reader is allowed four tickets. Membership of the County Library is free to county residents, and to others on payment of a subscription of ten shillings.

Norfolk, with a reputation for slow change has in fact a record of independence and enterprise in education no less than in farming. Twenty years ago the county showed a pioneer spirit in its approach to the Service of Youth unhappily frustrated by the war and post-war national apathy towards the adolescent. Since then it has pressed forward again and established new schools of quite excellent standard, and a relationship between all branches of the service which is cordial and co-operative. It is not content to accept without question patterns imposed from the centre nor to be unduly influenced by what is done elsewhere. It has withstood pressures, both personal and political, where it has felt the good of the service required resistance. It has welcomed, irrespective of sponsorship, every new opportunity of advance which it has felt could better its education service. In the spirit of Nelson and Coke, it continues what it believes to be sound reform and profitable experiment. It has no real doubt that in the end its stock in the field of education will appreciate.

TABLE VII

| | 1949–50 | | 1959–60 | |
	Book-stock	Issues	Book-stock	Issues
Total of Non-Fiction	97,689	377,755	235,617	1,017,773
Adult Fiction	117,640	1,257,905	160,361	1,135,098
Junior Fiction	39,360	370,676	89,587	881,745
Total	**254,689**	**2,006,336**	**485,565**	**3,034,616**

place-names

O. K. SCHRAM

IN THIS brief survey only a certain number of the major names, those of parishes, villages, and some of the larger hamlets, can be individually considered. But the selection has been made as representative as possible in order to give what may be regarded as a fairly accurate picture of the local nomenclature as a whole.[1]

Of Celtic settlements in the region few traces now remain, although such names as have survived are not without interest. The British names, in Romanized form, of the two fortresses on the East Anglian coast that formed part of the defence system of the Saxon shore are preserved in the *Notitia Dignitatum* of the early fifth century. In this Brancaster (Nf) appears as *Branodunum*, explained as 'crow-fort', and Burgh Castle (Sf) near the mouth of the Yare, as *Gariannonum*, derived from the British name of the river called *Gariénnos* by Ptolemy, and later *Gerne* as in the early medieval spellings of Yarmouth (*Gernemwa* DB, *Gernemuta* 1254); the name may mean 'the babbling river' (ERN 478). The Celts also named the river Ouse; but the modern names of the other main rivers are of Anglian origin, although in a few cases their earlier British names can also be recovered. The Wensum (*Wenson* 1096, *Wensum* 1250) is 'the wendsome, winding one' (OE *wendsum*), identical with the river Wantsum in the isle of Thanet. The Waveney (*Wahenhe* 1275, *Wagenho* 1286, *Wawneye* 1485) probably derives from an OE *wagen* 'quaking bog', also found in the Yorkshire river Wawne. The Wissey (*Wissene* 1257, *Wissenhe* c. 1300, *Wise* 1314) is simply 'the river' (OE *wise*); its British name may be preserved in Wereham (*Wigorham* 1060, *Wigreham* DB) where the first element is traced back to a British river name (*Wigorā* meaning 'the winding one' ERN 476), and identical with the river

Wyre in Lancashire. The Nar was named in recent times from Narford and Narborough; its British name may have been *Pante* preserved in Pentney (*Panteneia* c. 1200, *Pantenay* 1232), found in Essex as the river Pont and derived from a British term which appears in modern Welsh as *pant* 'valley'. The Chet owes its name to Chedgrave; its older name appears to have been *Lodne*, which represents a British *Lutnā* 'the muddy river' (ERN 258), later transferred to the chief place on its banks, Loddon (*Lotna*, *Lodna* DB, *Lodena* 1195). Modern back-formations from the names of prominent places by which they flow are common in the names of many smaller rivers: the Tas was named from Tasburgh, the Thet from Thetford, the Bure from Briston, earlier *Burston*, near its source, the Ant from Antingham. The process still goes on, and we have recent names like the Hun from Hunstanton, the Mun from Mundesley, and the Ingol from Ingoldisthorpe.

Whether Breydon Water existed before the coming of the Scandinavians at the end of the ninth century the documentary evidence does not show; but it is clear that the name is due to them (*Breþinghe* 1269; *aqua de Brey-thing* c. 1450, *Bredyng* 1462; from ON *Breiþingr* 'broadening in a river').

The Broads did not come into existence until late in the medieval period, and earlier records contain no references to large sheets of water in the area, although 'brodings' of the rivers are mentioned from the fourteenth century (MBr 64 ff.). Sir Thomas Browne, appropriately enough, is the first to mention them by name, in his *Natural History of Norfolk c.* 1670.

Two well-known British terms denoting natural

O.K. SCHRAM is a Lecturer in the Department of English Language and General Linguistics, University of Edinburgh

features survive as place-names in the region, both in the north-west. King's Lynn (*Lena, Luna* DB, *Linna* c. 1150, *Lenna* 1160, *Lenn* 1195) derives from British *lindo-, later Welsh *llyn* 'pool, lake', which is the base also of Lincoln. The villages of North and South Creake (*Creic, Creich* DB, *Crech* 1177, *Crek* 1181) were named from one of the hills that are a local feature, and derive from a British term found in Old Welsh as *creic*, modern Welsh *craig* 'hill'. A possible third example of a surviving British name is Trunch (*Trunchet* DB, c. 1145, 1209, *Trunche* 1257), which may be 'the wood on a ridge', from a British *trun 'nose, promontory' which survives in modern Welsh *trwyn*, and the familiar British *ceto- 'wood', modern Welsh *coed*; although a different interpretation of this unusual name is possible (DPN).

The Roman occupation of the region gave rise to Caister near Yarmouth, and Caistor St Edmunds, the *Venta Icenorum* of the *Antonine Itinerary*, the only place-name now known which mentions the *Iceni*. It is tempting to connect them with the Icknield Way (OE *Icenhilde weg*; recorded in Dersingham near its northern end as *Ykenildesthrethe* c. 1250), but on historical as well as linguistic grounds the connexion can only be regarded as at best a remote possibility.[2]

Three villages were named from Roman roads (OE *stræt*) along which they lay. The east-west road after crossing the Ouse passed by Stradsett (*Strateseta* DB, *Stratset* 1222); near its eastern end, so far as it has been traced, is Stratton Strawless, although this village is now some distance from the presumed course of the road. Stretched out along the road that came northwards towards Caistor St Edmunds lies Long Stratton (*Stratuna* DB, *Langestrattone* 1257).

The region preserves two interesting survivals of Celtic Christianity in the Late Roman period, in Eccles on the east coast, whose position may have a special significance to be noted later, and Eccles near Attleborough.

To the invading Anglo-Saxons of the fifth century the Romanized Celts were known as *Wālas*, whose presence was denoted by the newcomers in the place-names Walcot (OE *Wāla-cot 'cottage of the Welsh') and Walton (OE *Wāla-tūn 'farm of the Welsh'). The appearance of Walcott on the east coast, in the near neighbourhood of Eccles, is worthy of note, and the survival of the two names in fairly close proximity in an area densely settled by the Angles may not be entirely fortuitous. Walcot Green in Diss (*Walecote* 1269, 1312) is an isolated example in the extreme south, and its survival appears to be due to mere chance. The name Walton occurs four times in the region, but in no single instance does the derivation from OE *Wāla-tūn* seem justified. West Walton in the far west (*Waltuna* DB, *Walton* 1206, *Westwalton* 1257) was no doubt named from a local sea-bank (OE *wall*), as were its neighbours Walpole and Walsoken. East Walton, to the east of King's Lynn (*Waltuna* DB, *Walton* 1196) may well contain OE *wald* 'wood', as may Walton Hall in Ludham (*Walton* c. 1105, 1250). A lost *Waltone* c. 1260 in Poringland may have the same origin, but the few early references that can be found make the identification of the first element uncertain.

Although it is not unlikely that a certain number of other British names survived the Anglian invasions at the beginning of the fifth century, and remained in use until the Danish Conquest at the end of the ninth, if not later, the ultimate appearance of a mere handful in 'Domesday Book' and other early medieval records must in the main be due to the intensity of the Anglian colonization of the region. The Scandinavians made their own distinctive, and considerable, contribution to the local place-names; but the overwhelming majority of the names, both major and minor, is of Anglian origin. Those ending in *-ing*, *-ham*, and *-ingham* are generally regarded as belonging to the earliest stratum of Anglo-Saxon place-names in England, and the Norwich region has an impressive number of them (see fig. 1). Except in a few cases, like Weeting (*Wetinge* DB, *Wetinga* 1187, *Wetinge* 1257; 'the wet place', from OE *wæt*), Scarning (*Scerninga* DB, *Skerning* 1253; 'the dirty place', from OE *scearn* 'dirt, filth'), and Docking (*Dochinga* DB, *Docching* 1158, *Dockinge* 1222; 'place where docks grow', from OE *doce* 'dock plant'), the *-ing* names denote not the settlements but the settlers themselves. As repeatedly shown by the early spellings, they are old plural nouns describing a group of people associated with a leader whose name was used to designate them. A good instance of the creation of these names occurs on the east coast: here is Happisburgh (*Hapesburc* DB, *Hapesburg* 1220, *Hapesburge* 1269) 'the fort of *Hæp*', whose followers and associates were called the *Hæpingas* and settled in the area around

Happisburgh, which later became the hundred of Happing (*Hapinga* DB, *Happinges* 1230, 1266). Occasionally, the 'folk-name' was formed from the name of the river or other natural feature near which the newcomers settled; thus, the settlers along the river Chet, earlier *Lodne*, were called the *Lodningas*, which became the name of the hundred of Loddon (*Lothninga* DB, *Lodninges* 1199, *Lodenynges* 1275). But in the large majority of the two dozen *-ing* names in the region the first elements are personal names which give the impression of extreme antiquity. Many of them, as in Fring, Blickling, Elsing, Snoring, Dalling, have not been noted anywhere outside East Anglia. Others can be paralleled in neighbouring eastern counties but nowhere else. For some, only continental parallels can be adduced to establish their identity in England. With them must be closely associated the names in *-ingham*, of which there are over three dozen. Here the terminal indicates a settlement by a group of people many of

whose names are of the same archaic character as those in the *-ing* names. Particularly noteworthy are Erpingham (*hām* of the *Eorpingas*), Felmingham (of the *Felmingas*), Framingham (of the *Framingas*), Hassingham (of the *Hasingas*), Ketteringham (of the *Cytringas*, also found in Kettering, co. Northants.), Longham (*Lawingham* DB, *Lawingeham* 1198; from *Lāwa*, whose name also occurs in the Launditch: *Lawendic* DB, *Lawendich* 1160), and Wramplingham (of the *Wræmpelingas*). But the most characteristic and most widely distributed names in the region are those in *-ham*. They number more than ninety and indicate the main strength of the early Anglian settlements. Many contain personal names that are rarely met with in OE sources, or are otherwise unrecorded; e.g. Crimplesham, Frettenham, Quidenham, Weasenham, Snettisham (*Snetesham* DB, 1190, 1220; from *Snæt*, also found in Neatishead: *Snateshirda* DB, *Neteshirde* 1150, 1254, 'the household of *Snæt*; from OE *hīred*). One, Swaffham, contains the name of the

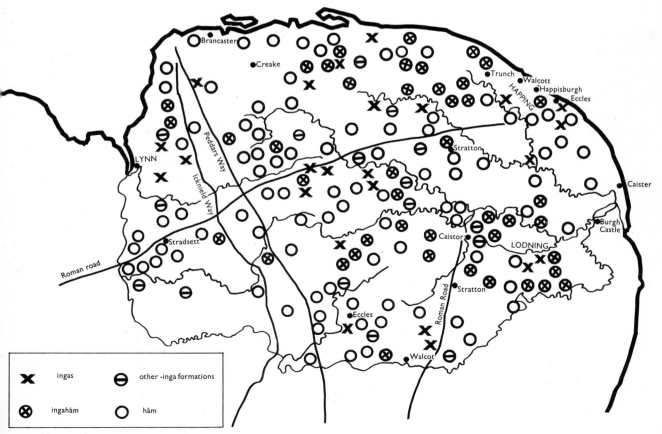

Fig. 1   *Celtic and early Anglian place-names of the Region*

Germanic tribe the Swabians known in OE as *Swæfe*, who also occur in Swaffham and Swavesey (C). Another, Wereham, has as its first element the old British name of the river Wissey. Some, like Congham, Shouldham, Shropham, and Taverham, are compounded with OE topographical and other terms that are rarely found anywhere else in England, but for which continental, specifically Low German, parallels can be adduced.[3] The names in -*ham* and -*ingham* must have been given to large estates which may well have covered most of the area of the modern parishes.[4] They designate vills in DB without exception; few have declined in status, most of them have remained as villages and parishes and now denote the bulk of the larger centres and market towns of the region. Four, Erpingham, Shropham, Taverham, and Walsham, also became the names of the hundreds in which they are situated. A number of the settlements were already divided into two or more separate units before the Norman Conquest. Characteristic instances are: Great and Little Snoring, Great and Little Walsingham, Framingham Earl and Framingham Pigot, Dersingham and Sandringham (*Santdersincham* DB; 'the sandy part of Dersingham'), and East, West, and South Raynham; they readily acquired outliers and hamlets, as in Honingham and Honingham Thorpe, Great Bircham, Bircham Newton, and Bircham Tofts, and the remarkable group comprising Burnham Market, Burnham Norton, Burnham Sutton, Burnham Westgate, Burnham Thorpe, Burnham Overy (*Overhee* 1346, *Overe* 1437; OE *ofer ēa 'across the river'), Burnham Ulph, where the manor in 1066 was held by *Ulf*, a man of Scandinavian descent.

There are a remarkable number of identities or close similarities between the early Anglian names of Nf and Sf; both counties have Barningham, Barsham, Brettenham, Elmham, Fakenham, Helmingham, Ingham, Needham, Rougham, Shimpling, Thornham, Tuddenham, and Walsham. Identical though with slight modern variations are Ludham (Nf) and Loudham (Sf), Shotesham (Nf) and Shottisham (Sf), Saham (Nf) and Soham (Sf); and there are a number of others where the first element, usually a personal name, can be closely paralleled in the two counties: such are Dalling (Nf) and Dallinghoo (Sf), Framingham (Nf) and Framsden, Framlingham (Sf), Hevingham (Nf) and Heveningham

(Sf), Harling (Nf) and Herringfleet (Sf: *Herlingaflet* DB). It cannot be mere coincidence that the similarities and identities are almost entirely among the three types -*ing*, -*ham*, and -*ingham*; these may be regarded as constituting a clear proof that the two counties, making up the Kingdom of East Anglia, formed a distinct linguistic as well as an ethnic unit from the earliest centuries of the Anglo-Saxon period.

To the three types may be added a further small group of names which are also made up of 'folk-names' combined with topographical terms like *ford*, as in Billingford on the Wensum (*Billingeford* 1212) and Billingford on the Waveney (*Billingeforda* DB), settlements of the *Billingas*; *land*, as in Poringland (*Porringalanda* DB, *Porringeland* c. 1180; of the *Porringas*) and Haveringland (*Heveringalanda* DB; of the *Hæferingas*); *halh* 'nook, corner of land', as in Arminghall (*Hameringahala* DB, *Ameringehale* 1212; of the *Hameringas*) and Kenninghall (*Keninghehala* DB, *Keningehal* 1191; of the *Cēningas*); *set* 'dwelling', as in Whissonsett (*Witcingkeseta* DB, *Wicingesete* 1196; of the *Wīcingas*) and Letheringsett (*Lavingaseta* DB, *Letheringesete* 1250; of the *Lādheringas*); *lēah* 'wood', as in Babingley (*Babinghelea* DB, *Babingele* 1198; of the *Babbingas*); *ēg* 'island' used of higher ground in the midst of marshland, as in Hilgay (*Hidlingheia* DB; of the *Hȳdlingas*), Wormegay (*Wermegay* DB, *Wirmingai* 1173, *Wyrmingeheye* 1257; of the *Wyrmingas*), and Swangey in Attleborough (*Swanegeya* 1219, *Swanegeye* 1298; of the *Swaningas*), which are analogous in their later development to Bungay (Sf) and Gamlingay (C); and *hȳþ* 'landing place', as in Methwold Hythe, formerly Ottering Hythe (*Otringheia* DB, *Otheringehethe* 1257, *Oteringhith* 1290; of the *Otringas*), for which Sf provides the parallel in Lakenheath (*Lacingahið* c. 945, *Lakingahethe* DB; of the *Lācingas*, the people of *Lāca*, who also occurs in Lakenham, Norwich).

The distribution of the four groups well illustrates the extent of the Anglian settlements (see fig. 1). Together they constitute more than one-sixth of all the parishes in the region. Some occur on the coast or are within easy reach of the sea; most of them lie some distance inland in the valleys of the main rivers and their tributaries. They are scarce in Broadland, where some may have been supplanted by Scandinavian names during the Danish Conquest;[5] they are prominent in the Loam

Region of the north-east, and well represented in south-east and mid Nf; quite a number occur in Breckland; except for some coastal settlements, they avoid the Good Sand Region of the north-west; but there is a remarkable string of them near the Wash in the Greensand Belt, in which every one of the types is represented; they occur in the Fenland only to the east of the Ouse; to the west of that river they are totally unknown until one is well into Cambridgeshire.

Whereas names in -ingham and -ham denoted large estates comparable to the later medieval manor, those in -ton (OE tūn 'enclosure, farm') were given to more modest settlements. The term is as common in the region as anywhere else in England; some 200 examples have been noted. But few places with names in -ton have become of any importance; a number ranked as Domesday vills, that never became villages and parishes; the majority of them are hamlets or minor places; some only appear in late documents; many have disappeared altogether.[6] To judge by the elements of which the names are composed, they must have come into existence at various times during the pre-Conquest period. Easton, Weston, Norton, Sutton, and Newton imply secondary settlement, usually associated with a larger estate in -ingham or -ham. Some two dozen contain old Scandinavian personal names, a form of 'hybridism' well known in other Danelaw areas, and cannot be older than the end of the ninth century. This latter type, represented by Garveston (*Gerolfestuna* DB, *Geroluestone* 1269; from ODan *Gerulv*), Thuxton (*Turstanestuna* DB, *Turstanestone* 1212; from ODan *Thursten*), Scoulton (*Sculetuna* DB; from ODan *Skule*), Griston (*Gerdestuna* DB; from ODan *Gyrdh*), Aslacton (*Aslaketuna* DB; from ODan *Aslakr*), Tharston (*Therstuna* DB; from ODan *Therir*), Hellington (*Helgeton* 1204, *Helgetone* 1254; from ODan *Helgi*), and Thurlton (*Thuruertuna* DB, *Thurvertun* 1234; from ODan *Thurverdh*) is chiefly found south-west, south, and south-east of Norwich, although there is a significant cluster of them in the Fakenham area, which comprises Kettlestone (*Ketlestuna* DB; from ODan *Ketill*), Helhoughton (*Helgatuna* DB; from ODan *Helgi*), and Hindolveston (*Hildolveston* c. 1060; from ODan *Hildulv*) among others, where they are closely associated with a number of 'pure' Scandinavian formations in -thorpe.

To the Anglo-Saxons of the ninth century the pirate Dane was known as *æscmann* and *flotmann*; the former occurs in Ashmanhaugh (*Asmanhawe* c. 1160; *Assemaneshaghe* 1269; 'the pirate's enclosure'; from OE *haga*); the latter in Newton Flotman (*Neuton Floteman* 1294, *Floteman Neuton* 1308). The Danish Conquest and destruction of the Kingdom of East Anglia resulted in a considerable introduction of Scandinavian place-names. The newcomers were sufficiently numerous or prominent among the population in the north and south-west to name the hundreds of Brothercross, Gallow, Grimshoe, and Wayland; but nowhere do the Scandinavian names predominate except in the area to the north of Yarmouth, the hundreds of East and West Flegg (*Flec* DB, *Fleg* 1193; from ME *flegge*, the name of a marsh plant, found in modern Danish as *flæg*), where nearly every village name ends in -by, usually containing a personal name of ODan origin (see fig. 2); of the twenty-one examples noted, the large majority lie in this area; none occurs in the west or south-west; they must be regarded as constituting the main settlements of the Scandinavians in the region. The term *by* denoted a village, whereas *þorp* was essentially a hamlet of a larger place; this is well borne out by the numerous names in -thorpe, over forty of them, which occur in every part of the region except the Fenland. Many of them contain well-known ODan personal names, and these are particularly prominent in the Fakenham area and south-west of Norwich. But a number of them are still designated merely as *Thorpe*, with various distinguishing additions, like Thorpe next Norwich, Thorpe Market, Thorpe Abbots, Thorpe Parva; some were known as *Thorp* in the pre-Conquest period and did not acquire a first element until the twelfth century or even later; a quarter of them are named from the neighbouring Anglian settlement which they did not displace, as in Burnham Thorpe, Gayton Thorpe, Shouldham Thorpe, Honingham Thorpe; a number declined in status after being Domesday vills and, like those in -ton, were lost altogether.

The major place-names of the region present few examples of other Scandinavian terms, like *topt* 'messuage', usually found in the plural, as in Buckenham Tofts, Bircham Tofts, Toft Monks, and Toftrees; *þveit* 'cleared woodland', as in Thwaite, Guestwick (*Geghestueit* DB, *Geistweit* 1203; 'the clearing belonging

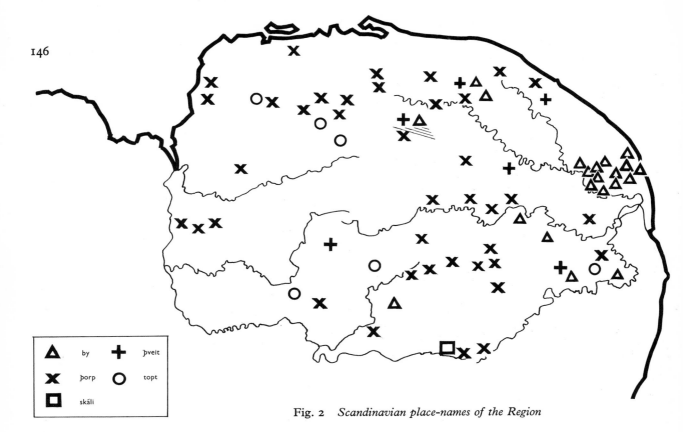

Fig. 2   *Scandinavian place-names of the Region*

Legend:

△	by	✚	þveit
✕	þorp	○	topt
□	skáli		

to Guist': *Geeysæte* 1037, *Gegeseta* DB, *Geiste* 1200, 'the dwelling of *Gæga*', also found in Gayton and Gaywood), Crostwick (*Crostueit* DB, *Crosthweyt* 1302) and Crostwight (*Crostwit* DB, *Crostweit* 1211; 'clearing by a cross', from ON *kross*). The term occurs more frequently in field and minor names, often in a modern corrupt form, as in Weight Farm in Saham Toney (*Thueit* 1219, *Thweyt* 1257) and Lingwhite in Hingham (*Langthweyt* 1257). A solitary example of *skáli* 'hut' occurs among the major names in Scole near Diss.

Two names of local interest indicating the frequent 'hybridism' of Anglian and Scandinavian elements are Costessey (*Costeseia* DB; 'the island of *Kostr*', originally a Scandinavian nickname) and Corpusty (*Corpestig* DB, *Corpesti* 1196; perhaps 'the pigsty of *Korpr*', also originally a nickname).

In an area that has been noted for centuries for its broad acres of arable there is a surprisingly large number of place-names indicating woodland in pre-Conquest times (see fig. 3). A rare British example may be Trunch. Terms of Anglian origin denoting woodland are: *wudu*, as in Gaywood, Lingwood, Southwood, Wicklewood, Woodbastwick, Wood Norton, Wood Rising, Wood Dalling, Woodton, North and South Wootton; *wald*, as in Hockwold, Methwold, and North-wold, and probably also in East Walton, Walton Hall in Ludham, and the lost *Waltone* in Poringland; *hrís*, as in Ryston, East Ruston, Sco Ruston, Castle Rising, Wood Rising, and Toftrees (*Tofteris* 1268, *Toftesris* 1302); *holt*, as in Holt and Mousehold; *sceaga*, as in Strumpshaw (*Stromessaga* DB, *Strumeshag* 1212, *Strompeshawe* 1273; from OE *strump* 'tree-stump'); *gráf*, as in Palgrave ('where poles were cut') and Chedgrave. But by far the most prolific is *léah*, found with a 'folk-name' in Babingley, with early Anglian personal names, as in Brisley, Cantley, Kimberley (*Chineburlai* DB, *Kinburllee* 1198, *Kineburlee* 1250; from OE *Cyneburg*, a woman's name), Mundesley, and Pattesley, and in many cases with names of trees, as in Acle (*Achelai* 1159, *Aclee* 1197; from OE *ác* 'oak'), Ashill (*Asscelea* DB, *Aschele* 1219; from OE *æsc* 'ash'), Bixley (*Biskele* DB, *Bischele* 1163, *Biskelee* 1283; from OE *byxe* 'box'), Sall (*Salla* DB, *Sallee* 1198; from

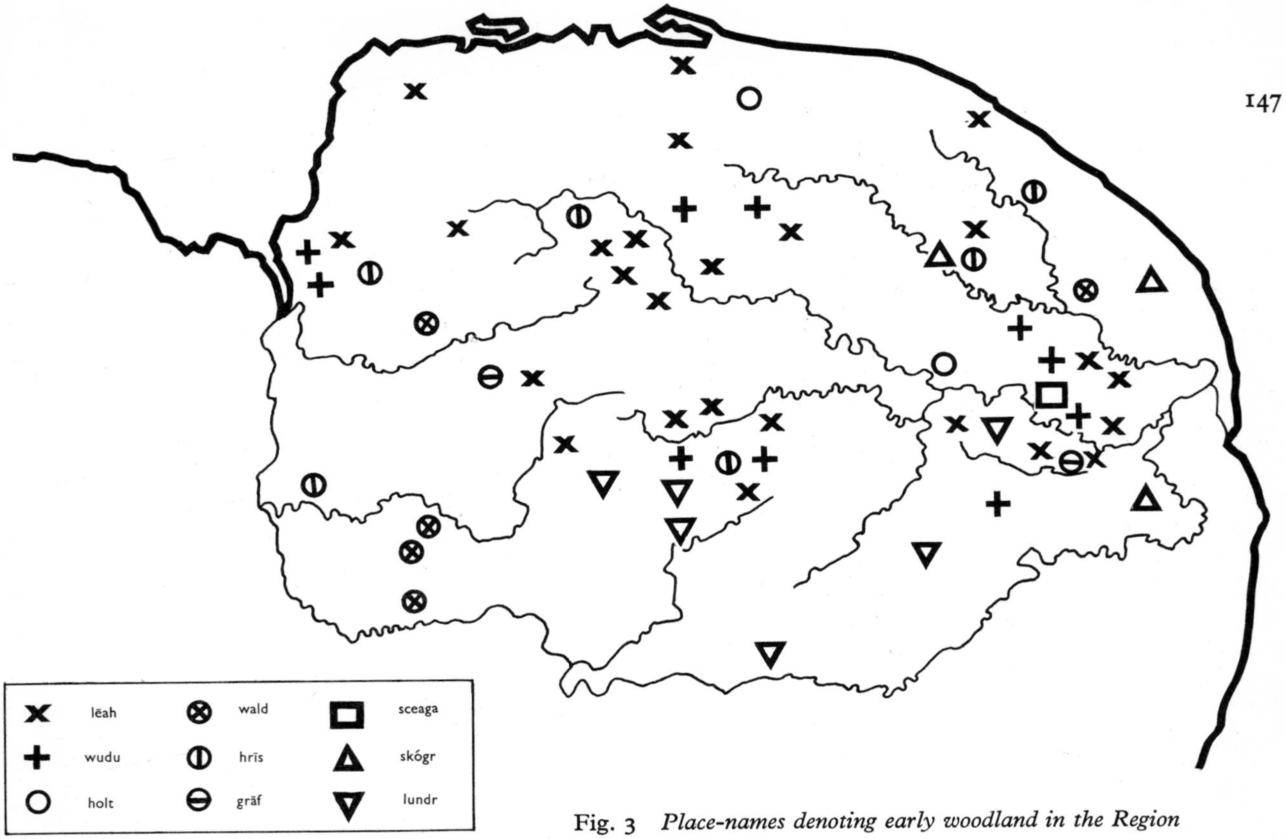

✗ lēah	⊗ wald	☐ sceaga	
✚ wudu	Φ hrīs	△ skógr	
○ holt	⊖ grāf	▽ lundr	

Fig. 3 *Place-names denoting early woodland in the Region*

OE *salh* 'willow', also found in the plural in Salhouse: *Sallus* 1235, *Sallowes* 1535), and Sloley (*Slaleia* DB, *Slalee* 1207; from OE *slā* 'sloe'). To these the Scandinavians further added their own terms *skógr*, as in Haddiscoe, Sco Ruston (where both English and Norse indicate woodland), and Sco in Martham, found repeatedly in field names; and *lundr*, as in Boyland Hall in Morningthorpe (*Boielund* DB, *Boilund* 1199), Boyland Hall in Bressingham (*Boilund* 1236), Wayland Wood in Watton, which gave its name to the hundred of Wayland (*Wainelund* DB, *Weinelund* 1188, *Wainlund* 1210), and the three separate Rocklands (*Rokelund* DB; from ON *hrókr* 'rook', no doubt the earlier equivalent of the modern *The Rookery*). The local birds are otherwise but little represented: we have the crow in Cromer and perhaps Brancaster, the crane in Cranwich and Cranworth, the cuckoo (OE *gēac*) in Yaxham; to these may be added Foulden (*Fugalduna* DB; 'bird hill', from OE *fugol* 'bird').

Some clearing of forest land is indicated in the occurrence of the OE term *bræc* 'land newly cleared' in Bircham (*Brecham* DB, *Brechham* 1176, *Brecheham* 1200) and Breckles (*Brecles* DB, 1257, *Brekeles* 1287; from OE *læs* 'meadow') as well as the ON *þveit*, as in Thwaite, etc.

Open country was generally denoted by OE *feld*, as in Blofield (*Blauuefelde* DB, *Blafeld* 1198, 1212; from OE *blāw* with the sense 'bleak, exposed', also found in Blo Norton, and in Blofield in Trimley, Sf), Fersfield (*Fersfelde* 1212; from OE *fyrs* 'furze'), Catfield (*Catefelda* DB, *Katefeld* 1269; probably from OE *cætt* 'wild cat', also found in Catton and a lost *Cattone* in Postwick), Edgefield (*Edisfeld* DB, *Edichfeld* 1191; from OE *edisc* 'pasture'), Swafield (*Suaffelda* DB, *Swathfeld* 1197, *Suathelfed* 1206, apparently 'land crossed by a track', OE *swæþ*).

Meadowland is indicated in Metton (from OE *mæd* 'mead'), Gresham (from OE *gers*, *gres* 'grass'), Etling Green in East Dereham (*Etlinge* 1277, *Ettlynge* 1325; from OE **ete-hlinc* 'grazing hill'), and a number of names formed with OE *edisc* 'pasture', as in Edgefield, Oxnead (*Oxenedes* DB, *Oxenedich* 1254), Thornage (*Tornedis* DB, *Thornedis* 1198, *Thornedisch* 1254), Brockdish (*Brokedis*

1166; from OE *brōc* 'river', here the Waveney), and Brundish in Raveningham (*Bornedis* 1209, *Brundis* 1257; from OE *burna*, ON *brunnr* 'spring'). The rare OE term *winn* 'pasture' appears to occur in East and West Winch (*Eastuuininc*, *Westwinic* DB, *Westwiniz* 1198, *Estweniz* 1234, *Westwenich* 1202) combined with OE *wīc* frequently used in the sense 'dairy farm', as in Oxwick, Bolwick in Aylsham (*Bolwyc*, *c.* 1130, *Bulewic* 1168; from OE *bula* 'bull'), Keswick near Norwich (*Chesewic* DB, *Kesewyk* 1252) and Keswick in Bacton (*Casewic c.* 1150, 1254, *Casewyke* 1286); identical with Casewick, co. Lincoln where cheese (OE *cēse*) was made. Sheep-farming is indicated in Hardwick near King's Lynn (*Herdeuuic* DB, *Herdewic* 1228) and Hardwick near Long Stratton (*Herdewich* 1167, *Herdwic*, 1199), which contain OE *heord* 'flock of sheep', as well as in Shipdham and the lost Shipden (*Scipedana* DB, *Shipeden* 1234; from OE *denu* 'valley') in Cromer.

Arable land is rarely mentioned as such in the major names. The OE term was *æcer*, which is found in East, West, South, and Castle Acre, and Wheatacre. References to crops grown are equally infrequent: barley (OE *bere*) may be referred to in Barford (*Bereforda* DB, *Bereford* 1168), beans (OE *bēan*) in Banham (*Benham* DB, *Banham* 1168, 1203), rye (OE *ryge*) certainly is indicated in Roydon near Diss (*Regedona* DB, *Reidune* 1198) and Roydon near King's Lynn (*Reiduna* DB, *Reidon* 1172).

Peasant communities were denoted by two terms, OE *swāna-tūn* and OE *ceorla-tūn*; the latter is found in three village names, Carleton Rode, Carleton Forehoe, and East Carleton, where the first element has been replaced by the equivalent ON *karl*; the former occurs in Swanton Morley, Swanton Novers, and Swanton Abbot, this last an important manor of the abbey of St Benet of Hulme.

The city of Norwich and its neighbourhood present in the local names a good epitome of the early settlements of the region. Its Anglian name (*Norþwic* 925–40, *Norðwic* 1004, *Norwic* DB) remained unaltered during and after the Danish Conquest, the local Scandinavian influence was not strong enough to change the terminal, OE *wīc*, into ON *vík*, as happened in *Eoforwīc* to make it *Jórvík* and subsequently York. The oldest street in the city is Ber Street (*Berchestrete c.* 1140, *Bergstrete* 1280) 'hill street' (OE *beorg*), in which the terminal may

indicate that it was part of a Roman road (OE *stræt*). Most of the other streets have names ending in -*gate* (ON *gata* 'road'), as in most towns in the Danelaw counties; but their component elements are words that can hardly have been in use before the medieval period. Apart from a few, like Fyebridge Street (*Fifbriggegate c.* 1300) which led to the Fyebridge (*Fifbrege c.* 1140, *Fifbrigge* 1176, *Fyfbrigge* 1257; hardly perhaps 'five bridges'; possibly one five times the width of an ordinary footbridge); Fishergate (where the fishermen lived), Cowgate (perhaps where the dairymen lived), Hungate (*Hundegate* 1257, *Houndegate* 1395; perhaps fouled by dogs; from OE *hund*), the majority indicate the medieval tradesmen's quarters, like Mountergate (*Parmenteregate* 1269), Westlegate (*Wastelgate* 1381; from ME *wastel* 'cake'), Finkelgate (*Fenkelgate* 1508; from ME *fenkel* 'fennel'), Sadelgate 1255, now White Lion Street, Hosieregate 1287, now part of London Street, and Souteregate 1355 (from ME *soutere* 'cobbler') now Muspole Street. Among the wards of the city are Conesford (*Cunegesford* 1166, *Cuningesford c.* 1200; from OE **cyninges ford* 'king's ford' with early substitution of the equivalent ON *konungr* for OE *cyning*), Mancroft (*Mannecroft c.* 1145, 1210, *Manecroft* 1257; from ON personal name *Manni*), Westwick (*Westwic c.* 1160; perhaps originally in distinction to *Norþwic*). The meeting-place of the citizens was originally at Mustow (*Motstowe* 1257, 1289; from OE *mōt* 'meeting'); the space in front of the cathedral was left empty of buildings and called Tombland (*Tomeland* 1287, 1307, 1314; from OE *tōm* 'empty'). Other places in and around the city have names composed of well-known Anglian elements; such as Bracondale (*Brakendele c.* 1140, 1256, *Brakendale* 1257, 1269; from OE **bræcen-dæl* 'fern valley'), Carrow (*Carho* 1159, 1196, *Karhoge* 1198, *Carhow* 1212; from OE **carr-hōh* 'stone hill'), Earlham (*Erlham* DB, 1163, *Eorlham* 1254; from OE **eorl-hām* 'the estate of the earl'), Eaton (*Aietuna* DB, *Etone* 1205, 1257; from OE **ēa-tūn* 'river farm'), Harford Bridge(s) (*pons de Hertford* 1205, *Herteford* 1235; from OE **heorot-ford* 'ford frequented by harts'), Mousehold (*Musholt c.* 1260, *Musholte* 1269; from OE **mūs-holt* 'mouse infested wood', as in Mousewood in Hingham), and Trowse (*Treus* DB, 1228, *Trowes* 1250, *Trouse* 1254; from OE **trēow-hūs* 'wooden house').

The influence of Norman feudalism upon the local names was slight. The new owners of various manors added their official titles or family names to Framingham Earl, Framingham Pigot, Kirby Bedon, Kirby Cane, Melton Constable, Saham Toney, Stow Bedon, Stow Bardolph, Swanton Morley, and Swanton Novers. In a few isolated cases the presence of a French-speaking family permanently affected the pronunciation and subsequent spelling of a place-name. The most significant example is Diss (*Dice* DB, *Dize* 1158, *Disze* 1161, *Disce* 1196, *Disse* 1374; OE dative singular of *dīc* 'ditch' referring to Diss Mere). In the French-looking Hautbois (*Hobuisse* DB, *Hobwise* 1200, *Hautboys* 1250; from OE *hobb-wisse* 'meadow with tussocks'), where the owner of the manor is called *Peter de Hobwisse* in 1199, but *Peter de Hobois vel de Alto Bosco* in 1211, the spelling was altered but the pronunciation has remained 'hobbis'.

Elsewhere, however, many local pronunciations have had to give way to more 'standardized' ones. Norwich is still pronounced 'noridge' – unless it be 'narridge'; Cley still rhymes with 'fly', and Guist with 'priced'; Happisburgh is still 'hazebro', and the Haisbro Light-house will probably retain its distinctive spelling as long as the Englishman goes to sea. But the local 'hunston' for Hunstanton is rapidly being superseded by a tri-syllabic spelling pronunciation made popular by the ever-increasing number of summer visitors; and with every month that the U.S. Air Force continues to remain in East Anglia, Wymondham is becoming more widely known as 'wye-mundham' instead of 'windum'; this last change is the more to be regretted, as the local pronunciation gave rise to the family name Wyndham, and has a respectable ancestry (*Wimundeham* DB, *Wymedham* 1250, 1286, *Wemedham* 1431, *Wyndham* 1548; 'the estate of *Wīgmund*').

NOTES

1 The following abbreviations are employed:

C Cambridgeshire.
DB 'Domesday Book.'
DPN E. Ekwall, *The Concise Oxford Dictionary of English Place-Names* (1960). Fourth Edition.
ERN E. Ekwall, *English River-Names* (1928).
MBr *The Making of the Broads* (1960). R.G.S., Research Series No. 3.

ME Middle English.
Nf Norfolk.
ODan Old Danish.
OE Old English.
ON Old Norse.
Sf Suffolk.
* denotes hypothetical form.

2 The similarity between Ickburgh (Nf), Ickworth, Icklingham, and Iken (Sf), and Ickleton (C), which are all derived from well-established OE personal names, and the name *Iceni* is purely fortuitous.

3 Taverham (*Taverham* DB, *Tauerham* 1168, 1191, 1198) appears to contain OE *tēafor* 'red pigment', the later *tiver* used for marking sheep; perhaps the term is used here in the sense 'red earth', which has otherwise not been noted. Shropham is unexplained by Ekwall (DPN). The earliest spellings (*Scerepham*, *Scerpham* DB, *Serepeham* c. 1120, *Schrepham* 1166, 1219, *Shrapham* 1225, *Sharpham* 1226, *Screpham* 1252, *Schropham* als. *Schrepham* 1303) suggest that it contains a term that may be descriptive of the local topography; it might be OE *scearp* 'steep'; there is an appreciable rise from the low ground by the river to the centre of the village in less than a mile; south-west of the village is Linger Hill.

4 It could be argued on semantic grounds that some of the names in -*ham* which contain animal or bird names are more likely to have OE *hamm* 'enclosed piece of ground' as their terminal. This would apply to East and West Dereham, which might well mean simply 'deerfold' rather than 'large estate where deer were kept'. Similarly with Horsham which might be merely a variant of its neighbour Horstead; and with Shipdham (*Scipedeham* DB; from OE *scip-ēde* 'sheepfold') and Yaxham (*Jakesham* DB, *Jackesham* 1199, *Iakesham* 1254; from OE *gēac* 'cuckoo'). But the early spellings give no indication that the terminal was in fact -*hamm*, which should occasionally appear in medieval sources as -*hom* as well as -*hamm*. It is, however, possible that the prevalence of -*hām* in the region obliterated the distinction from early times.

5 Martham in West Flegg (*Martham* DB, 1211, 1198) derived from OE *mearþ* 'marten, weasel' (DPN) might possibly be a Scandinavian importation in this intensively Danish area. The identical name occurs in Denmark as Mårum, earlier *Marthæm*. But the name may well belong with the small group discussed in note 4, above.

6 Among those that have recently come to light are *Dentone* 1302 (OE *denu-tūn* 'valley farm') and *Gattun* c. 1230 (OE *gāt-tūn* 'goat farm'), both in Flitcham, and *Faverton* in Thetford (*Fahertune* c. 1100, *Fagertone* c. 1160, *Favertone* 1205; from OE *fāg-ærn-tūn* 'farm by the painted house'; Mr R. Rainbird Clarke reports that traces of a Roman building have been found near the presumed site of this place.)

introduction
A. R. CARTWRIGHT | A. FITCH

THIS SECTION of the Survey examines the ways in which the people of Norfolk earn their living. The basic employment statistics are shown on pages 151–3 and the diagrams (figs. 2a and 3a) arrange some of these figures into four groups – for Norwich, Great Yarmouth, King's Lynn, and for the rest of Norfolk.

An attempt is also made (in figs. 2b and 3b) to present the figures in their national context by calculating the total number of workers in each Ministry of Labour category as a percentage of the overall total of employed persons, and then comparing the results with similarly derived national percentages. Thus a category which has more than the national proportion of workers is represented by a column extending above the line of value 1 and vice versa.

The areas to which these statistics relate are shown on the map (fig. 1). It will be seen that the Norwich, Great Yarmouth, and King's Lynn districts include substantial agricultural hinterlands. Furthermore, the figures relate only to those areas whose Employment Exchanges are situated within Norfolk. Consequently, the parts which are referred to as 'The Rest of Norfolk' include portions of neighbouring counties while in other instances they fall short of the county boundary.

It has seemed appropriate in this section to deal first with the economic activities related to the soil and to the sea, then with the Region's manufacturing industries and, finally, with its professional and commercial services.

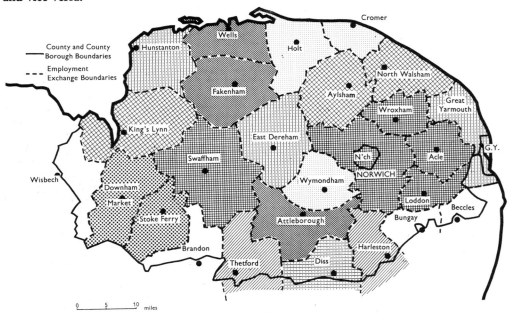

Fig. 1 *Employment Exchange Areas*

EMPLOYMENT STATISTICS: TOTAL, MALES AND FEMALES OVER 15

Order No.	Industry Minimum List Heading	THE URBAN CENTRES			THE REST OF THE COUNTY												TOTALS
		Norwich	Great Yarmouth	King's Lynn	Attleborough	Aylsham and North Walsham	Cromer including Holt	Dereham	Diss	Downham Market including Stoke Ferry	Fakenham including Wells	Harleston	Hunstanton	Swaffham	Thetford	Wymondham	
I	Agriculture and Fishing	5,180	1,723	2,925	1,845	3,307	1,864	2,240	1,745	2,270	3,054	1,262	1,194	2,363	660	896	32,528
II	Mining	196		168			24	92					20	8	9	37		554
III	Food, Drink, and Tobacco	5,698	3,552	2,237	281	958	68	403	143	341	263	335	99	229	293	100	15,000
IV	Chemicals, etc.	337	99	636					17	26	21		6	36	15		1,193
V	Metal Manufacture	355			40			58			40			8			501
VI	Engineering and Electrical Goods	5,157	3,440	810	71	115		667	70	126	100	105	26	65	66	35	10,853
VII	Shipbuilding, etc. Marine Engineering	515	418	16		10	4									1	964
VIII	Vehicles	501	23	24			73	262			1						884
IX	Metal Goods	1,104	17		12	39		6	4	4			4		27	8	1,225
X	Textiles	566	977	24			57		139				6			19	1,788
XI	Leather, etc.	337		4				8			4						353
XII	Clothing and Footwear	9,816	627	38		8	103	33	92		4	130		63		4	10,918
XIII	Bricks, etc.	379	149	12		6		15	41		49		27			27	705
XIV	Timber, Furniture, etc.	1,835	693	169		30	100	461	8	11	65			10	18	25	3,425
XV	Paper, Printing, and Publishing	2,615	606	195		8	22	9	28	1	208		17	17	134	21	3,881
XVI	Other Manufacturing Industries	152	17	78	107		4		91				2			528	979
XVII	Construction	7,387	2,069	1,399	479	471	478	390	312	338	756	228	515	551	372	331	16,076
XVIII	Gas, Electricity, and Water	1,612	707	344		42	108	31	60	53	49		28	36	39	48	3,157
XIX	Transport, etc.	4,999	1,699	1,885	217	232	380	389	191	143	375	118	126	178	224	180	11,336
XX	Distributive	11,769	4,161	2,829	461	914	966	661	483	464	937	326	557	459	211	265	25,463
XXI	Insurance, Banking, and Finance	3,560	260	223	19	46	115	88	65	29	43	29	26	21	21	19	4,564
XXII	Professional, etc. Services	7,776	1,981	1,554	317	811	1,185	373	229	335	410	185	344	316	257	526	16,599
XXIII	Miscellaneous Services	7,870	4,347	1,751	229	756	1,447	768	476	337	1,151	318	598	434	407	360	21,249
XXIV	Public Administration	3,975	1,164	594	295	175	292	250	50	309	395	86	350	295	144	66	8,440
	Other Miscellaneous	20	2	7			7		4		·			4	2		46
	TOTALS	83,711	28,731	17,922	4,373	7,928	7,297	7,204	4,248	4,787	7,925	3,144	3,935	5,092	2,925	3,459	192,681

ESTIMATED NUMBER OF INSURED EMPLOYEES, JUNE 1959
Source: Ministry of Labour

EMPLOYMENT STATISTICS: MALES OVER 15

Order No.	Industry Minimum List Heading	THE URBAN CENTRES			THE REST OF THE COUNTY												TOTALS
		Norwich	Great Yarmouth	King's Lynn	Attleborough	Aylsham and North Walsham	Cromer including Holt	Dereham	Diss	Downham Market including Stoke Ferry	Fakenham including Wells	Harleston	Hunstanton	Swaffham	Thetford	Wymondham	
I	Agriculture and Fishing	4,855	1,614	2,400	1706	3,034	1,709	2,046	1,603	1,843	2,693	1,225	1,059	1,956	578	806	29,127
II	Mining	185		165				24	89				20	8	9	37	537
III	Food, Drink, and Tobacco	3,279	2,026	1,067	219	449	45	260	125	275	167	261	64	63	116	77	8,493
IV	Chemicals, etc.	242	82	561					17	24	19		2	7	13		967
V	Metal Manufacture	344			36			54			37			8			479
VI	Engineering and Electrical Goods	4,434	1,502	735	61	113		390	68	109	94	98	24	54	21	27	7,730
VII	Shipbuilding, etc. Marine Engineering	437	391	16		10	4									1	859
VIII	Vehicles	498	22	21				72	248		1						862
IX	Metal Goods	870	8		12	14		6	4				4		16	8	942
X	Textiles	207	426	15				42		65			2			6	763
XI	Leather, etc.	176		4					8		4						192
XII	Clothing and Footwear	4,580	123	4				2		3		43		2			4,757
XIII	Bricks, etc.	369	96	12		6		14	26		41		27			25	616
XIV	Timber, Furniture, etc.	1,575	647	152		26	95	389	4	11	63			9	14	25	3,010
XV	Paper, Printing, and Publishing	1,494	548	99		6	18	9	25	1	137		11	12	57	13	2,430
XVI	Other Manufacturing Industries	106	12	21	16				55				2			325	537
XVII	Construction	7,219	2,009	1,364	473	451	469	376	308	330	743	220	508	536	363	320	15,688
XVIII	Gas, Electricity, and Water	1,476	655	313		38	101	28	55	46	47		26	34	35	47	2,901
XIX	Transport, etc.	4,453	1,590	1,675	197	185	351	326	153	127	288	105	117	151	178	173	10,069
XX	Distributive	6,671	2,299	1,532	279	471	523	345	298	268	473	202	266	272	121	152	14,172
XXI	Insurance, Banking, and Finance	1,973	163	158	10	32	78	68	54	19	29	20	18	14	12	9	2,657
XXII	Professional, etc. Services	2,529	708	523	62	257	352	78	71	98	114	34	70	90	59	189	5,234
XXIII	Miscellaneous Services	3,662	2,110	847	71	318	467	366	225	136	591	94	202	159	249	134	9,631
XXIV	Public Administration	2,974	978	449	263	147	247	206	39	241	339	76	308	258	125	55	6,705
	Other Miscellaneous	20	1	7				7		4				4	2		45
	TOTALS	54,628	18,010	12,140	3,405	5,557	4,605	5,306	3,202	3,528	5,880	2,400	2,720	3,636	1,994	2,392	129,403

ESTIMATED NUMBER OF INSURED EMPLOYEES, JUNE 1959
Source: Ministry of Labour

EMPLOYMENT STATISTICS: FEMALES OVER 15

Order No.	Industry Minimum List Heading	THE URBAN CENTRES			THE REST OF THE COUNTY												TOTALS
		Norwich	Great Yarmouth	King's Lynn	Attleborough	Aylsham and North Walsham	Cromer including Holt	Dereham	Diss	Downham Market including Stoke Ferry	Fakenham including Wells	Harleston	Hunstanton	Swaffham	Thetford	Wymondham	
I	Agriculture and Fishing	325	109	525	139	273	155	194	142	427	361	37	135	407	82	90	3,401
II	Mining	11		3					3								17
III	Food, Drink, and Tobacco	2,419	1,526	1,170	62	509	23	143	18	66	96	74	35	166	177	23	6,507
IV	Chemicals, etc.	95	17	75						2	2		4	29	2		226
V	Metal Manufacture	11			4			4			3						22
VI	Engineering and Electrical Goods	723	1,938	75	10	2		277	2	17	6	7	2	11	45	8	3,123
VII	Shipbuilding, etc. Marine Engineering	78	27														105
VIII	Vehicles	3	1	3			1	14									22
IX	Metal Goods	234	9			25					4				11		283
X	Textiles	359	551	9			15		74					4		13	1,025
XI	Leather, etc.	161															161
XII	Clothing and Footwear	5,236	504	34		8	101	33	89		4	87		61		4	6,161
XIII	Bricks, etc.	10	53					1	15		8					2	89
XIV	Timber, Furniture, etc.	260	46	17		4	5	72	4		2			1	4		415
XV	Paper, Printing, and Publishing	1,121	58	96		2	4		3		71		6	5	77	8	1,451
XVI	Other Manufacturing Industries	46	5	57	91		4		36							203	442
XVII	Construction	168	60	35	6	20	10	14	4	8	13	8	7	15	9	11	388
XVIII	Gas, Electricity, and Water	136	52	31			4	7	3	5	7	2	2	2	4	1	256
XIX	Transport, etc.	546	109	210	20	47	29	63	38	16	87	13	9	27	46	7	1,267
XX	Distributive	5,098	1,862	1,297	182	443	443	316	185	196	464	124	291	187	90	113	11,291
XXI	Insurance, Banking, and Finance	1,587	97	65	9	14	37	20	11	10	14	9	8	7	9	10	1,907
XXII	Professional, etc. Services	5,247	1,273	1,031	255	554	833	295	158	237	296	151	274	226	198	337	11,365
XXIII	Miscellaneous Services	4,208	2,237	904	158	438	980	402	251	201	560	224	396	275	158	226	11,618
XXIV	Public Administration	1,001	186	145	32	28	45	44	11	68	56	10	42	37	19	11	1,735
	Other Miscellaneous		1														1
	TOTALS	29,083	10,721	5,782	968	2,371	2,692	1,898	1,046	1,259	2,045	744	1,215	1,456	931	1,067	63,278

ESTIMATED NUMBER OF INSURED EMPLOYEES, JUNE 1959
Source: Ministry of Labour

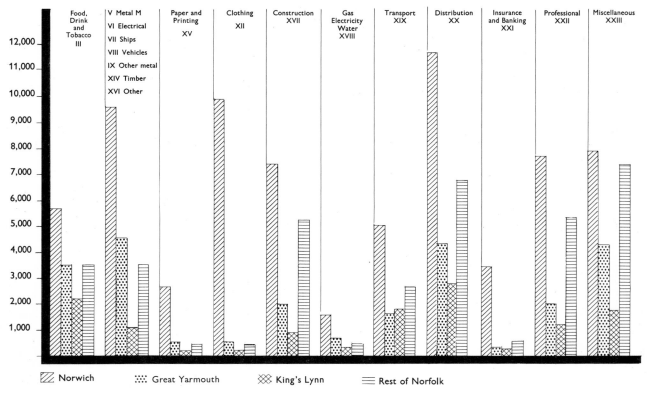

Fig. 2a *Employment by Category*

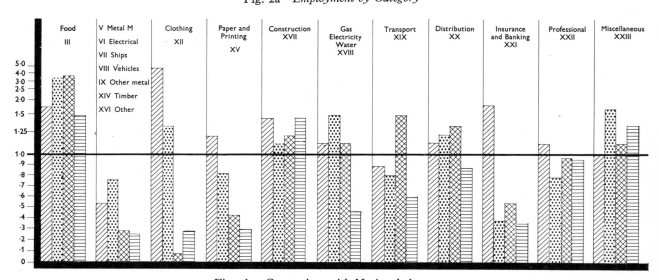

Fig. 2b *Comparison with National Average*

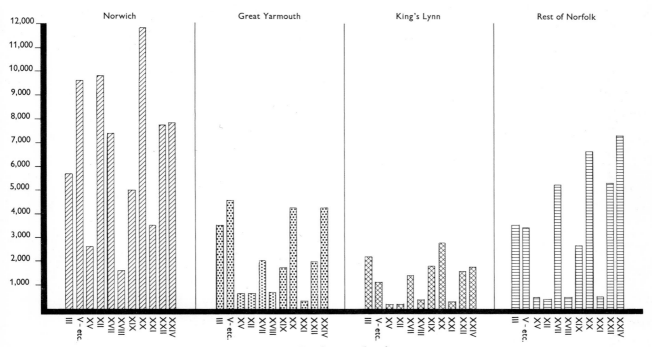

Fig. 3a   *Employment by Area*

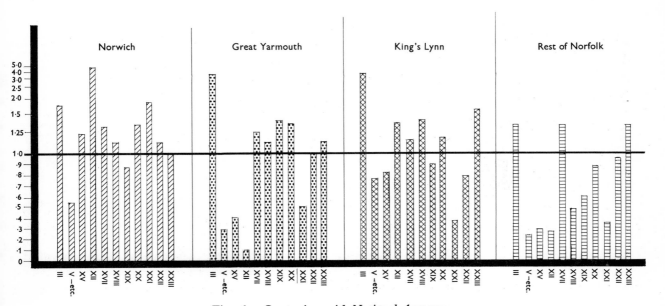

Fig. 3b   *Comparison with National Average*

agriculture F. E. SHOTTON

THE COUNTY of Norfolk is proud of its agricultural industry. Not only is this large in scale – as in the third largest English county it could hardly fail to be – but it has a long tradition of agricultural innovation and progress, a worthy record of achievement during the wartime Food Production Campaign, and a recent history of increasing crop yields and technical advance quite in keeping with its past. Almost every product known to British agriculture is produced within the county and the prefix 'Norfolk' can justifiably be attached to a wide range of commodities – beef, turkeys, ducklings, barley, lavender, asparagus, and lucerne meal – which it exports to the rest of the country and even overseas. The type of farming which is practised in the county, its variety and its importance in the overall agricultural output of England is shown by Table I. Not only in such basic arable crops as wheat, barley, and sugar-beet but also in carrots, celery, and strawberries Norfolk is the largest producer of all the English counties.

TABLE I
NORFOLK'S CONTRIBUTION TO THE AGRICULTURAL PRODUCTION OF ENGLAND
(1959)

	Crop acreage or livestock numbers in Norfolk as a percentage of the total for England	Norfolk's position as a producer of crops and stock in relation to other English counties
Crops and Grass	4·6	2nd
Arable	6·4	1st
Tillage	8·1	1st
Permanent Grass	2·0	23rd
Rough Grazing	1·8	12th

Crops

Wheat		7·1	1st
Barley		10·1	1st
Oats		3·9	9th
Rye		25·1	1st
Potatoes		5·6	6th
Sugar-beet		24·3	1st
Vegetables		13·3	1st
including	Carrots	36·0	1st
	Peas	26·1	1st
	Asparagus	22·4	3rd
	Celery	29·8	1st
Orchards		5·6	6th
Strawberries		23·1	1st
Mustard for seed		14·6	1st
Lucerne		13·7	1st

Livestock

Total Cattle	2·7	14th
Total Sheep	0·6	33rd
Total Pigs	4·8	4th
Total Poultry	5·8	2nd

Later sections of this report will deal in greater detail with individual products and practices but here, at the outset, we may consider certain factors which have contributed to the development of so diversified a pattern of farming.

F.E. SHOTTON is Director of the Experimental Husbandry Farm, Terrington St Clement

CLIMATE AND TOPOGRAPHY

The geography, geology, and climate of the county form the subject of other sections of this survey, and it is necessary here to consider these factors only in so far as they affect farming practice. Topographically Norfolk is favourable to arable cultivation having no high hills and very few unploughable slopes. Such rough grazing as now remains – and the acreage has been halved since 1939 – exists either on heaths, in waterlogged river valleys or as unenclosed saltings of the coastal alluvial plain.

Ministry of Agriculture. Aerial photograph by infra-red, June 1959

Fig. 1 *Breckland Croxton. The effect of an eroded chalk subsoil on barley, the crop is green in the dark areas where there was good chalky loam at 18 to 24 inches, and withered by drought in the light areas where the loamy sand topsoil is deep. The pattern may have resulted from frost cracking under tundra conditions followed by gullying under wet conditions*

The Norfolk climate can be both a help and a hindrance to farming. The rainfall is low, averaging 26 inches a year, but varies considerably from place to place, year to year, and from one month to another. In so far as August tends to be the wettest month of the year, it can create difficulties at harvest as was the case in 1958 and 1960. But in Norfolk the rate of evaporation is high, and in most seasons strong breezes and hot sun will rapidly dry out the standing corn after a shower. In the same way, though less beneficially, heavy land ploughed wet in the spring will rapidly dry to intractable clods under the strong north-easters which blow in March and for this reason spring ploughing of strong land is rigorously avoided whenever possible. Ploughed before Christmas such land will usually be brought to a good tilth by winter frosts which are frequently severe, although this has not been the case during recent winters. Late snow, in February and persisting well into March, not only interrupts drilling in the exposed northern and eastern parts of the county with annoying regularity but also, blown by the wind, forms drifts which may isolate villages for days at a time.

Over the greater part of the county spring or early summer drought is a potent influence whose effect can be detected in such varied facets of Norfolk agriculture as the technique of cultivation, drilling dates, the lucerne acreage, seed mixtures, and the distribution pattern of milk production both geographically and seasonally. Within very broad limits the whole pattern of Norfolk farming is planned to minimize the effects of drought and yet, in seasons such as 1960 and especially on the lightest soils, excessive drought in May and June can nullify the best of planning and reduce crop yields to uneconomic levels.

TYPES OF SOIL

As yet science has contributed little to the systematic classification of the soils of Norfolk. An adviser going about his duties will identify silt and peat, skirt and breck, sand, loam, and clay, which may be further described as heavy, medium or light, deep or shallow. They may also be acid, alkaline or organic, drummy, marly, raw or sticky, and, although it may be both useful and informative to identify a soil as a 'deep drummy light black peat', the description clearly lacks scientific

Ministry of Agriculture photograph, August 1960

Fig. 2 *Breckland, Gooderstone. Barley failure due to May drought. Crop yielded 7 cwt/acre where chalk loam within 1 foot of the surface and died completely where loamy sand 3 feet deep*

precision. The Land Utilization Survey of 1938[1] took account of the origin and character of the soils, but it dealt with the county by broad regions and was insufficiently detailed to be of great practical value. For, although there are areas of Norfolk which are sufficiently uniform for the farming to assume an overall similarity and to contrast strongly with that practised elsewhere, significant variations of soil-type may occur in a single farm – or even in an individual field. The successful cultivator studies these variations, and selects his crops and adjusts his sequence of cropping, his tillage, and his manurial practices to suit them.

Farmers themselves make a primary distinction between 'upland' Norfolk and the rest: between land lying above the 15 feet contour and the marshes and fens below that level. The greater part of the upland area consists of glacial deposits overlying the Norwich Crag, the Chalk, and much of the Greensand and Gault Clay. The arable soils are therefore mainly of glacial origin, mixed in varying degrees with the underlying deposits. Chalk sometimes reaches the surface on eroded valley sides and round the lips of the old marl-pits which pockmark large stretches of light land Norfolk, limiting the depth of ploughing and hampering seedbed preparation; but these areas are rarely extensive. Broken chalk does, however, form the subsoil of many farms and increases the water-holding capacity where the topsoil is sandy. This effect is most clearly seen in the Brandon-Swaffham-Garboldisham triangle of the Breckland where many fields have a sandy soil superimposed upon an eroded and gullied chalk subsoil (fig. 1). The depth of the chalk below the surface may drop from 1 to 3 feet and rise to plough-depth again all within a few yards, and in a dry year crop yields vary inversely with the depth of sand over the chalk (fig. 2).

As the chalk dips eastwards the glacial deposits deepen and contribute both topsoil and subsoil, tending to become heavier as they deepen so that, as a broad generalization, a steady increase in the clay fraction of the soil may be traced from north-west to south-east across the county. In the Docking rural district the typical soil varies from a loamy coarse sand to a coarse sandy loam; from Fakenham through mid-Norfolk towards Wymondham loams and sandy clay loams predominate, becoming fractionally heavier until the only really difficult clays are found in the parishes of Woodton and Hempnall and on the eroded slopes of the Waveney valley. The soils across this transect have a great family likeness in the coarseness of the sand fraction and even the clay loams of south Norfolk retain a distinctly gritty texture.

North and east of Norwich, in the Rural Districts of Smallburgh and Blofield and Flegg, lie the deep loams and very fine sandy loams which are the pride of east Norfolk. The coarseness of the sand has gone and these soils, which are more like silts and brickearths than sands or boulder clays, retain moisture without needing elaborate drainage-systems. Now that the lime and phosphate status has been built up the better soils of this district can grow most horticultural or agricultural crops in competition with the county's best soils.

Alongside the upland loams – frequently intersecting them and forming part of the same farms – are the estuarine marshes and valley-meadows of the Broadland area. In the silted estuaries of the Yare, Waveney, and Bure the typical soils are of marine clay or silty clay overlaid with a relatively shallow organic or even peaty layer. Higher up the valleys, and throughout the length of all the little rivers and streams of Norfolk, may be found peat, sand, and gravel – with very varied mixtures of these components.

The county's largest river – the Great Ouse – flows through the two remaining principal soil-types of

Norfolk. The silt soils of Marshland are products of recent marine deposition and lie in a belt, some 10 miles deep, south of the Wash. At their best they are deep, stone-free silty loams affording unlimited root range and abundant water-supply for crops. A small part of the Norfolk silt area is light, with patches of 'raw silt', while much of the south-eastern part is heavy silty clay loam or silty clay which is difficult to drain and to cultivate, and here the range of profitable crops is more restricted. On a line between Downham Market and Wisbech the soil changes through 'skirt' to peaty loam, and a light peat with up to 65 per cent of organic matter occurs where the peat fen abuts the upland from Methwold to Hockwold. The best soils of this organic group are the peaty loams and those 'skirts' – soils from which most of the organic matter has been oxidized – which overlaid silty-loam or silty-clay so that the soil is now organic or of a predominantly silty nature.

Less than 5 per cent of Norfolk therefore has extremely heavy soils. Heavy soils of sandy or silty-clay loam character, which require good artificial drainage and skilful handling for successful arable cropping occupy a further 20 to 25 per cent of the county, and almost three-quarters of the area has medium, light or very light soils. The criterion here is solely the clay-content of the soils, and no distinction is made between good or bad soils or even between those which are wet and those which are naturally drained. The fact that many Norfolk soils can be worked with relatively light power has undoubtedly encouraged a system of farming based on large-scale tillage rather than on pastoral husbandry.

SOIL FERTILITY

The lightness of much of the Norfolk soil is not, of course, an unmixed blessing. A twelfth-century monk of Peterborough reported his view of the county as follows:

> Every land and every sea
> Have I crossed, but much the worst
> Is the land of Norfolk cursed.
> That the land is poor and bad
> I the clearest proof have had,
> If you plant the choicest wheat
> Tares and darnel you will meet
>
> Satan on the road to Hell
> Ruined Norfolk as he fell.

Farmers everywhere strive to return to the soil that which they take out in order to preserve fertility for those who will follow after them. Clearly earlier generations of Norfolk farmers must have done more than this. It is apparent even today – by soil examination quite apart from the historical record – that on the light lands they were faced with a task of vast proportions, and the record of their efforts is preserved in the marlpits of north-west Norfolk and in the shelter-belts of Breckland. On these soils extreme acidity, low organic content, and overall poverty had to be corrected. To a reduced extent these problems remain. Liming is today a simple operation carried out on contract by mechanical spreaders but crop losses from acidity continue to recur though to a much reduced extent than a few years ago. Applications of inorganic fertilizers, particularly of nitrogen, were at a higher rate in upland Norfolk than in any other region surveyed by the Survey of Fertilizer Practice.[2] Phosphate deficiency, which before the war was very serious on some of the best east Norfolk soils, has been corrected and even the potash status of the light soils has been brought to a level where further abnormal dressings are no longer necessary.

Soil organic matter on some Norfolk soils remains, however, at an extremely low level and on light soil under arable cultivation in a dry climate it is doubtful if it will ever be raised. To what extent organic matter is important, and at what level, remains to be clearly demonstrated experimentally. Vast areas of light-land Norfolk contain well under 2 per cent of organic matter and much of the coarser soil is at about 1 per cent. Most of these soils continue to crop successfully, according to season, at this level of organic matter, and crop yields have in fact improved over recent years. The majority of Norfolk farmers act on the assumption that they should return to the soil as much organic matter as possible, and if all their straw is not made into farmyard manure they will normally plough in the residue: straw burning does occur but on a relatively small scale. The beneficial effect of farmyard manure, especially for potatoes and sugar beet, is well known in practice and has been clearly demonstrated by long-term experiments at the Norfolk Agricultural Station.[3,4] What is not clear is whether the sort of dressing which can in practice be applied – some 2–3 tons of dry matter incorporated in a thousand tons of topsoil once every five to eight years – produces any lasting improvement in the level of organic matter remaining in the soil over and above that which results from the inevitable annual additions of such crop residues as roots, stubble, leaves, and the crowns of sugar beet.

At the 1959 Meeting of the Association a condition of sugar beet named 'Docking Disorder' after the parish of that name in north-west Norfolk, was reported to the Agricultural Section by Professor H.G. Sanders.[5] This condition, a virtual failure of the beet crop, occurs on patches of extremely poor loamy sand where the organic matter content is usually less than 1 per cent. To what extent there is a direct relationship between these facts has yet to be proved. Applications of bulky organic materials such as farmyard manure, shoddy, sugar-beet tops or the residue of lucerne leys have increased the yield of the succeeding sugar-beet crop but the material which has had the greatest and most lasting beneficial effect has been DD (an impure mixture of dichloro-propane and dichloropropylene – a by-product of the petroleum industry) which is a soil sterilant and nema-ticide. Moreover, a very similar but distinct condition of beet has been observed during the last five years to occur on fields which have recently been ploughed out of grass or lucerne. In this case it appears that there may be some indirect relationship with the soil fungus *Rhizoctonia solani* although the fungus cannot be found to be actively pathogenic on sugar-beet though it may be pathogenic on barley which is similarly affected. The present thinking of those most nearly concerned with the investigation of these problems is that 'Docking Disorder' may be due to some indirect biological effect, possibly due to some organic toxin, which in its turn may be affected by the level of soil organic matter.

It is not only the light soils which present problems of fertility in its widest sense. For a county which is frequently thought of as consisting solely of light soil and which has a dry climate the volume of drainage work which constantly goes on may surprise visitors. The major schemes of river maintenance, embankment and flood and coast protection which are the responsibilities of the River Boards are of direct consequence to about 15 per cent of the county. Leading to the main rivers are the tributaries and watercourses over which the Internal Drainage Boards exercise control. In the low-lying parts of the county and especially in the arable silt and fen areas of west Norfolk these Boards, composed of interested land-owners and occupiers, are most vigilant and active bodies whose jurisdiction extends not only over the watercourses themselves, but also over the pumping stations which lift the water into the main rivers and without which such land would revert to marsh and fen. The importance of these Boards may be gauged by the size of the rates which they levy, which today over large areas of the black fen amount to between 20s. and 30s. per acre.

The farmers themselves are responsible for their own dykes and ditches, and over the last five years have been carrying out improvements at the rate of £70,000 per annum quite apart from the costs of routine maintenance. Norfolk is well served by contractors, and increasingly major drainage work is carried out by mechanical drag-line excavators. Similarly, with the tile drainage of the fields, the traditional skill of the land-drainer – and a very high skill it was – is being replaced by mechanical trench cutters and even tile laying machines. Thorough tile drainage today costs not less than £30 per acre and there is relatively little land in Norfolk with a subsoil of sufficient clay content to be satisfactorily mole-drained at lower cost.

Liming on light land and drainage of heavier or wetter soils are both fundamental to rotational cropping and unless each is properly attended to other aspects of soil fertility are largely irrelevant, for acidity and bad drainage will each inhibit the free ranging of roots which is necessary for a crop to collect its moisture and mineral nutrients from the soil.

CROPS IN RELATION TO SOIL

The volume of production of any crop is conditioned by several factors. In the first place there must be an outlet for the product – either a market or an appropriate live-stock enterprise – and it is clearly desirable, essential in fact for major crops, that this outlet should be profitable. The present system of Government price support for certain commodities tends to encourage the production of these commodities at the expense of others which are denied such support. A favourable climate is also a necessity for continued extensive production of any crop and it is essential that adequate skilled labour should be available to cultivate and harvest it. To the extent that these factors leave the farmer any freedom in the choice of which crops he will grow he will favour those for which his soil is best suited. There are, of course, cases where the soil will be so eminently suitable for – or so adverse to – the production of a crop that its effect may override that of all other factors. The effect of the soil may also be an indirect one as when its unsuitability for one crop leads to an increase in the proportion of another.

The effect of the soil on the volume of crop production is quite marked for the range of soils which occurs in Norfolk, for the economic factors and labour supply are reasonably constant throughout the county. The exception is those crops such as vining peas which are grown on contract, for without a contract there is no market. Sugar-beet, although a contract crop, is not restricted in the same way – in the past contracts were freely available throughout the county, and the present distribution of the crop is fairly closely related to soil type.

In Table II the relative size of the principal crops in 1959 is shown both for the county as a whole and for the main soil regions defined by the Land Utilization Survey. At the head of the Table appear estimates of the proportion of the total area of the county covered by each type of soil, and also the percentages of the agricultural area of Norfolk for which it has been possible to extract detailed statistics. These statistics do not in fact cover the whole area as it has been necessary to exclude farms lying on the boundaries of adjacent regions where soils are very mixed. The peat fens have been split into Light Fen and Mature Fen as these two types contrast quite markedly with one another.

The permanent pasture acreage is shown as a percentage of the *total agricultural area* giving, by difference, the arable area which includes rotational temporary leys. The principal crops are shown as a percentage of the *arable* acreage.

Permanent pasture in Norfolk is very variable both in nature and usefulness. On the heavier soils of south and central Norfolk where dairy herds predominate, a proportion of old pasture is retained for winter grazing as an established sward is less liable to 'poach' than the more open turf of a younger ley. Nevertheless, much of the acreage returned as 'permanent' will in fact have been sown down in the last ten years – most farmers regarding as 'permanent' any ley which is older than three years. In other parts of the county, as for example in east Norfolk, the permanent pasture tends to be concentrated in the valleys of the numerous rivers and streams, and may well be on river gravels or even peats very different from the normal soil of the district – though differentiation of the statistics is not possible. These valleys are frequently very narrow, and would require extensive and costly drainage to make them fit for arable cropping, and there is a strong tendency for them to be left in grass. Nevertheless, their acreage is continually being eaten into: the acreage of permanent pasture in Norfolk having been reduced by 80,000 acres since 1939. The acreage of pasture is lowest in the silt and fen areas where much of what remains is on unploughable river banks and washes. The county's only extensive block of permanent pasture – totalling some 20,000 acres – lies in the estuaries of the east Norfolk rivers where some excellent and erstwhile fattening pastures exist on land which could not be cropped without complete reorganization of the whole drainage system and the construction of many new access roads and bridges. Most of these marshes are let seasonally and to a large extent the grazing, which was once almost entirely devoted to bullocks and colts, is today occupied by dairy heifers and dry cows.

When we turn to consider the utilization of the arable acreage we find a closer relationship between the acreage of temporary leys and the type of soil than exists with permanent pasture. The ley acreage is lowest on the best arable soils – silts, mature fen, and east Norfolk loams – where it is more profitable to grow cash crops. There is an appreciable proportion (15 per cent) of leys on the heavier soils of south and mid-Norfolk which are relatively drought-resistant. The highest acreage is, however, found on the lightest soils – the sandy brecks and the light peats – not because leys do especially well on these soils (though grass does grow luxuriantly on the peats) but mainly for rotational reasons. In Breckland and also in north-west Norfolk a considerable proportion of the ley acreage is in lucerne or lucerne-grass mixtures. Lucerne is the most drought-resistant of our herbage plants and a notable fertility builder on poor land. A large proportion of the lucerne crop is artificially

TABLE II NORFOLK CROPPING IN RELATION TO SOIL TYPE (1959)

PRINCIPAL SOIL TYPE REGIONS OF NORFOLK: THEIR TEXTURE AND EXTENT

Soil Type Regions	East Norfolk[1]	Mid-Norfolk	South-Norfolk	Breck-land	North-west Norfolk[2]	Holt-Cromer Ridge	Marsh-land[3]	Light Fen	Mature Fen	Whole County
Soil texture (U.S. classification)	SL-VFSL-L	CSL-CSCL	CSCL-CL	S-SL	LCS-CSL	CS-CSL	VFSL-ZyL-ZyCL	Peat-Loamy Peat	Peaty loam-Org. ZyCL	—
Estimated extent as a percentage of the gross area of Norfolk (1,307,333 acres)	17	18	14	8	17	3	8	2	2	—
Percentage of the county acreage of crops and grass (1,002,852 acres) from which the following statistics are drawn	5.4	9.0	7.1	6.9	13.9	2.1	5.3	1.7	1.8	—

PERMANENT PASTURE AS A PERCENTAGE OF THE TOTAL CROPS AND GRASS ACREAGE OF EACH REGION

	East Norfolk	Mid-Norfolk	South-Norfolk	Breck-land	North-west Norfolk	Holt-Cromer Ridge	Marsh-land	Light Fen	Mature Fen	Whole County
Permanent pasture	16.3	20.1	22.9	16.7	12.4	13.8	9.3	6.0	5.9	18.5

PRINCIPAL CROPS AS A PERCENTAGE OF THE ARABLE ACREAGE OF EACH REGION

	East Norfolk	Mid-Norfolk	South-Norfolk	Breck-land	North-west Norfolk	Holt-Cromer Ridge	Marsh-land	Light Fen	Mature Fen	Whole County
Wheat	19.0	14.3	16.2	5.1	14.7	12.5	25.1	21.6	36.8	15.9
Barley	30.6	39.8	40.7	40.3	37.4	39.2	12.5	3.9	6.6	34.0
Oats	6.8	5.1	6.5	3.0	3.3	8.4	2.3	0.6	1.3	4.7
Rye	0.1	0.1	—	2.9	0.6	0.1	—	0.1	—	0.4
Total Cereals	**56.5**	**59.3**	**63.4**	**51.3**	**56.0**	**60.2**	**39.9**	**26.2**	**44.7**	**55.0**
Potatoes	4.1	1.0	0.5	0.6	0.8	2.3	17.9	8.4	21.1	3.7
Sugar beet	16.2	11.7	9.3	10.9	12.7	11.8	5.9	15.5	14.9	12.4
Fodder roots, kale and cabbages	2.9	5.2	5.8	6.1	3.5	7.3	1.4	1.4	1.5	4.5
Total Root Crops	**23.2**	**17.9**	**15.6**	**17.6**	**17.0**	**21.4**	**25.2**	**25.3**	**37.5**	**20.6**
Vegetables	**6.6**	**2.8**	**1.9**	**4.3**	**8.6**	**2.1**	**13.7**	**22.4**	**8.7**	**6.7**
Grass, Clover, Lucerne and Mixed Leys	**6.3**	**15.8**	**15.4**	**21.8**	**15.3**	**13.6**	**2.8**	**21.9**	**3.7**	**13.1**

Note 1. The statistics given in no case add up to 100 per cent. Minor soil types have been omitted and it has not been possible to supply statistics representing the whole of the land within each region. Similarly minor crops have been omitted from the Table.

Note 2. Soil type descriptions are those shown on the map on page 49 except:
1 'East Norfolk' corresponds to 'Flegg' and 'Loam Region';
2 'N.W. Norfolk' corresponds to 'Good Sands';
3 'Marshland' corresponds to 'Silt Fen'.

KEY TO SOIL CLASSIFICATION

CS	Coarse sand	SL	Sandy loam	L	Loam	ZyL	Silty loam
S	Sand	CSL	Coarse sandy loam	CSCL	Coarse sandy clay loam	ZyCL	Silty clay loam
LS	Loamy sand	VFSL	Very fine sandy loam	CL	Clay loam	Org.	Organic

Ministry of Agriculture photograph, August 1960

Fig. 3 *Marshland, Terrington St Clement. Hybrid 46 wheat taken after potatoes. The crop lodged at the end of July but yielded over 47 cwt/acre*

dried and sold for compounding, as also is much of the cocksfoot which is grown on the light peat.

Wheat is grown by all farmers to a limit set by the fertility of their soil and its acreage is highest on the mature fens and silts (fig. 3), the proportion on the silts would be higher were not such a large proportion (11 per cent) of this land devoted to fruit. Almost the whole of the Norfolk wheat crop is autumn-sown except on the light peats where it is almost entirely spring wheat and where the acreage has almost doubled in the last ten years as new varieties, and a fuller understanding of the minor element deficiencies of these soils, have raised yields to economic levels. The 1959 wheat acreage on the heavy soils was reduced by the wet autumn of 1958 otherwise the proportions of wheat in south and mid-Norfolk would have been higher than the present figures show.

Barley is Norfolk's principal cereal crop as it will succeed on lighter soils than wheat, and is less affected by footrot diseases. On all the upland soils it occupies about two-fifths of the arable area, but the acreage declines sharply on the richer alluvial soils where lodging is so great a danger. This problem is most severe on the light peats where excess nitrogen and deficient manganese combine to produce extremely weak straw, and here the acreage is a trivial 4 per cent. The oat crop is nowhere of great consequence and succeeds well only in the eastern and southern parts of the county where

there is the greatest demand for the crop for stock feeding. Rye cannot compete financially with wheat or barley on reasonable soil and is grown only on the lightest sand where wheat is out of the question and barley not entirely reliable.

The outstanding root crop in the county is, of course, sugar beet which occupies an eighth of the arable area. Such is the economic and rotational importance of the crop that nowhere does it diverge very widely of this proportion except on the silts where, because of the established success of the potato crop, labour competition with potatoes and other crops, and difficulty of harvesting on the heavy silts, the crop has not gained such wide acceptance. Harvesting difficulties also restrict the acreage on the heavier loams while drought reduces yields on the very light soils in Breckland and on the Holt-Cromer ridge.

More than any other crop, potatoes reflect soil suitability. The problem here is not simply one of yield: quality is also of great importance, and whereas with suitable preparation and in a moist season reasonable yields may be grown on upland loams, scab (*Streptomyces scabies*) or poor cooking quality frequently limit the market value of the crop. Potatoes are the principal 'root crop' on the silts and mature fens. On the light fens the acreage is limited because of variable quality and high populations of potato root eelworm (*Heterodera rostochiensis*). Since the war certain farmers on the good loams of east Norfolk have shown themselves to be extremely good potato growers and during recent moist years have produced yields to rival and even exceed those of the silts. As these loams are deep, stone-free, and relatively moisture-retentive, there is no reason to think that successful potato growing will not continue to thrive in this area, especially as there is a local demand for varieties suitable for the manufacture of potato crisps.

The fodder root acreage bears little direct relationship to soil quality, but is mainly conditioned by the livestock population. Nowhere is the acreage lower than on the alluvial soils of west Norfolk but nowhere can higher yields of mangolds be grown. The mangold acreage has, of course, been much reduced by the expansion of sugar-beet: it can, however, easily be handled by the existing labour supply and involves little extra cash outlay.

Today kale almost equals mangolds in acreage and is concentrated in the dairying areas.

The remaining item in Table II – vegetables – is in fact a group of crops, the most important being peas (25,000 acres), carrots (11,000 acres) and brassicae (8,000 acres). These crops vary in their soil requirements and market outlets and collectively their relationship to the soil does not emerge clearly from the Table. None of these crops are, however, grown to any extent on the heavier loams or on the stony soils of the Holt-Cromer ridge. In east Norfolk and in Marshland the predominant vegetable crop is peas for canning or quick-freezing, for these areas lie closest to the processing factories. There is, however, a soil relationship here for the factories were established in areas where the crop succeeds well. In contrast the bulk of the vegetables in north-west Norfolk are carrots and brassicae partly because the soil is reasonably suitable but mainly from rotational requirements, because they can be grown extensively and because labour is available to handle these crops during the winter. On the light fens vegetable crops occupy almost a quarter of the area and include celery, carrots, lettuce, red beet, onions, and similar intensive crops.

ROTATIONS

Norfolk has given its name to the four-course rotation of clover-wheat-fodder roots-barley which held sway, and with legal force, over most of the upland part of the county throughout the nineteenth and into the twentieth century. Today, in its original form, it exists no more. The virtual disappearance of hurdled flocks from the arable land reduced the need for turnips and swedes and for the large acreage of grazing ley. The effect of so great a change might well have been to alter the whole concept of crop rotation in the county, and to have led either to a system of alternate husbandry based on leys and cereals or, more probably, to an almost all-cereal rotation. This has not happened, and it will be seen from Table II that over the county as a whole cereals amount to only 55 per cent of the arable acreage while roots and vegetables occupy over a quarter. Thus the overall statistics of the county indicate the existence of a system very similar to the old rotation, and it is interesting to consider how such continuity has been achieved.

In the first place it would be wrong to overlook the importance of tradition. The Norfolk four-course rotation worked. Not only did it persist for over a century but during that time it built up the fertility of the light lands and converted sheep walks into profitable arable land. Such a system would not lightly be abandoned.

Many developments have contributed to the continued diversity of Norfolk farming, but undoubtedly the most important was the development of the British beet-sugar industry. The first English factory was opened at Cantley in 1912, and began continuous operation in 1920, to be followed by other factories, at Wissington in 1925 and at King's Lynn in 1927. The sugar-beet acreage rose from 1,087 acres in 1920, to 15,515 in 1925, to 74,627 in 1930 and so to its present limit of 96,000 acres or almost a quarter of the English crop. Valuable pioneer work at the Norfolk Agricultural Station established both the husbandry of the crop and the value of the by-products for livestock feeding. Sugar-beet, in the depression years when the acreage was first built up, had the virtues of being a cash crop which enabled the labour to be profitably retained on the farms, of being a root crop which continued to fulfil the traditional role of the fallow crop in rotational husbandry and, while it replaced the fodder root acreage, yet of itself producing fodder in the form of crowns and pulp for livestock feeding. Without sugar-beet Norfolk farming must surely have been very different today.

The vining pea crop is to a lesser extent performing similar functions though, as we have seen, its influence is more limited in area. This is a leguminous break which provides cash, employment, and feeding by-products. Such crops are much sought after, and so in fact are any crops which offer a substitute to cereals. Thus the county grows over 4,000 acres of mustard for seed – not a vast acreage but another means of maintaining balance in the rotation. Similarly, contracts for herbage seeds, chicory and lucerne for drying are eagerly sought and even oil-seed poppies have been tried – failing only because suitable varieties for alkaloid extraction are not yet available. Without the urge to follow a sound rotation many of these crops would never have been tried. As it is, it is well known that if any crop can be grown the Norfolk farmer will be in the forefront of those who grow it. Thus a variety of crops is maintained and rotational farming has been preserved.

By courtesy of the Eastern Daily Press, *Norwich*

Fig. 4 *Quick-freeze Peas. A battery of viners in East Norfolk to which crops from neighbouring farms are carted for shelling*

In spite of all this there is today no 'Norfolk' rotation and on few farms is there any set rotation at all. On upland farms the rotation is based on the principles (i) that wherever possible a cereal should follow a root or 'black' crop; (ii) that if one cereal must follow another the second crop should not be winter wheat; and (iii) that no crop other than barley should occur more frequently than once in three, or preferably four, years. Within these limits many combinations are possible and serious difficulties can usually be avoided.

The figures in Table II show that on the upland soils the proportion of cereals varies between 50 and 60 per cent – between two crops in four and three crops in five – with wheat occupying less than a fifth and barley up to two-fifths of the acreage. For east Norfolk the rotation

might be idealized as a five-course – peas, wheat, sugar beet, barley, barley or oats – and many farmers do in fact follow some such rotation. Over the region as a whole the pea acreage is less than the necessary 20 per cent to make a full shift and leys, potatoes, and a part of the early lifted sugar-beet will precede the wheat crop. Similarly, the third shift, while predominantly of sugar-beet, will include the fodder roots and crops such as mustard. One of the few fixed rotations, this time followed on the lighter loams of north-west Norfolk, is a three-course – sugar-beet, winter wheat, barley. This involves December drilling of part of the wheat crop, but this rotation, in one farmer's hands, is eminently successful. On most of the lighter farms the rotation will, however, be varied to suit individual fields; the wheat and sugar-beet being kept on the better soils and their place taken by barley, carrots, and cabbages on the lighter land. Frequently similar crops whose acreage is insufficient to make a whole 'shift' follow one another at the appropriate place in succeeding rotations so that eight- or ten-year rotations eventuate with, for example, peas in the first year and ley in the fifth. At this stage changes in market conditions, labour supply, livestock policy or even in mechanization are liable to intervene so that in fact such extended rotations become opportunist – though not necessarily any the worse for that.

On silt soils a good rotation is peas, potatoes, wheat, sugar-beet, barley. Few people, however, have sufficient pea or sugar-beet acreage to follow this strictly and these shifts may be augmented with leys, beans, and crops of turnips, mustard, sugar-beet or mangolds taken for seed. On the mature peat the basic rotation is potatoes, sugar-beet, wheat, but circumstances make it necessary to lengthen this by bringing in peas, carrots, and seed crops. On light peat rotations range widely from ley, ley, mustard, spring wheat, spring wheat, roots on one large farm to onions, celery, sugar-beet, carrots, potatoes, chicory, sugar-beet – or some such arrangement of root and vegetable crops – on small holdings.

FARM SIZE

Apart from its effect on the crops which are grown and the rotation of those crops the type of soil exercises a very marked influence on the size of the farms, and on the size and shape of the fields. The effect on field size can most clearly be seen on the 6-inch Ordnance Survey maps but variations in farm size can to a large extent be demonstrated by statistics. In 1950 over 13,000 occupiers made an agricultural return but of those almost 40 per cent occupied less than 10 acres of land. The influence of the type of soil becomes apparent in the distribution of the larger holdings and interesting comparisons may be drawn for holdings above 200 acres – Table III. The soil type regions are as given in Table II except that both types of fen are now grouped together.

Soil productivity and hence land value limits the size of holding on the silt and mature fen though a number of larger holdings occur on the light fen. On the lighter upland soils the size of holding increases markedly as larger acreages become necessary to make a good living,

and in these areas the bulk of the land is in fact farmed in large units. In the county as a whole three-quarters of the holdings are smaller than 100 acres (though half of these are smaller than 15 acres and except on the best land would not be viable units), whereas three-quarters

TABLE III

Soil Type Region	Percentage of holdings larger than 200 acres	Percentage of land occupied in units larger than 200 acres
Marshland	3.4	35.6
Black Fen	5.5	53.3
South Norfolk	9.5	43.0
East Norfolk	10.1	54.1
Holt-Cromer Ridge	10.5	52.8
Mid-Norfolk	13.8	60.2
N.W. Norfolk	23.5	82.9
Breckland	24.7	83.3

of the land is held in units larger than 100 acres. Of 6,649 holdings larger than 15 acres only 359 are larger than 500 acres. Over 60 per cent of the land (a) in the silt area is in units smaller than 200 acres; (b) in the south Norfolk area is in medium-sized farms between 100 and 500 acres; and (c) on the sandy loam of north-west Norfolk is in large farms of over 500 acres.

WEEDS, PESTS, AND DISEASES

As a body Norfolk farmers have always been most ready to adopt the chemical aids of good husbandry which have appeared in such profusion since the end of the war, and it is a point for argument whether the plant breeders or the chemists who developed chemical weed-killers have done more to increase cereal yields in the county. Until the war the area of light land around Cromer was justly known as 'Poppy Land', while vast acres of the county were yellow with charlock (*Sinapis arvensis*) or white with the more serious wild radish (*Raphanus raphanistrum*). These colourful fields have now entirely disappeared and one would be hard put to find such a sight in a day's drive through the county.

Not only have crop yields improved as a result of the removal of weed competition but spring sowing can be somewhat earlier and seedbed working, and consequently moisture loss, can be reduced as the need to control weeds by harrowing is reduced.

In much the same way many pests, such as turnip flea-beetle (*Phyllotreta* spp.), wheat bulb fly (*Leptohylemyia coarctata*), aphids and wireworms (*Agriotes* spp.) can now be controlled chemically and it is rare for failures to occur from these causes. Diseases of arable crops have yet to be brought under the same measure of control. Knowledge of the control of potato blight (*Phytophthora infestans*) is improving but recent developments have mainly concerned the *technique* of fungicide applications: a systemic prophylactic has yet to make its appearance. During the last three years there has been a spectacular development in the control of virus yellows of sugar-beet via the control of the aphid vector (*Myzus persicae*) by chemicals, notably demeton methyl, so that during 1959 and 1960 this disease was virtually eliminated from the Norfolk sugar-beet crop with tremendous benefit to crop yield.[6] Little attempt has been made to control potato virus diseases in a similar way and the importation of virus-free seed from Scotland or Northern Ireland, supplemented by English H certificate seed grown in isolation in the county, is still of prime importance.

Where chemical control of a weed or pest is feasible the technique becomes routine practice on most Norfolk farms but there still remain many weeds, pests, and diseases for which there is as yet no satisfactory chemical control and for which cultural and rotational methods are still needed. It seems possible that wild oats (*Avena fatua*) may shortly pass out of this category as promising chemicals appear to be on the way. Eelworm pests of potatoes (*Heterodera rostochiensis*), sugar-beet (*H. schachtii*) and cereals (*H. major*) and the footrot diseases of cereals – Take-all (*Ophiobolus graminis*) and Eyespot (*Cercosporella herpotrichoides*) – still require sound rotations and crop hygiene for their control. Potato root eelworm can be very damaging on silts and peats, as can cereal root eelworm on light soils in time of drought. Sugar-beet root eelworm is kept under good control by official action under the Sugar Beet Eelworm Order 1952 which prescribes special areas in the Fen and elsewhere where cropping with beet and brassicae is regulated by licence and failures from this pest are now very rare.

MECHANIZATION

Between 1949 and 1959 the number of whole-time men between the ages 18–65 employed on Norfolk farms fell from 26,655 to 22,607, a reduction of 4,048 men (16.7 per cent). Almost all these men would be employed on the 6,103 holdings in the county larger than 20 acres which total 961,889 acres, so that we now have 2.35 men employed per 100 acres of crops and grass. During the years 1939–58 the number of horses used in agriculture fell from 26,689 to 4,529 – to such a very low figure that in 1959 farmers were not even required to make a return of their horses! During the same period the number of tractors rose to an estimated 17,000 so that from having had one horse per man in 1939 we now have one tractor to 1.33 men. In this way Norfolk farmers have participated in the great mechanical revolution which has been such a feature of British agriculture since 1939. In a corn-growing county it is not surprising that, after field cultivations, the greatest strides should have been in the harvesting of grain crops and the handling and storage of grain after harvest. We now have one combine harvester to approximately 180 acres of grain, and if these were distributed evenly over the cereal acreage they would be more than adequate to harvest every acre of corn which is grown. In fact not all corn is combined but the acreage which is cut by binder diminishes year by year, and where binder harvesting is retained it is for other reasons than the efficiency of the corn harvest – reasons such as the need of good straw to cover potato clamps.

With increasing quantities of corn harvested by combine, arrangements had to be made to dry the corn in a wet harvest and to store it until the market could absorb it. Corn driers have been installed in ancient barns which once heard the thump of flails, and surplus aerodrome hangars have been adapted by merchants and farmers alike. Until 1950 relatively little was done about bulk storage – sacks could be hired or corn could be stored loose in barns and buildings without capital outlay – but since that date many farmers have constructed silos into and out of which their corn can be delivered and emptied mechanically. Some corn, chiefly wheat for milling and some feeding barley, is now never sacked but is handled in bulk from the tanker combine to trailers, to the intake pit of the drier and thence by mechanical conveyors through the drier into the silos and eventually out again into a bulk-delivery lorry.

Drying and storage installations have been built up gradually and modified from time to time as new developments came along. In consequence, the final layout of many of them is open to criticism. On the other hand the work has been done and the expenses incurred over a period of years, whereas the equipping of a large grain-growing farm with all the necessary equipment for combining, drying, conveying, storage, and delivery at the present time might well cost more than the pre-war freehold value of the farm and in some cases has done so.

The mechanization of the corn harvest on most Norfolk farms is thus well on the way to completion. A very different situation obtains with the harvesting of the next most important crop – sugar-beet. Although Norfolk grows more sugar-beet than any other county, and has grown the crop for the longest period, mechanical beet harvesting is less developed in the Norfolk factory areas than anywhere else.

King's Lynn and Cantley growers who between them grow two-thirds of the Norfolk crop are the least mechanized body of sugar-beet growers in England and only half of the Wissington crop is harvested mechanically. The peat fens which fall within the Wissington area are stone-free and thus favourable to machinery while such crops as potatoes and celery also demand labour for harvesting in the autumn and create an incentive for the mechanization of the beet harvest. In contrast, in the bulk of the King's Lynn area and in much of the Cantley area soils are stony and depreciation on machinery is high. But of far greater importance is the availability of skilled hand labour in regular employment on the farms. The sugar-beet crop makes heavy demands on labour twice during the year: in May-June when the crop has to be thinned and from September to Christmas when it is harvested. Wholesale successful spring mechanization has not yet been achieved – here again a stony and variable soil is a handicap – and until this is done labour is necessary to carry out this part of the work. The sugar-beet crop is not at risk from the weather to the same extent as the corn harvest and there is a long period in

TABLE IV

PERCENTAGE OF CROP ACREAGE HARVESTED MECHANICALLY IN EACH FACTORY AREA (1959)

Factory	per cent
Norfolk Factories	
CANTLEY	37·2
KING'S LYNN	21·4
WISSINGTON	50·9
Other Factories	
Allscott	54·2
Bardney	77·5
Brigg	73·3
Bury St Edmunds	62·8
Colwick	70·0
Cupar	83·5
Ely	81·3
Felstead	69·4
Ipswich	40·6
Kelham	77·6
Kidderminster	42·1
Peterborough	85·5
Poppleton	59·1
Selby	71·7
Spalding	84·7
Southern Area*	56·0

* This is an administrative area, not a factory (source: *British Sugar Corporation*)

which to harvest the beet – twelve weeks at least – with the factories regulating their intake of beet from the farms over the whole period of the 'campaign' by a permit system. There is therefore as yet little to be gained on most upland farms by speeding up the beet harvest. The Norfolk farm-workers have developed such skill in handling the sugar-beet crop that they can work at great speed, and in consequence earn good wages on piece-work rates. These earnings help to lift the annual income

By courtesy of the Eastern Daily Press, *Norwich*

Fig. 5   *Sugar-beet. The bulk of the Norfolk beet crop is still 'topped' by hand*

of most Norfolk farm-workers well above the statutory minimum wage and hence help to retain the workers on the land. On a large farm one man may chop out and single and then 'score' (second hoe) 10 acres of beet in the spring and lift possibly 12 acres in the autumn. On an average crop he will have hoed in the season 55 miles of rows with a 7-inch hoe once in May and again in July, and will then lift about 300,000 roots by hand, and individually cut off their crowns with a short hook. It is clearly desirable that such repetitive labour should be accomplished mechanically if this can be achieved, but no one concerned wishes to see the farm-workers suffer in the process.

SOIL CULTIVATION

In this most fundamental aspect of his work – the handling and management of the soil in which the crops are to grow – the arable farmer has received least assistance from the scientists and technologists, and is most reliant on tradition and intuition. We are at the stage where we can now offer some explanation of facts which good farmers have known for generations but as yet can go no further. The only exception to this general position was introduced into Norfolk farming some six years ago to cope with a situation which was itself exceptional, and concerns the use of gypsum to prevent the breakdown of the structure of soil which had been flooded with salt water. This technique, in the particular situation, was of outstanding benefit to the farmers concerned. It is not possible to instance a similar newly introduced technique concerned with the handling of soil which has produced comparable results in a normal situation.

The basic implement of cultivation is still the mould-board plough – fundamentally the same in design as it has been for generations. Ploughing in Norfolk is generally of a high standard; the soil being well inverted and trash completely buried to give a clean seedbed for the following crop. In part this cleanliness of work is due to the depth to which the land is ploughed, which is deeper than in most other parts of the country; and is in turn a function of the mechanical power now available to draw the plough, and of the workable depth of soil over most of the county. To what extent the depth of ploughing is of importance has yet to be determined satisfactorily by experiment: to date the general result of experiments is that depth of ploughing, within quite wide limits, is of little consequence but this answer does not find favour with practical farmers whose views are worthy of respect.

Relatively recent developments of round-and-round ploughing and one-way ploughing have enabled open furrows to be dispensed with, and have consequently led to more level seedbeds which are an advantage for sugar-beet drilling and for combine harvesting. Experiments on the amount of cultivation needed to produce a satisfactory, crop of sugar-beet, or even of potatoes, have been of value in demonstrating that more work is not necessarily better work, and the object of most expert cultivators today is to plough in such a way that a satisfactory seedbed can be produced by the minimum of cultivations in the spring. This is particularly the case with sugar-beet where excessive working of the soil under drying March winds can cause the surface soil to dry out to such an extent that germination is delayed or impaired. The plough and winter weathering are accepted as better agents of cultivation than such vigorous implements as disc-harrows and rotary cultivators which, though extremely valuable in certain circumstances, are best kept for such circumstances and not used in conditions where a spiked harrow will do all that is necessary.

As a general summary: good drainage, good ploughing, the essential minimum of seedbed operations when the soil is in a fit condition, and early drilling is a recipe for success for almost all crops in Norfolk.

LIVESTOCK

On most Norfolk farms, though subsidiary to crop production, livestock nevertheless contributes substantially to the farm income and is closely integrated with the arable enterprises. The distribution pattern of the various classes of livestock can often be related to changes in soil, topography or farming system. Cattle are kept both for milk production and for beef, and the two enterprises are on most farms distinct and mutually exclusive. Milk production has largely replaced the traditional bullock fattening on the heavier soils in the south, south-east, and centre of the county where the soil is sufficiently moisture-retentive to produce a reasonable output of summer grass, and elsewhere in the county along the river valleys and coastal marshes where, again, summer grass can be produced. Only rarely are dairy herds encountered on the light uplands. Fattening bullocks in their various present-day forms retain their position in the areas which the dairy cows have not penetrated and also on marshes in the Broadland area.

Sheep numbers have declined dramatically from three-quarters of a million in 1870 to half a million at the turn of the century, and then to a mere 48,000 in 1950, from which low point they have now increased to 86,000. The full story of their decline is beyond the scope of this paper except to mention that in the years of depression between the two wars hurdled flocks became increasingly unprofitable, and that during the 1939–45 food-production campaign the need for crops for direct human consumption finally swept sheep from the arable land. Today large flocks, mainly of the grassland types, remain only on the lighter lands from Thetford to Fakenham

grazing on leys put down in the arable rotation. Pigs and poultry are widespread throughout the county, and are especially valuable on the smaller holdings and in the more intensively cultivated areas where, while making small demands on farm acreage, they provide a second storey to the farm business. Poultry now constitute the county's most important livestock enterprise.

DAIRY COWS

Production of milk for the liquid market is a relatively recent innovation in Norfolk agriculture, and output doubled between 1939 and 1957, when it achieved a peak production of over 41,000,000 gallons, since when it has declined slightly. During the last ten years the number of registered milk producers has fallen by one-third to its present level of 2,000: the smaller uneconomic herds have gone out of production with the introduction of more stringent regulations often entailing considerable capital outlay on improvements to buildings. During the same period the number of cows and heifers in milk or in calf fell by less than 2 per cent while production rose by over 6 per cent. Herds have in fact become larger, more efficient and more hygienic, and in October 1959 the whole county became an attested area.

Today the black and white British Friesians are the dominant breed. The tendency is increasingly for cows to be housed in yards and milked in milking parlours. In this way not only does the dairy cow continue to play the traditional role of neat stock in an arable county – an instrument for converting straw into farmyard manure – but very considerable labour economies in littering, feeding, and milking the cows become possible: factors which are of great consequence in the increasing efficiency of milk production.

To a considerable extent the cow's winter maintenance ration comes from the by-products of the arable crops. Sugar-beet tops, sugar-beet pulp and more recently pea-haulm silage have considerably reduced the cost of winter feeding, and thus make winter milk production an attractive proposition. The quantity of hay fed to cows in commercial herds is extremely small, and is normally kept for after Christmas when beet tops and kale are replaced by the lower-protein mangolds or beet pulp. At other times the herd relies on barley- and oat-straw for its long roughage. Silage making from grassland proved unattractive to Norfolk farmers until the development first of the buckrake, and more recently of forage harvesters, enabled the crop to be collected without the need of a large labour gang, and hence without seriously competing for labour at a time when spring work in the sugar beet crop was at a peak. Effective mechanization in fact achieved what years of exhortation failed to do.

Zero grazing – the technique of cutting all grass, even during the summer, and hauling it to the cows which are kept in a yard or stamping ground – has as yet found few converts in Norfolk, though it has several features which will tend to commend it to Norfolk farmers if the present pioneers find that it can be successfully operated under our conditions. The fact that under this system cattle do not go out on to the land would reduce the need for fencing and watering, and thus enable grass as a rotational crop to be brought on to fields from which, for lack of these facilities, it is at present excluded. As yet it is too early to know whether these and other advantages will outweigh the equally apparent disadvantages of the system.

The improvement in the yield of dairy cows to which reference has been made can in part be ascribed to the improved type of dairy cow which is kept today, and this in no small part is due to the availability of top-quality sires through artificial insemination. The majority of dairy herds in the county may obtain services from the A.I. centre at Beccles – just over the Suffolk border – or from its sub-centres at Wymondham and Aylsham, though in west Norfolk service is available from the Cambridge centre. The Beccles centre, which started as a co-operative venture of Suffolk and Norfolk farmers at the end of 1943, and was taken over by the Milk Marketing Board a year later, carried out almost 50,000 inseminations in 1958–9 of which about one-third were in Norfolk. During the short life of this centre the number of bulls being maintained for service on Norfolk farms fell by over 50 per cent to the present level of 1,175. Great as have been the advances in the techniques of crop husbandry in the same period, there can be no doubt that the commercial development of artificial insemination for cattle is the most revolutionary and profound application of science to agriculture which the present generation of farmers has witnessed.

BEEF CATTLE

The change which has occurred in the Norfolk fat cattle industry is illustrated by the following figures for store cattle sold in Norwich market.

TABLE V

	English	Fresh Irish	Total
1929	3,939	62,759	66,698
1939	9,834	23,947	33,781
1949	24,821	4,189	29,010
1959	21,889	1,370	23,259

(source: Clerk of the Markets, Norwich)

The figures for total store sales should not be taken as indicative of a decline in the cattle population of Norfolk; the June Returns show an increase in the total number of cattle on Norfolk farms from 139,127 in 1930 to 200,969 in 1959. What Table V does show is a swing from imported big Irish stores to 'homebreds'. This is again illustrated by the June Returns which show an increase of over 33,000 (125 per cent) between 1930 and 1959 in the number of calves under one year old. The vast droves of Irish cattle have gone: more farmers are rearing cattle but only some of these find their way to the markets as stores, the rest being fattened on the farms on which they were reared. This reversal of the tradition that the arable counties should fatten stores produced in the grassy west has been brought about by the narrowing margins on beef fattening, market requirements for the smaller beast, and the discovery that the steer calves from the Friesian dairy herds can grow into very acceptable butcher's beasts. Friesians do in fact account for a large proportion of the beef production. Shorthorns and Shorthorn-Hereford crosses are very popular, while the pure beef breeds – Herefords, Aberdeen Angus, Galloways and Lincoln Reds – account for a relatively small proportion of the trade. The two principal fatstock markets are Norwich and King's Lynn from each of which some 20,000 beasts were sold in 1959. The Fatstock Marketing Corporation purchased a further 8,200, while considerable numbers are sold at other local markets. To a greater extent even than dairy cattle, fattening bullocks are expected to make use of arable by-products: the days when they received a stone of linseed cake a day having long since passed. The extreme stringency of the wartime period has, however, been relaxed as the demand for younger, leaner beef has required better calf rearing and the virtual elimination of the store period to produce a beast of 9 to 11 cwt. at eighteen to twenty-four months of age. Big bullocks weighing 13 cwt. are rare and are generally not required, though well-finished beasts which are not over-fat can still command top prices from the local butchers. A few cattle are fattened off the grass throughout the summer and 100 to 200 cattle will be on offer at both Norwich and King's Lynn markets each week. From the end of January sales increase sharply as the forward beasts are drawn out of the fattening yards, and numbers continue to rise until in each market from 800 to 1,000 cattle a week are coming forward during April and into the beginning of May. Two-thirds of the fat cattle sales take place during the four months February to May when prices are highest and English beef supplies from the grassland counties have dried up.

PIGS

Pigs are the principal type of livestock on many Norfolk farms. At a time when the barley trade is – to say the least – slow, they provide an alternative outlet for a considerable proportion of the crop while they also make profitable use of surplus potatoes on farms where these are grown. Otherwise, apart from their own direct contribution to the farm income – which is, of course, the reason why they are kept – they are valued as makers of farmyard manure, especially on intensive market garden holdings where limited acreage excludes cattle.

The cost of feeding-stuffs account for over 80 per cent of the cost of a bacon pig, and there is a tendency for large pig farmers to install their own milling or mixing plants in order to keep feed costs as low as possible. Such economies are not open to the smaller pig producer, and in fact the majority of pigs are fed on proprietary mixtures compounded either by the port millers or by local merchants in the county.

Pig numbers are liable to fluctuate from year to year, but since 1954 the total pig population in June has been between 191,000 and 215,000 with breeding sows ranging from 26,000 to 29,000. Deliveries of fat pigs to the markets are relatively steady throughout the year, and between 750 and 1,000 pigs are likely to be on offer in both Norwich and King's Lynn markets in any week of the year with the exception of the week before Christmas when the number in each market soars to about 1,500. During a year each market will put through about 44,000 pigs, most of which go to the pork trade. In addition farmers contract direct with the bacon factories at Elmswell and Ipswich in Suffolk, or with other factories through the F.M.C. who purchased 32,678 bacon pigs in Norfolk in 1959–60, while an as yet limited number of heavy pigs (220–340 lb. liveweight) are sold on contract to processing companies who produce bacon, hams, sausages, and pies from the various parts of the pig according to the housewife's requirements. As in certain other counties a movement is now afoot to popularize Norfolk bacon with the county's housewives in an attempt to obtain a larger share of the retail trade.

Pigs on Norfolk farms are housed in every type of building and even without permanent buildings at all. The pork and the heavy pig markets are attractive to many farmers as they do not demand such a closely graded product as the bacon factories and therefore housing standards can be correspondingly less precise. Many pigs are in fact kept in large bunches in yards, and are only brought into fattening pens for the final weeks of fattening. The chief breeds are Large White, Essex, and Landrace while Large White × Essex and Landrace × Large White crosses are very popular.

POULTRY*

Norfolk has the second largest poultry population in the United Kingdom and is the only county where the three species – chickens, ducks and turkeys – are found in large numbers. Since the end of the war poultry numbers have increased from 1,423,021 to 4,783,078 in 1959. Modern breeding techniques, intensive methods of management, and revised feeding standards have all played a part in this expansion.

Prior to 1939 laying hens were mainly kept on free range on general farms. Today the position is quite different. Specialist intensive farms are now producing

* This section has been contributed by Mrs J.M. Cullington, County Poultry Adviser.

a very large proportion of the eggs and the stock is kept mainly in batteries or deep litter units. Improved knowledge of ventilation, insulation, nutrition, and disease control has enabled us to maintain such artificial conditions, and we are now able to do successfully what was inconceivable some years ago. To find 7,000 birds on one site is common enough and the tendency is still to increase flock size. This has resulted in the use of mechanical devices whenever possible, and where one man could previously look after a thousand head of stock he can now attend to three times that number without difficulty. The hybrid with its usually superior performance has become popular on commercial egg units, and Norfolk farmers have been quick to realize its value. Owing to the expense involved it has been developed in the main by large breeding and hatchery organizations, and this has resulted in the elimination of some of the smaller breeding flocks which in many ways is regrettable.

Changes have also taken place in table poultry, and the rapid growth of the broiler industry since the war is one of the outstanding features of the county's agricultural development. A specially bred bird is required, and during the last six years extensive breeding programmes have been put into operation to cater for this trade – again largely by the big hatcheries. The 'group system', the basis on which producers operate, is worthy of note. It began with the growers setting up their own packing station and supplying the birds for processing at pre-arranged times to ensure continuity of throughput. It has now become even more organized as in some cases chicks, food, and litter are bought in bulk, which has tended to encourage the larger producer, and today it is not unusual for 10,000 to run together in one flock and 100,000 to be found on one site.

These small fryer chickens, as the Americans call them, are reared in insulated, mechanically ventilated houses and submitted to certain controlled hours of light and darkness. Diets are designed to produce rapid growth and contain drugs to combat disease, tranquillizers to calm the birds and antibiotics for growth stimulation. Much research has gone into the broiler industry, and it has now resulted in the lowering of food consumption with larger weight gains. To produce a bird with a conversion rate of 2.5 weighing $3\frac{1}{2}$ lb. in seventy days is becoming a common occurrence.

Norfolk's contribution to the trade is substantial and approximately eight million will be produced in 1960.

Norfolk is, of course, renowned for its turkeys. The days when they roamed the hay fields and stubbles and slept under the stars are passed, the easier intensive methods are now more or less universally adopted due largely to the introduction of drugs to combat disease. This has not been the only major change, as the birds we know now are quite unlike their ancestors, their shape having appreciably altered during the last ten to fifteen years. The present-day turkey is no longer high-breasted and long legged, but broad or dimple breasted carrying a high percentage of meat to bone. This change in body conformation has not escaped the vicissitudes that are to be expected if Nature is tampered with inordinately; indeed, in some cases the birds are incapable of mating and fertility is consequently impaired. Some of Norfolk's most enterprising farmers have adopted artificial insemination and, although not pioneers, have done much to improve the technique. It is probable that much of the future breeding will be undertaken by this means.

This in itself has tended to alter the pattern of the industry, and big organizations are being set up to supply poults to the fatteners, whilst the finished birds are bought back for processing and marketing. The larger farms in Norfolk have quite extensive freezing and storage plants, and in some cases the whole process is done on the farm – a position that rarely applies in other branches of farming and says much for the enterprise and foresight of the Norfolk turkey producer.

The sixteen-week-old 'broiler' turkey is a recent innovation, and one of our larger producers is gearing his entire efforts in this direction. This trade is in the early stages of development and we have without doubt much to learn about it. The birds are being accommodated in large intensive houses on similar lines to broiler chickens, and the implantation of oestrogens together with the use of high energy and well fortified rations contribute to the production of a well finished carcass.

The eminently suitable sandy soil of Breckland has undoubtedly been one of the reasons for the establishment of the large duck farms of that area. The majority of ducks are produced by a few men in a big way, and although this county has been associated with duck production for over half a century no serious competition has occurred from elsewhere in this specialized field. Approximately one million are sold each year which represents 75 per cent of the national output.

In the past the day-old ducklings were brought in from outside, but during the last few years greater interest has been taken in breeding, and large farms have developed to supply the fatteners with ducklings. After the brooding stage they are put on to the fields where they remain until they are killed between eight and nine weeks. Waxing to remove the down feathers is a comparatively recent practice and gives a better finish, whilst wrapping and boxing to improve presentation is now the general rule. A more detailed knowledge of

By courtesy of the Eastern Daily Press, *Norwich*

Fig. 6   *Poultry. Duckling production on a Breckland farm*

nutrition has helped to produce a better duckling in a shorter time and Virus Hepatitis, a disease that can have a catastrophic effect, is now controlled by the use of a vaccine. The duck trade, unlike that of broilers and turkeys, is confined largely to hotels and restaurants and a duck is rarely offered for sale directly to the public. With the introduction of super-markets to this country, oven-ready ducks will no doubt compete with oven-ready turkeys.

AN ESTIMATE OF THE TOTAL VALUE OF THE PRINCIPAL PRODUCTS

Now that the main enterprises which make up Norfolk agriculture have been surveyed, it is desirable to bring them together so that their financial importance may be compared. Annual economic surveys, *Reports on Farming*, which include data for a sample of farms in central Norfolk, are available from the Farm Economics Branch of Cambridge University.[7] These reports, which show how the farmers conducted their businesses from year to year, are both factual and valuable, but an alternative method of analysis is used for present purposes.

The figures in Table VI have been obtained by estimating the volume of production for a particular crop and then attaching a potential gross sale value to it. In most cases these estimates are only approximations – 'guestimates' is the coined word – because the detailed statistics required for accurate assessments are not available. The figure for barley, for instance, assumes that the whole crop is sold, whereas a considerable proportion is retained for feeding to pigs and is ultimately sold as pig-meat. It follows that these figures will tend to over-estimate the gross income of the farms, to which the Cambridge Reports are a more reliable guide. The intention here is merely to compare the estimated values of the various products on a county-wide basis.

These figures contrast markedly with those for the United Kingdom as a whole in the relative importance of crops and livestock. For the United Kingdom livestock sales account for over two-thirds of the gross output[8] whereas in Norfolk crops are of greater value than livestock – and our figures do not include the truly horticultural crops and some minor agricultural ones. On the other hand it is equally clear that the farmers of Norfolk are not solely concerned with crop production, for livestock and livestock products account for at least two-fifths of their total output.

The most important products are barley, sugar-beet, poultry, and milk in that order; followed by beef, wheat, pig-meat, and potatoes. The importance of a good barley crop to Norfolk is very clear. This report is being written following the 1960 harvest when yields are estimated to be about 25 per cent below those of 1959 as a result of the dry spring, and the potential value of the 1960 crop will probably be £2–3,000,000 below that of

TABLE VI

AN ESTIMATE OF THE GROSS VALUE OF THE MAIN AGRICULTURAL PRODUCTS OF NORFOLK 1959

Crops		
Wheat	5,105,000	
Barley	9,205,000	
Rye	63,000	
Sugar Beet	8,980,000	
Potatoes	3,540,000	
Carrots and Peas	2,180,000	
Total Crops		**£29,073,000**
Livestock		
Milk	6,197,000	
Beef	5,457,000	
Pig Meat	4,200,000	
Eggs and Poultry	7,145,000	
Lamb, Mutton, and Wool	400,000	
Total Livestock		23,399,000
	Total	**£52,472,000**

1959. Such a drop, averaging £2–3 per acre over the total agricultural acreage of the county, will inevitably cause a very serious reduction in farm income on most farms.

Dr Hull has estimated[6] that the control of aphids and virus yellows in the 1959 sugar-beet crop raised national yields from 4,500,000 to 5,500,000 tons of roots. This is not thought to be in any sense an over-estimate for the county of Norfolk, and we may therefore conclude that this new technique added over £2,500,000 to the value of the 1959 crop. The 1960 sugar-beet crop shows signs of being as good as that of 1959 – better in the Cantley area – and certainly many farmers are looking to this crop to offset in part the reductions which they foresee, not only from barley, but also from wheat, potatoes, and carrots. In spite of this, income from crop sales in 1960 will be much below the level of 1959.

The size of the modern poultry industry comes out quite clearly from the figures, and it is probable that in 1960 poultry will be second only to sugar-beet in gross value. Milk, eggs and, on the larger farms, pigs, have the great value of being products which bring in an income throughout the year, and thus help to tide the farm over the period before the cereal harvest when farm exchequers are always running low. Beef, on the other hand, has quite a tendency to be an annual 'crop' with the bulk of sales in the spring. Although it is not intended that our figures should be used as a basis from which to start calculations on farm income or profitability one point should be made to avoid leaving an entirely erroneous impression of the importance of beef in the Norfolk economy. For every £100 of revenue from milk over £50 will be available as 'gross margin' from which the farmer must pay his labour and overheads and find his profit. For bacon pigs the corresponding figure will be about £20 but for yard-fattened beef it is likely to be less than £6 per £100 of revenue. The labour and overhead costs of these products are very different, but it will be clear that beef fattened in the traditional manner has little chance of showing a profit comparable to that from milk or bacon and that the yard-fattening of bullocks should be regarded as a means of making farmyard manure to keep up the fertility of the arable land rather than as a profit-making venture *per se*.

THE EXPERIMENTAL FARMS

The Norfolk Agricultural Station has made a tremendous impact on farming theory and practice in the county, and has also achieved an international reputation.

Towards the end of the last century, the farmers and landowners of Norfolk took a keen and characteristic interest in the growing applications of science to their industry and, by 1885, the Norfolk Chamber of Agriculture was already organizing experimental work on various farms in the county. In 1908, it was decided to concentrate all this work on a single farm, and a public subscription raised £1,000 for the purpose. The Jex Farm at Little Snoring was made available – rent-free for five years – by the late Lord Hastings, and the work continued there until 1919, when it was moved to St Faiths. It was finally transferred to the Church Farm at Sprowston and, in 1924, Mr F. Rayns was appointed Director during a very difficult phase of Norfolk

Agricultural history. The excellence of the Station's work – particularly on the comparatively new crop, sugar-beet, is nationally recognized.

The Station has financed its work largely by its own farming activities, and by a contributory membership scheme – though grants have been received from the Ministry, the Royal Agricultural Society of England, the National Institute of Agricultural Botany, the Sugar Beet and Research Education Committee and others. The Station's work is controlled by an executive committee elected by its members and it enjoys a unique independence. Moreover, although the problems of Norfolk and East Anglian farming are its chief concern, it has always collaborated in research of far wider significance.

The Ministry's Experimental Husbandry Farm at Terrington is concerned with problems peculiar to crops grown on silt and fen soils, while the one at Boxworth in Cambridgeshire has obtained results of value to the farmers of the heavier Norfolk soils. It is hoped that another experimental farm will be established on the black fen, and the county's farmers should then have all the information needed to keep them in the forefront of progress.

SOME OTHER FACTORS OF IMPORTANCE

More might well have been said, had space permitted, about the Norfolk farm-workers, and the various ways in which they have adapted themselves to the post-war mechanical and chemical revolutions, helped by the Farm Machinery Clubs and Stockmen's Clubs which both originated in the county. Educational facilities and information services, which are both of special importance at a time of rapid technical advance, deserve fuller discussion. Formal education for young farmers is available at the Norfolk School of Agriculture, and at the day courses run by the Education Authority, while less formal instruction is provided by the Young Farmers Clubs. For the farmers, visits to experimental farms and winter programmes of conferences, lectures, and demonstrations are arranged, and the Press, radio, and television produce special features. Most farmers receive visits from advisers and a considerable volume of advisory leaflets from commercial concerns also help to disseminate information on new developments.

It has not been possible here to discuss the role of the landowner – many of Norfolk's largest farmers are tenants – nor have land values and rents been reviewed.

Works of land reclamation might well have been more fully described. Feltwell and Methwold Fens, which had been derelict, were reclaimed during the war, and the grazing-marshes round Dersingham were converted to arable land. Since 1948, 1,800 acres of fertile soil have been added to the county by the enclosure of saltings south and east of the Wash and, since 1954, new techniques have made it possible to grow wheat as little as three years after enclosure.

For the Flood Protection Scheme of the Great Ouse River Board, a 300 feet-wide relief channel has already been dug to the east of the tidal river from King's Lynn to Denver, and a cut-off channel is to be excavated from this point to Mildenhall to intercept the water from the Lark, Little Ouse, and Wissey. This water will then be led around the eastern edge of the peat fens in order to reduce flooding.

The author hopes that this mere mention of these important topics may draw them to the reader's attention and that papers and visits during the course of the Meeting will add flesh to this scant skeleton.

REFERENCES

1. L. DUDLEY STAMP. *The Land of Britain*. Report of the Land Utilization Survey. Pt. 70, 'Norfolk.'

2. *Survey of Fertilizer Practice* (1952), (Pt. 1). By the Advisory Chemists of the N.A.A.S. and the staff of Rothamsted Experimental Station.

3. RAYNS, F. and CULPIN, S. (1948). 'Rotation Experiments on Straw Disposal at the Norfolk Agricultural Station.' *J.R.A.S.E.*, **109**, 128–39.

4. HARVEY, P.N. (1959). 'The Disposal of Cereal Straw.' *J.R.A.S.E.*, **120**, 54–63.

5. 'Balance in British Farming' (1959). Address of the President of Section M. *Journal of The Advancement of Science*, XVI, No. 62.

6. HULL, R. (1960). 'The New Factor in Sugar Beet Growing.' *British Sugar Beet Review*, **28**, No. 3, 113–14.

7. *Report on Farming 1958–59*. Farm Economics Branch Report No. 50. Cambridge University.

8. *Annual Review and Determination of Guarantees 1960*. Cmnd. 970. March 1960. H.M.S.O.

horticulture R. W. KEMP

OF THE 800,000 acres of arable land cultivated in this predominantly agricultural county, some 70,000 acres, or nearly 9 per cent are used for horticultural purposes. Every crop for which there is a market demand, and which can be cultivated profitably under the climatic and other conditions of this part of England is represented.

The pattern of production has become extensive rather than intensive in that, wherever possible, the tendency is to grow crops in large units on a field scale for processing. This state of affairs was already well under way when described by P.E. Cross,[1] with many references to Norfolk, in 1943. It has enabled farmers to achieve at last two important objects, namely the introduction of one or more valuable cash crops and the opportunity to break an otherwise close rotation of corn crops.

More intensive methods of cultivation are still practised by a great number of growers but they and their acreages are outnumbered and exceeded by those operating on the larger scale.

Norfolk has produced many great horticulturists and has a fine tradition, but the high place it occupies nationally in this industry today is vastly different from that which would have been envisaged by some of the commercially minded pioneers of the nineteenth and early twentieth centuries.[2]

Tables I and II show what a high percentage of the national acreage of horticultural crops is grown in Norfolk. It will be seen that no less than one-fifth of all the soft fruits are grown in the county and, in the case of certain vegetables of which carrots, celery, and vining peas (for canning or quick freezing) are examples, the acreages are in the order of one-third of those for the whole country.

TABLE I
FRUIT ACREAGES

	Norfolk	England and Wales
Strawberries	3,942	16,712
Raspberries	262	2,452
Black Currants	2,392	12,347
Red and White Currants	106	747
Gooseberries	864	5,429
Cultivated Blackberries	102	1,203
Total Soft Fruit	**7,668**	**38,890**
Orchards	8,850	243,330

Table based on 4 June 1958 Agricultural Returns

In terms of cash value, W.L. Hinton,[3] Farm Economics Branch, Cambridge University, has estimated the total farm gate value of horticultural produce grown in England and Wales during 1958 to be £117,000,000. Unpublished work by the same author, used with his kind permission, shows Norfolk's share of this to be nearly £10,000,000, of which 48 per cent was from vegetables, 33 per cent from fruit, 10 per cent from glasshouse crops, and the remaining 9 per cent from flowers, etc.

CROPPING IN RELATION TO SOIL TYPE
Visitors to Norfolk are constantly expressing their surprise at its varied topography. So many arrive with the preconceived notion that they are coming to a uniformly flat coastal plain.

R.W. KEMP is Norfolk County Horticultural Advisory Officer

TABLE II
ACREAGES, PRINCIPAL VEGETABLES, BULBS, GLASSHOUSE CROPS

	Norfolk	England and Wales
Brussels sprouts	2,213	47,439
Winter Cabbage—Savoys	5,093	48,122
Carrots	10,973	32,936
Parsnips	815	4,104
Onions, for harvesting dry	407	4,552
Beans, Broad	1,272	11,280
Beans, Runner and French	1,412	13,250
Peas, for canning and quick freezing	15,466	55,452
Peas, for harvesting dry	8,993	72,458
Asparagus	269	1,377
Celery	1,532	5,472
Bulbs and Bulb Flowers	833	10,320
Crops under glass	143	4,392
Total vegetables and crops under glass	**53,199**	**440,301**

Table based on 4 June 1958 Agricultural Returns

Equally surprising to some is its wide diversity of soil types which range from blowing sands to heavy clays and silts or black fen peats. For the grower on mineral soils of drift or alluvial origin, there is often the complication of soil variation, not only from farm to farm or field to field, but even within the boundaries of an individual field.

Although the distribution of crops has to some extent followed a pattern set by tradition, evolved in some cases no doubt from the special interests of one pioneering individual, it is more closely associated with soil type or other topographical feature.

Modern techniques and aids such as irrigation have broken through some of the tradition and extended the areas in which certain crops are grown. This is particularly the case with crops grown for, and under the direction of, processing firms. For their purpose it is essential to have a planned programme of cropping which will ensure a steady flow of produce over a long period to keep production lines working. This is largely achieved by appropriate arrangement of sowing dates to provide a succession, but also by spreading the crops geographically over early and late areas.

Against the general background just described it will be of interest next to consider the principal crops grown in Norfolk in relation to the soil areas depicted on the survey map.

The Silt and Peat Fens. For fertility and high-cropping capacity there are few areas in the country which can equal (and probably none which can surpass) either the peat or silt fen soils. Because of this and their correspondingly high purchase or rental value every available square inch is usually well and intensively cropped.

On the silt fens we find the extensive fruit growing area known to horticulturists throughout the country as 'the Wisbech district'. This area, some two-thirds of which lies in Norfolk, is characterized by its Bramley orchards intermixed with gooseberry plantations and strawberry fields.

The Bramley trees are very large and low-spreading. A habit of growth dictated in the past to match the capacity of spraying machines then available. Today, with machines of greater capacity in use but with labour more difficult and costly, it is still deemed an advantage to keep the trees as flat-topped as possible, if only to reduce expensive ladder work at picking time.

Plums and pears are also grown quite extensively, though acreages of the former have tended to fall in recent years on account of the reduced demand for plum jam or the canned fruit. At one time the biggest proportion of the gooseberries grown in Norfolk were to be found as an under-crop in these orchards, but the tendency now is to plant these as a crop on their own in open land. Nearly 100 per cent are of the variety 'Careless' and they are grown almost exclusively for picking green and sale to processors.

The deep, moisture retaining, silt soils are ideal for strawberry growing and nearly two-thirds of the county acreage is grown in this area. The recorded acreage would in fact be increased quite substantially if account were also taken of those grown in the large gardens, sometimes up to $\frac{1}{4}$ acre, attached to Council and other houses, or on allotments.

For many years there was, in effect, only one variety grown, namely 'Huxley's Giant' (syn. Brenda Gautrey). This is a heavy yielding sort especially liked because it keeps its flowers well hidden amongst the foliage and therefore less exposed to spring frosts – a great advantage in so open an area as the fens. However, it has some drawbacks, notably a large centre plug in the fruits which processors find difficult to remove. Other high-yielding varieties, e.g. 'Cambridge Favourite', are now tending to replace 'Huxley'.

Amongst other special features of this area are many large glasshouse holdings, especially those concentrated in the parish of Terrington St Clement. These produce a wide range of crops such as tomatoes, cucumbers, and chrysanthemums, including some all-the-year-round production of flowers, to be described later, and forced bulbs.

On the most modern of these holdings recent additions to the glass area have mostly been in the form of mobile structures as opposed to permanently fixed houses. The 'mobiles' are mounted on rails, in such a way as to be movable in a lengthwise direction where two or more alternative sites can be covered in turn. Thus coverage can be removed quickly from a crop which is finished or no longer requires protection and transferred to another site where another crop may be already established, or preparations for one are under way.

Besides greatly increasing the potential annual output of crops from a given area of structure, this system gives greater opportunities for crop rotation and reduces risk of serious build-up of pests and diseases.

Bulb growing is, in itself, an important industry, resembling that of neighbouring Lincolnshire, though on a smaller scale. Production takes two forms, namely, cutting and selling flowers and the harvesting of dry bulbs for sale, the latter being the major interest and usually the most profitable. In addition to bulbs, some growers have recently taken up the production of gladiolus corms for sale and, by careful attention to storage conditions, are producing corms which compare very favourably with imported ones.

The last, but by no means the least important, feature of horticultural production on the silt fens, is the very considerable acreage devoted to vegetables. In this connection the specialities are peas and beans for processing, and spring cabbage and early, frame or glasshouse raised, cauliflowers for the open market.

While orchards and strawberries dominate the scene on the silt fens, they are of little significance on the adjoining peat or black fens, where vegetable crops on the other hand are very extensively grown. Of these, special mention must be made of at least celery, carrots, and onions.

Reference to the entry for celery in Table II will show there were 1,532 acres in Norfolk or nearly one-third of all the celery grown in England and Wales. Relationship of crop with soil type is clearly illustrated in this case, for all but the odd 32 acres were located on these black fen soils in south-west Norfolk. In common with the celery grown under identical conditions in the adjoining counties of the Isle of Ely, Cambridgeshire, and Huntingdonshire, most of the growers have their plants raised for them under contract by other specialist growers, of whom there are a number in the Whittlesey area near Peterborough.

The scale of their task will be appreciated when it is revealed that, on average, it requires some 20,000 to plant one acre. Thus the south-west Norfolk area alone will require over 30,000,000 plants each year, and K.M. Round[4] has estimated that contracts with the Whittlesey nurseries have amounted to no less than 80,000,000 plants per year.

The acreage of carrots grown on these fens is greater than that of celery, but this crop is also extensively grown on the mineral soils of 'high' Norfolk. Carrots are grown both for canners and for supplying the fresh vegetable market. The crop is mechanized from drilling stage to harvesting by mechanical diggers and baggers. Lifting is followed by grading, and those for market consignments also go through washing machines before despatch.

Of onions, roughly two-thirds of the Norfolk crop are grown in the fens. As with other crops grown on these fertile soils, yields are usually high. One difficulty is that, because of their deep rooting habit in these conditions, they tend to keep growing until quite late in the season and in a wet year are slow to ripen off. Provided this is allowed for and lifting is commenced early enough, bulbs of very good quality can be produced.

In recent years an organized attempt has been made by local growers to obtain contracts with manufacturers

Mechanised bean picking with 2-row harvester

Birds Eye Food Ltd

for pickling onions. This trade requires onions of extremely uniform shape and size, which they have normally imported almost entirely from the Continent. It has been established that a satisfactory article can be grown locally, but the future depends upon enough growers being forthcoming to guarantee supplies in adequate quantity.

Weed control is a serious problem in growing horticultural crops, especially onions, under fen conditions, but increasing use is now being made of residual and other weed-killers of recent introduction.

Another hazard is that caused by the wind, especially in the spring or at any other time when the peats are dry and bare of crops or other herbage. It is no unusual thing for inches of topsoil to disappear during a sustained blow and seeds or fertilizers may often go as well. Wire netting/hessian shelters, or even rows of bushel boxes are sometimes set up across fields in an attempt to reduce the risk of this happening.

Although fruit growing in itself is not practised on the black fens, some contribution to the fruit-growing industry as a whole is made from at least one holding in the area. Considerable numbers of black currant bushes,

strawberry runners, raspberry, and loganberry canes are raised. These are grown, where applicable, under the Special Stock Scheme operated by the Ministry of Agriculture, Fisheries and Food from virus tested material supplied as 'Foundation' or 'Elite' stock by the Nuclear Stock Association. The site has the enormous advantage of complete isolation from any other fruit, so the risk of the stocks picking up any pest or disease during propagation is virtually eliminated.

The Loam Region and Broadland. Although designated as the 'loam region' on the survey map, the area next to be described has a considerable area of soil difficult to distinguish from the silts. These areas, and some closely associated fine sandy loams, are as inherently fertile as the silt fens and although having a less well controlled water table they usually withstand drought equally well.

To add to the similarity, a bulb-growing industry is in process of development, and bulbs equal in quality to those grown in west Norfolk or Lincolnshire are being produced on a number of farms. New areas such as this have a high chance of success, if only because they start off with virgin land so far as bulbs are concerned, and with reduced risk of pests or diseases as compared with the older and more congested areas. The flowers produced are of secondary importance (those of tulips grown for bulb production are not usually cut any way) yet a number of the growers have already combined to develop a scheme for marketing their daffodil flower crop on a co-operative basis.

However, the east Norfolk area is best known horticulturally for its black currant industry. In total Norfolk produces roughly one-fifth of this country's black currants and, as the bulk of the strawberry acreage was shown to be concentrated on the silt fens, so are the black currants in this part of the county. They thrive in the rich moist soils of the Broadland area, and can in fact be grown profitably on most of the east Norfolk soils, especially if given frost-free sites with good protection from cold east and north-east winds.

The black currant is an indigenous plant, and bushes can be found growing freely in thickets and reedy marshes associated with some of the Broads. E.A. Ellis, the Norfolk naturalist, has taken the trouble to measure some of these and has found specimens as much as

30 feet across. Fortunately they do not grow to this stature under cultivated conditions!

Formerly the biggest proportion of the currants went to the fresh fruit market in chip baskets, but the bulk now goes to preservers or to manufacturers of black currant cordials. There is a great deal of organized marketing associated with the crop both through fruit merchants and the local Fruit Grower Associations. As described elsewhere[2] there has been co-operative marketing of this and other soft fruit crops from the area since at least 1911.

Although co-operative marketing is now a well-established feature in east Norfolk fruit growing, the industry is much less specialized than it is in the Wisbech district, and there is not the close-knit fraternity of growers as exists in that area. In the aggregate there is a very considerable acreage of orchards, and all types of soft fruit, but it is mostly grown as an extra enterprise on a general farm or in association with other horticultural crops, on the numerous smallholdings and market gardens.

Numerous glasshouse and flower-growing holdings exist in this area with cropping programmes similar to those described for west Norfolk. The total acreage of glass in the county is almost equally divided between east and west, but the holdings here are more dispersed, and no big concentrations exist equivalent to that in the parish of Terrington.

When the first quick-freeze factories were established in east Norfolk at the end of the Second World War and the existing canning factories started their post-war expansion, new impetus was given to large-scale vegetable growing.

Vining peas were the first crop to be worked up and the acreage was still increasing up to 1960. The fact that there is such a concentration of factories in the Great Yarmouth, Lowestoft, North Walsham, and Westwick areas for handling peas, and the many other crops grown for canning and freezing, is indication enough of how greatly their cultivation has been taken up in this highly suitable area. Prominent amongst the other crops grown are runner, French and broad beans, brussels sprouts, sprouting broccoli and sweet corn.

Mechanical handling is practised wherever possible. The peas for instance are shelled by vining machines which may be mobile or static. The latter being either outstationed at some point serving a group of farms, or the peas may be hauled, on the vine, to vining stations at or near the factories. Within a few years it is possible that the acreage of runner beans will decrease in favour of the dwarf or French beans, some of which are already being harvested mechanically thus cutting out the heavy cost of hand-picking. For one other example, the case of brussels sprouts might be quoted where, instead of periodic pickings being made in the field, a growing practice now is to wait until the bulk of the sprouts are of suitable size, and then cut the stalk through at ground level and cart the whole plant into the factory where the sprouts are stripped off.

Good Sands, Mid-Norfolk and Greensand Area. These areas are notable for really large-scale vegetable growing on the 'mass production for market' scale. Large blocks of land are cropped in the farm rotation with such crops as brussels sprouts, cabbages, carrots and parsnips. Many are grown and marketed in association with local grower-merchants, though there is some contracting for carrots and for peas which are also grown quite extensively.

When trade for cabbage is poor whole fields will sometimes be ploughed in or fed off to livestock. In either case some contribution is made to soil fertility so the crop is not necessarily a total loss to the grower.

Not much soft fruit is grown and advantage has again been taken of this isolation to establish a number of sites for the propagation of virus-free strawberry runners. These are obtained as 'Foundation' or 'Elite' stocks from the Nuclear Stock Association and certified after inspection under the Ministry of Agriculture Scheme.

Orchards are widely dispersed and not very numerous. Most of those which do exist are of post-war planting, and consist mainly of 'Cox's Orange Pippin' and other up-to-date market dessert apples. Included amongst the fruit grown in this area is a unit of dessert apples and black currants on the Royal Estate at Sandringham. This is complete with a modern packing shed and cold stores for holding the produce.

No account of the horticulture of this region would be complete without reference to the lavender-growing industry carried on by a specialist firm in the extreme north-east of the county around Hunstanton and Ringstead. The fields in flower make a striking splash of colour. They can be seen for miles and are a constant source of interest to summer visitors.

The lavender oil is extracted in the firm's own stills and used in the manufacture of perfumes, etc. Peppermint is also grown and distilled by this firm though on a small scale compared with the lavender.

Breckland. Even Breckland makes its contribution to Norfolk horticulture despite its very light soils, for many of them are eminently suitable for growing carrots or parsnips. In fact quite large acreages of other vegetables, including peas for canning, are also grown. It is an area where peas usually mature fairly quickly, and at least one canning firm locates part of its acreage there to reap the benefit of this earliness and spread the supply of produce to its production lines.

Two other crops grown very successfully in Breckland are asparagus and black currants. The latter require adequate supplies of organic matter to improve the moisture retaining capacity of the soil. Given generous manurial treatment and the right choice of variety, yields compare surprisingly well with those on better soils.

Asparagus growing was started some thirty years ago on the initiative of the late Lord Fisher of Kilverstone. The inspiration which led him to see and develop its possibilities was alone responsible for putting Norfolk asparagus 'on the map'! Previously its cultivation in this county and elsewhere was on the raised, multi-row, bed system. Lord Fisher's researches into other methods of cultivation led him to introduce a wide, single row system of planting based on American practice. By this means the cultivation of the crop could be mechanized to a large extent and much costly hand labour eliminated. This set a pattern which others on similar soils throughout Breckland, and beyond the boundaries of Norfolk have, and are, successfully following today.

One other small but important enterprise which, so far as Norfolk is concerned had its origin in Breckland, is hop-growing. This takes the form of production of sets which are sold to growers in Kent and other production areas for planting new hop gardens. It is another example of taking advantage of isolated, disease-free, conditions to propagate stocks for production areas where infection is not so easy to control. Some half-dozen or so Norfolk growers now grow sets which are regularly inspected under another of the Ministry of Agriculture schemes.

CONTRIBUTION OF THE NURSERY TRADE

Having ended the survey of cropping practices in relation to areas and soil types on the subject of plant propagation, this is an appropriate place in which to mention the many nurserymen who contribute in one way or another to local and national horticultural prosperity.

Apart from growers who are producing special stock material as already described, there are several nurserymen who devote a good deal of time to plant breeding for the production of new and improved strains of various subjects. Included amongst these are such groups as herbaceous and alpine plants, roses, black currants, and strawberries. Some of these are helping to keep British horticulture to the forefront on an international as well as a national scale for, in addition to winning awards in Royal Horticultural Society and National Rose Society trial grounds, a number of local productions are being equally successful in American and Continental trials.

APPLICATION OF SCIENTIFIC AND TECHNICAL DEVELOPMENTS

It should be reasonably clear from the foregoing that horticulture as practised in Norfolk is extensive, full of variety, and a highly organized (and capitalized) industry.

To maintain this position in the competitive world of today it has to keep abreast of scientific developments in pest and disease control, manuring and growing techniques, and in the use of all modern aids to plant raising, crop harvesting, and marketing.

It is not the purpose of this chapter to catalogue the many facets of scientific knowledge now being applied to horticulture and used to increase, or cheapen, the output of produce from the land. In any case their adoption is by no means peculiar to Norfolk.

A few instances might, however, be quoted if only to confirm that growers in this rather out-of-the-way part of England are not slow in taking up new ideas.

To start with something of seeming commonplace, soil analyses have for a long time been taken as a general guide to manuring practice but never more so than is the case at the present time, especially in connection with glasshouse crops. Here there is a decided swing away from heavy application of dry fertilizers, which so often leave harmful residues of soluble salts behind in the soil. The change is in favour of liquid feeding through 'trickle', or 'low-level sprinkler', irrigation lines. By this means adjustments in watering and feeding rates in relation to sunlight or other climatic factors, and control of plant response, can be organized almost automatically and on a day-to-day basis.

Similarly, with the application of new knowledge of temperature control, it has become possible to influence the size of tomato fruits and even the number of fruits per truss or bunch.

Irradiation of tomato or cucumber seedlings for given periods at the propagation stage can substantially affect plant vigour and earliness of cropping. More recent research now being applied in practice to crops such as chrysanthemums, also concerns the photoperiodic, or day-length, factor. This has made it possible to work out growing schedules, by which a succession of crops can be producing flowers the whole year round.

Basically the chrysanthemum's habit is to make stem length in long days and start flower bud initiation under short day conditions in autumn. By controlling day length artificially, lengthening as necessary by lighting (usually with ordinary 60 watt or 100 watt incandescent lamps) or shortening by shading with black cloth, and providing the right temperature for bud formation, the plant can be made to respond almost at will.

Varieties differ in their requirements and adjustments have to be made to accommodate them. Most of those now in commercial use have been, or are being, tested and placed in their response groups so that growers can know how they should be treated.

This method of controlled flowering is in use for producing chrysanthemums as pot plants as well as growing them for cut flowers. There are indications that the principle can be used on other flower crops also, and Norfolk growers are awaiting these future developments with interest.

Possibilities of controlling environmental conditions for outdoor-grown crops are more limited but there are areas, of which the blowing fens already quoted are good examples, where knowledge obtained from research into

shelter screens is being applied with some success. A few growers in east Norfolk have also made use of this work in providing much needed shelter for soft fruit plantations.

Irrigation has been used on intensive horticultural holdings for a very long time, but it is now also being installed much more freely on farms and larger holdings for use on a wide range of crops. There is still a great deal to learn about the technique of how much water to apply, and when, and some growers are no doubt learning this the hard way by trial-and-error. The majority, however, do make some use of such information as is available. Some follow the method of Penmans' formula[5] for calculating moisture-loss on the basis of estimated potential transpiration, while others have installed proprietary instruments of a pattern similar to equipment designed at the National Vegetable Research Station,[6] which provides an alternative means of assessing the deficit.

For users of the former method the National Agricultural Advisory Service in Norfolk started a service, by postal and local paper notices, in 1960 which provided growers with a weekly guide of calculated moisture losses, and indicated which crops were likely to benefit most from irrigation applied at that particular stage.

Irrigation is also used as a means of protecting crops, e.g. soft fruits and early potatoes, from damaging spring frosts. This involves continuous sprinkling throughout the period of freezing. In one particularly interesting instance the grower has put the equipment into his field of blackcurrants as a permanent installation with underground mains.

In the realm of pest and disease or weed-control it is essential that growers keep up to date with new materials or new ways of using existing ones.

Good examples of the way Norfolk growers do this can be quoted for two such widely differing crops as carrots and apples.

Directly a new recommendation for control of carrot fly by a soil application of dieldrin was evolved at the National Vegetable Research Station, it was taken up by practically all the leading carrot growers. Within two years it was estimated that it had been adopted by at least 50 per cent of the growers and used on something approaching 75 per cent of the acreage!

The adoption by fruit growers of a new approach to

the control of apple scab – based on a means of determining infection periods worked out by Dr W.D. Mills of New York State, U.S.A. – has been equally notable. The 'Mills Tables' were not entirely applicable to local conditions, but served as the stimulus for an intensive period of investigation by N.A.A.S. officers working in the Wisbech district. Spore traps were set up in local orchards and warnings issued when spore releases were recorded. The new system of anticipating infection led to the dropping of protective sprays such as lime sulphur and the wide-scale adoption, for spraying Bramleys at least, of a spray programme using mercury-based materials.

Facilities for setting up apparatus of this sort and also light traps for confirming the emergence of codling moth, another serious problem for apple growers, are usually readily available on fruit farms in the area. The growers concerned also co-operate in placing orchards at the disposal of those who wish to set up experiments in pest or disease-control.

It is, however, a matter of regret that no general Experimental Horticulture Station has yet been established in the eastern region. Glasshouse and flower growers have welcomed the setting up of a station to serve their interests at Hoddesdon in the Lea Valley, and those more interested in fruit or vegetable growing look forward to the day when they too will have a local station to investigate their problems.

PRIVATE GARDENS AND PUBLIC PARKS

It is inevitable in a chapter of this sort that emphasis throughout has been on commercial matters, for an industry so extensive as horticulture in this county is so closely related to the economic life of the country.

However, it would be wrong to end without some reference to the standard maintained in private gardens and those under the control of local authorities.

In common with the general trend, all too many of the fine old gardens on big estates have either been closed down or semi-commercialized.

There are, however, a number which still maintain a good collection of interesting plants and put on a floral display of the very highest order. Furthermore many of these displays are accessible to the general public through the generosity of owners in opening their gardens on behalf of some good cause or other.

Examples quoted must of necessity be limited but three which regularly attract huge attendances by the public or in private parties are, Sandringham (H.M. The Queen), Blickling Hall (National Trust), and Fincham Manor (Mr L.M. Mason).

Public parks and gardens maintained by local authorities have a dual-purpose role and a great responsibility in these days of high pressure living yet, for some sections of the community, greater leisure.

Their first, and perhaps most obvious, duty is the provision and maintenance of recreational areas and floral displays in parks, streets or at civic functions.

In addition to this they have an educational function and are the means of making plant species and varieties, old or new, known to the general public for their own inspiration and advantage.

Norfolk is well served by its Parks and Garden Departments. The local authorities of Norwich, King's Lynn, Great Yarmouth and other seaside resorts in particular, put on floral displays of great imagination and beauty, and also meet their educational and recreational responsibilities to the full.

REFERENCES

1. CROSS, P.E. (1943). 'Extension of Market Gardening into Agriculture.' *J.R. Soc. Arts.*, **91**, 4639.

2. KEMP, R.W. (1957). 'Horticulture in Norfolk.' *Agriculture*, **4**, 161.

3. HINTON, W.L. (1960). 'Distribution of Horticultural Output in England and Wales.' *Agriculture*, **4**, 184.

4. ROUND, K.M. (1960) 'Celery Growing in the Fens.' *Agriculture*, **4**, 189.

5. PENMAN, H.L. (1949). 'A General Survey of Meteorology in Agriculture and an Account of the Physics of Irrigation Control.' *Quart. J.R. Met. Soc.*, **75**, 249.

6. STANHILL, G. 'An Irrigation Gauge for Commercial Use in Field and Glasshouse Practice.' *J. Agric. Eng. Res.*, **3**, 292.

forestry   G. F. BALLANCE

TRADITIONALLY the region is renowned for the intensity of its agricultural activities, and until recently forestry has not been a feature of the rural economy. At the same time the large farming estates always retained some woodlands for their sporting value. From the point of view of forest economy such woodlands carried a large proportion of inferior tree growth with only sporadic stems of real timber value.

The heavier land in the centre and south of the county carried a mixed crop partly natural and partly planted of oak (*Quercus pedunculata*), elm (*Ulmus varieties*), ash (*Fraxinus excelsior*), and in places beech (*Fagus sylvatica*), with many subsidiary species in association and an understorey of coppice hazel (*Carpinus betula*), ash, and other shrubby growth. In places sweet chestnut (*Castanea sativa*) coppice was introduced but without any large-scale success.

In the Breckland and again to the north of Norwich up to the Cromer ridge the heaths carried open stands of birch (*Betula* spp.) and Scots pine (*Pinus sylvestris*), together with sparse oak (*Quercus pedunculata*). These heaths are suitable for the natural regeneration of these two main species, but the ground vegetation of heather,

bracken, and gorse is liable to recurring fires which destroy all regrowth. It is said on good authority that some of the natural Scots pine found on the commons and open heaths near Holt are direct descendants of very old native pine, contemporary with the Caledonian forest in Scotland.

A third type of woodland is met with in the swampy land on the Broads and alongside the slow-running rivers of the region, where one finds a dense scrub tree vegetation dominated by alder (*Alnus glutinosa*), ash (*Fraxinus excelsior*), willows and sallow (*Salix* spp.).

Throughout the county the skyline is broken by the tops of tall trees of innumerable species, mainly conifers which were planted by the estates about the middle of last century in the form of arboreta or pleasances. Such trees indicate the timber potential of the region but have received a measure of attention in their development far beyond the means of the commercially minded forester.

The calls on the timbered estates in two world wars were exceptionally heavy, and the residual tree crops were in most cases of little value and very far from the potential of the region.

After the first war the Forestry Commission came into being and undertook a vigorous afforestation scheme in the Breckland, around Thetford and Swaffham, which towns gave their names to the forests growing up around them. Most of the planting was of pines, both Scots and Corsican (*Pinus sylvestris* and *P. laricio* var. *Corsicana*); these were the most suitable species for the open heaths but amenity was cared for with the establishment of roadside belts of oak and beech, and a proportion of these hardwoods mixed with the pines in places.

Drawing by Noel Spencer

G.F. BALLANCE is a Divisional Officer of the Forestry Commission

During this period sound forestry was practised on a few estates only, and most of the woodlands were left to come on by themselves with occasional felling of anything that became marketable. A few notable exceptions include the intensive forestry carried out at Weasenham, Westwick, and Ryston.

The advent of the Second World War brought about a further felling of almost any species of timber which could be put to use in the war effort, and left the woodlands of the region very largely devastated and with considerable areas carrying little more than scrub as a crop. However, it is in post-war years that truly progressive forestry has been practised on a wide scale. The economic pressure to make the best use of land coupled with the development of further markets which can absorb early thinnings have been the two fundamental causes, but the educational and subsidizing activities of the Forestry Commission and the felling licence regulations often requiring replanting have all helped to bring a proper perspective to the art and science of forestry in the region.

Today there are some 83,000 acres of woodland in the county of Norfolk which represents about 6.5 per cent of the land area, this is on a par with the national average for woodland. Of this area some 33,000 acres are managed by the Forestry Commission, and over 20,000 acres of privately owned woods and plantations are operating on realistic and progressive lines helped by subsidies. There remain, however, a further 30,000 acres in need of attention to bring them into full productivity.

The private woodlands are fairly evenly distributed over the county, while the Forestry Commission has a concentration of some 23,000 acres forming part of Thetford and Swaffham forests in the Breckland (a similar acreage exists in the Suffolk Breckland). The balance of their areas are scattered through north and east Norfolk forming Wensum forest, and in the heathlands around King's Lynn, called Lynn forest.

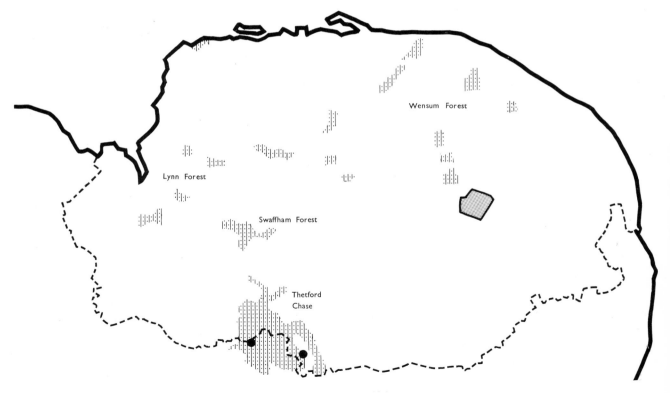

Fig. 1   *Main Forestry Areas*

The application of scientific and commercial forestry to a region like East Anglia presents the forester with some rather special local problems, the principal of which are climatic. The general maritime climate of the kingdom associated with the hilly country in the west changes to a much drier one in the flat country of the region with its low rainfall (22 to 25 inches) and all-round exposure. Again the absence of hills drawing a cloud layer often gives rise to clear skies and late spring frosts which can cause great losses among young trees at the height of their growing season. Frosts of 10 degrees in June and 8 degrees in July have been recorded within a few miles of Norwich, and ground-frosts have been noted in every month of the year.

On the matter of soils, the more fertile woods occur in those parts of the county where agricultural requirements are most pressing, and large-scale forest expansion is confined to the heathland areas where the soil is very poor; this limits the choice of species for at least the first rotation until a deeper and more favourable forest soil is built up.

An important factor in the development of commercial forestry is the location of markets: all timber produced in the region, unless consumed locally, must go westwards, and the large national consumers are not seeking a great variety of timber but rather, large quantities of one or two species. When these several factors are weighed up the forester finds himself somewhat limited in his choice.

Undoubtedly the most satisfactory and widely used species are the Scots pine (*Pinus sylvestris*) and the Corsican pine (*P. laricio* var. *Corsicana*), both thrive in the low rainfall conditions and the poor soils of the heathlands. The latter is more susceptible to frosts, and should be avoided when planting low-lying areas. The Douglas fir (*Pseudotsuga Douglasii*) and the European larch (*Larix europea*) can develop to reasonable timber sizes on selected sites, while the Norway spruce (*Picea abies*) is a very suitable choice on the better soils where it is much favoured for its early returns either as Christmas trees or small poles, but rainfall is against it growing to really large-sized timber. Limited and well-chosen sites can grow very good western red cedar (*Thuya plicata*) and silver firs (*Abies* spp.).

In general the climatic conditions are against the large-scale use of hardwoods as an economic forest crop but the demands of amenity, sport, and shelter combine to make it desirable to maintain a proportion of hardwoods in the woodlands, either as mixtures or surrounds, and for this purpose oak (*Quercus pedunculata*), beech (*Fagus sylvatica*), elm (*Ulmus* spp.), sweet chestnut (*Castanea sativa*), and other species are in common use.

The exception to the above is poplar (*Populus* spp.) which is about the only suitable choice for the low-lying and swampy riverside areas, where it grows extremely well.

In the matter of silvicultural techniques, some significant variations have been developed in the region compared with standard practice in the rest of the country; for instance, while normal practice on open land or heathland is to plough with a forest plough to turn up mineral soil, in East Anglia ploughing is very shallow, usually with sub-soiler attachment to give a mechanical screefing, and the plants are planted in the bottom of the furrow instead of on the upturned furrow slice. Another practice which has developed with great success in the clearing of old woodland and scrub areas is the technique termed 'through planting', which involves clearing a proportion of the scrub only, and retaining a scattering of the straighter stems of coppice, etc., as overhead shelter. The young trees planted under these conditions are protected from frost and exposure in their early life, and become established much more rapidly.

Thinnings become necessary as the plantations develop, in order to give light and growing space to the best stems, and experience in the region has shown that these should not normally commence until about the eighteenth year, after which they should be carried out periodically in cycles at four-year intervals extending to eight and even twelve years in the later stages of the rotation. The three-year cycles practised in other parts of the country have proved unsuitable in most cases in Norfolk.

In the commercial atmosphere of modern forestry one must be on the alert to take advantage of changing markets, and while within the region there is a demand for saw timber great enough to absorb production, greater knowledge is needed on the grading of timber. Marketing problems exist, however, on the disposal of the large quantities of pole-sized thinnings now coming

Drawing by Noel Spencer

forward, and it is to be anticipated that bulk consumers will appreciate the potential of the region and establish themselves here, thus reducing the heavy transport costs to the producer.

In addition to all the factors which have to be taken into account in planning the silviculture in a forest scheme there are many further hazards to be met with before success is assured, and the forester is in constant conflict with the enemies of the forest. These can take the form of animals such as deer, hares and rabbits, insects, and fungi. Deer are present in several areas in the county, hares are increasing commensurate with the gradual decrease of rabbits since myxomatosis became common. Many insects can cause serious damage but can be controlled by using common sense and forest hygiene. Perhaps the greatest cause for concern is the butt-rot fungus *Fomes annosus* which is present in most East Anglian soils and which can spread from root to root. Vigorous action such as the treatment of all cut stumps of felled trees with creosote can prevent excessive spread of the fungus from spore infection and continuing research into methods of control are proceeding both by the Forestry Commission and by Dr Rishbeth of the School of Botany, Cambridge. Fire, invariably the result of human carelessness, can cause terrible losses in the dry climate of the region and calls for constant vigilance.

In conclusion, it has been possible to outline but briefly a number of the facets and problems which confront the forester in the region. The true forester is an idealist, and the fascinating and exacting studies to achieve the optimum results will continue for many decades, but in the process the county of Norfolk will undoubtedly benefit in many ways from his labours.

REFERENCES

1. TANSLEY, SIR A.C. (1949). *The British Isles and their Vegetation*. Cambridge University Press.

2. RAINBIRD-CLARKE, R. (1937). *In Breckland Wilds*. W. Heffer & Sons Ltd., Cambridge, 2nd edition.

3. TAYLOR, W.L. (1925). 'New Forests in East Anglia.' *Quart. J. For.*, **29**, 1935, 245–55 and *ibid.*, **19**, 192–212.

4. MACDONALD, J. 'Thetford Chase with notes on Swaffham and the King's Forest.' *Forestry*, **13**, 139, 1–18. *F. Abs.*, **1**–124.

5. BACKHOUSE, G.W. (1957). 'Thetford Chase, Swaffham and King's Forests, further notes.' *Forestry*, **30**, 57–68. *F. Abs.*, **18**–4810.

6. WOOD, R.F. and NIMMO, M. (London, 1953-4). 'Trials of Species in Thetford Chase.' *Rep. For. Res. For. Comm.*, 106–14. *F. Abs.*, **17**–1449.

7. RISHBETH, J. (1950). 'Butt Rot by *Fomes annosus* in East Anglian Conifer Plantations and its Relation to Tree Killing.' *Forestry*, **24**, 114–20. *F. Abs.*, **9**–708.

8. GUNSTON, J. (1947). 'Prevention of Coastal Erosion by Planting Conifers (Holkham).' *Trees, Abbotsbury*, **40**, 49–53. *F. Abs.*, **9**–2063.

9. MONRO, D. (1908). 'The Planting of Sand Dunes at Holkham.' *Quart. J. For.*, **2**, 130–8.

10. ANON. 'Conifers in Norfolk'. (List of notable trees.) *Report of the Conifer Conference*, 1932, 435–6. *R.H.S. Book*, 667.

11. PRATT, E.R. (1950). 'The Fastest Growing Trees.' *Quart. J. For.*, **44**, 142–4.

12. WALLIS, G.W. (1960). 'Survey of *Fomes annosus* in East Anglian Pine Plantations.' *Forestry*, **33**, No. 2, 203–14.

fishing

G. J. Y. THORPE

FISHING is an industry of great antiquity in East Anglia – and still remains of major importance today. Lowestoft and Yarmouth are the two principal ports, although – save for landings by inshore fishermen – Yarmouth is now used only during the autumn herring season. There are also a number of small ports within the district at which mainly shellfish landings are made. In the past the district was best known for its autumn herring fishery, but this has now become of secondary importance to the growing whitefish industry based on Lowestoft, the value of which exceeded £2,000,000 in 1960.

THE HERRING FISHERY

Compared with the prosperous years before 1914 the present-day fishery has declined drastically. For instance: in 1913, the heyday of the industry, a fleet of 1,650 vessels made 33,496 landings at Yarmouth and Lowestoft totalling nearly 1,500,000 crans, whereas in 1960 a fleet of only 104 vessels made 1,680 landings totalling just over 39,000 crans. Quantitatively, 1960 was the worst season ever known, and it is difficult to foresee how the industry can overcome its present problems.

There was a number of reasons for this decline, some of which are of a deep-seated nature. Since 1913 landings have fallen steadily, but until recently this was not from any shortage of herrings on the grounds. The pattern of the industry for most of the first half of the century was one of over-supply and declining markets; and it is only in the last decade that catches from the traditional East Anglian herring season have begun to fail. The causes of this failure cannot be precisely stated. Some attribute the changes in the herring stock to biological factors; others to over-fishing – and, particularly, the growth of industrial fishing, i.e. the catching of immense quan-

tities of both mature and immature herrings for conversion to animal food and the extraction of oil. This fishing is not prosecuted by British vessels. In pre-war years it was mainly fall in demand that caused the herring fleet to shrink; but in recent years the dwindling catches from the traditional grounds, coupled with the greater profitability of whitefish and the attraction of shore employment, have all played their part. Exports of herrings, once the mainstay of the industry, have been hard hit by the growing self-sufficiency of former importing countries, notably Russia and Germany, the political barriers to trade and the rising standards of living in countries which formerly imported large quantities of cured herring. Moreover, as a highly seasonal industry it depended on a good reserve of casual labour which is no longer available following the post-war development of alternative industries in Great Yarmouth and Lowestoft. For example, the new quick-freezing industries utilizing fruit, vegetables, meat products, and fish now account for the employment of between 10 and 15 per cent of the insured populations of both towns. The growth of shipbuilding, too, is another important post-war development, as well as more light industries. Furthermore, the old steam drifters, which made up the bulk of the fleet, rapidly became uneconomical with the rising price of coal; conditions in these vessels, too, were not attractive, and as they began to be scrapped so the crews found ready employment in the growing fleet of whitefish trawlers. Lack of capital in the immediate post-war phase, coupled with the greater profitability of whitefish trawling, halted the replacement of these old drifters. The skipper-owner, once the backbone of the herring industry, is now no longer to be found, mainly

G.J.Y. THORPE is District Inspector of Fisheries

because of the growth of large concerns and more integration; this trend towards greater horizontal integration within one section of the industry has been a feature of post-war development.

The present-day East Anglian drifter is a dual-purpose steel motor vessel, able to drift for herrings or trawl for whitefish, and now costs up to £65,000. By contrast, a Scottish wooden-built motor vessel, also capable of various types of fishing, costs less than half this amount. It is not difficult to see therefore why the modernization of the East Anglian drifter fleet went more slowly apace than in Scotland where, incidentally, the traditional herring fisheries have not shown the same decline as the East Anglian fishery.

The pattern of the herring industry before 1939 – and to a lesser extent up to 1953 – was one of large fluctuating landings, the best of which were absorbed by the home market for freshing and kippering, but the greater part being cured and exported either in the form of the relatively cheap and simple pickle cure, klondyking (lightly salted and iced) or as red herring (prolonged salting and smoking). After 1946, and up to about 1953, reduction to meal and oil was an important outlet, but with the rapidly dwindling catch in recent years there has been a change in the pattern of traditional usage. For example, during the 1960 East Anglian season the home market, which includes kippering, absorbed about 40 per cent of the total catch, with purchases by the redders and freezers accounting for another 50 per cent. Canning, which absorbed some 26,000 crans in 1952, took only 112 crans in 1960, less than 1 per cent of the total catch; pickle curers' purchases were only 96 crans;

and for the third year in succession there was no klondyking. Similarly, the H.I.B.'s reduction plant at Great Yarmouth, which in 1953 processed 23,000 crans, purchased only 242 crans during the season which has just passed.

WHITEFISH

While the herring industry has declined the whitefish industry at Lowestoft grows annually, although whitefish landings are no longer made at Great Yarmouth. Lowestoft has been one of the leading ports in building new diesel-powered trawlers, a policy which has been greatly aided since 1953 by the White Fish Authority's grant and loan scheme. The advantages of diesel trawlers are greater economy, and the power and range to fish grounds hitherto beyond the capabilities of the old steam trawlers. Whitefish landings at Lowestoft in 1960 reached the considerable total of 374,000 cwts., and these figures do not include another 57,000 cwts. which were landed by East Anglian vessels at Grimsby and Fleetwood. During 1960 alone, nine new trawlers were added to the fleet; a further sixteen have been ordered, and are expected to join the fleet within the next eighteen months. This rapid expansion of the trawler fleet – which now numbers over one hundred vessels – has caused certain manning problems only partially alleviated by an increase in the number of boys recruited through the pre-apprenticeship training scheme of the Lowestoft Education Authority and the scrapping or laying up of drifters. In addition, successful vocational courses for fishermen were also held.

The main types of fish caught are shown in this Table:

CATCH IN CWT

	1955	1956	1957	1958	1959	1960
Plaice	115,584	100,778	97,719	112,975	165,235	171,241
Sole	14,941	11,171	7,614	8,671	8,970	10,183
Turbot	9,381	11,293	13,035	12,140	14,401	15,382
Cod	40,862	39,897	65,839	77,206	88,887	119,220
Haddock	16,601	24,375	34,586	19,926	12,422	12,695
Whiting	22,214	15,607	13,248	15,257	14,893	9,384
Skate	20,182	15,786	13,463	13,135	14,166	13,988

INSHORE FISHING

About 200 men are engaged in the inshore fisheries along the Norfolk coast. Varieties landed include crabs, lobsters, whelks, mussels, cockles, sprats, herring, mackerel, shrimps, and a few cod and flat fish.

From an economic aspect the most important of these fisheries are those concerned with crabs, whelks, mussels, herrings, and sprats.

In the northern part of Norfolk, from Brancaster to Blakeney, the main varieties are whelks and mussels, the landings of which have remained reasonably steady in recent years, and in 1960 consisted of 20,000 cwts. of whelks and 9,000 cwts. of mussels. The substantial cockle industry in the same area was seriously reduced by pests, poor spatfalls, and storm damage in the early 1950's, and has not yet recovered to any extent.

In the Cromer–Sheringham area a thriving crab and lobster fishery exists, and in 1960 some forty boats landed over 10,000 cwts. of crabs valued about £58,000. The crab landings during the past three years have shown a steady improvement.

Since 1958 a notable development on the Norfolk coast bordering the Wash has been revival of the previously neglected sprat fishery. A family of Whitstable fishermen, with six boats, settled at Wells, and now land upwards of 14,000 cwts. of sprats per annum at that port alone.

Further south, fishing is more spasmodic. In the Yarmouth area, for various reasons, the inshore fleet has fallen steadily. Shrimps and sprats, which in the past have been landed in valuable quantities, have been unaccountably hard to find, and the herrings – so scarce in recent years on the deep sea grounds – have been equally elusive inshore. In the Yarmouth/Lowestoft area less than 3,000 cwts. of fish of all varieties were landed in 1960 from inshore boats.

Compared with the more stable whelk, mussel, and crab fisheries in north Norfolk the rather more variable – and considerably lower – earnings from shrimps, herring, and whitefish have resulted in a drift from this minor side of the industry at Yarmouth and Lowestoft.

The traditional steam-drifters of the herring industry are being replaced by steel motor vessels able to drift for herring and to trawl for whitefish. Great Yarmouth has developed other industries alongside its traditional herring fishing in the post-war period

Norfolk News Co. Ltd

manufacturing industries

A. R. CARTWRIGHT | A. FITCH | D. L. J. ROBINS

DR ALLISON has taken his account of the growth of local manufacturing industry up to the end of the Second World War. Before describing the present-day nature of these industries, it will therefore be helpful to outline developments in the intervening post-war years.

In Norwich, two tendencies may be noted: the reconstruction of bomb-damaged premises and the growth of additional productive capacity. One hundred and twenty-nine factories were destroyed during the war, and many of the firms affected seized the opportunities afforded by their rebuilding to modernize their plant. As examples we may instance: Harmers' new clothing factory; the successful resurgence of John Mackintosh's factory in which chocolate manufacture had been brought completely to a standstill by enemy bombing in 1942; and the revival of the shoe industry which achieved an output of over eight million pairs in 1960, the three largest firms each contributing over a million. Such re building does not require a Board of Trade certificate and does not therefore appear in fig. 5. Additional significant capacity is seen: in engineering, firms like Balding's and Autowrappers being post-war enterprises; in clothing, where growth has tended to come from existing firms; and in food and drink, printing, and chemicals. The limited area of sites suitable for further industrial development in central Norwich and the growing difficulties of traffic circulation have directed much of the factory growth to the fringes of the city, the single industrial estate at Harford being now fully occupied. Recent decisions by Boulton & Paul illustrate this tendency. To expand production, they have taken over, for the making of wire netting and chain link fencing, premises on the northern outskirts no longer required for the weaving of silk and nylon. They have gone even further afield to develop a site at Lowestoft for the production of builders' joinery.

Unlike that of Norwich, Norfolk's post-war industrial development has not included the restoration of productive capacity lost by war damage so much as the extension of existing firms and the introduction of completely new industries. Shortage of land within the city of Norwich has meant that considerable industrial development has taken place in the administrative county immediately adjacent to the city boundaries yet still within the urbanized area. Shortage of female labour in Norwich has brought branches of some firms into the country towns. Furthermore, a fair amount of sub-contract work is being done in the county for Norwich engineering firms.

Extension of existing premises has been most marked in the food industries, but as the Table on page 210 shows, growth has occurred mainly in those industries producing prepared foods – in canning, for example, rather than flour-milling. This is a reflection of increasing national prosperity, for such goods reduce kitchen chores but are more expensive than raw fruit and vegetables.

Agricultural engineering has also developed because of increased capital investment in farm mechanization – itself the result of Government subsidies to agriculture.

The food industries prefer to be near their sources of raw material. By contrast, the main location factor common to the industries of recent introduction has been the availability of labour. Between 1958 and 1960 about two million square feet of industrial floor space

A.R. CARTWRIGHT and A. FITCH, assistant masters at the City of Norwich School, are part authors of *The Norfolk We Live In*
D.L.J. ROBINS was, until recently, Research Officer in the Norfolk County Planning Department

were built in Norfolk, much of this in new locations. The policy of the Board of Trade in restricting industrial expansion in the London area has made firms look further afield and the local authorities in Norfolk, aware of this trend, have been keen to attract new industry, in order both to broaden the basis of the county's economy and to absorb civilian labour becoming redundant by the closing of armed forces' establishments, of which there was a considerable number in the county at the beginning of the post-war period. The unemployment rate exceeded 4 per cent over much of the county during the winter of 1957–8 – helped by the above trend, a bad winter, and a recession in building and civil engineering on account of a 'credit squeeze' – and parts of the county qualified for government assistance under the Distribution of Industry (Special Finance) Act, 1958. Since that date, however, the volume of new employment made available in the county has gone far to take up any surplus labour.

There now follows a description of manufacturing industry at the present day: first in the Norwich area, then in Great Yarmouth and King's Lynn, and finally in the rest of Norfolk.

NORWICH

Dr Allison has made it clear that any description of Norwich industry before the nineteenth century would have to begin with the cloth industry, which, in those days, dominated the industrial scene. In 1961, only one textile firm remains, Fras. Hinde & Sons, which employs about 275 workers, of whom about 100 are men and about 200 are skilled. Post-war rebuilding has enabled this company to compete in the use of the newer synthetic fibres which have tended to vie with its traditional raw-material, silk.

It is equally clear from fig. 3a on page 155, on the other hand, that there is today no corresponding dominant category on which employment in the Norwich area may be said to depend. The largest single industry, clothing, is nevertheless an important one, giving work to nearly 10,000 people, 8.4 per cent of the total employed population, or almost exactly 30 per cent of the total manufacturing population of about 30,000. Of these, about 9,000 (50 per cent men, 50 per cent women) are engaged in the shoe industry, in 23 factories which vary greatly in size.

In terms of total annual production, Norwich as a footwear manufacturing centre ranks fourth in the whole country with over 8,000,000 pairs, behind Leicester (14,000,000 pairs from 68 factories), Leicestershire (21,000,000 from 58 factories), and the London area (10,000,000 from 46 factories). Though Norwich contributes only about $5\frac{1}{2}$ per cent, worth about £14,000,000, to the total national production, it has an acknowledged superiority in the manufacture of ladies' fashion shoes and children's shoes, which include many nationally known brands. On average, only about 4 per cent is exported, to all parts of the Commonwealth, to western Europe and to the U.S.A., though some firms look forward to selling as much as one-third of their output overseas. Most dispose of their production to the large retail chains, but one manufactures for the C.W.S., and therefore distributes its shoes through Co-operative stores, while another has developed its own chain of retail stores through which it sells one-third of its output and, incidentally, keeps closely in touch with market trends.

This can be most important. Ever since skirts left the ground and shoes became visible, 'style' and 'fashion' in the design of shoes for women have been the chief considerations, and never more so than now, when Italian styles are being freely imported to compete with the local product, and when teenagers, who buy on average five pairs of shoes a year (twice the number bought by more mature women), are the most sought-after consumers. One company has engaged a 'teenage council' to advise it and last year took this view of its problems: 'Fresh from the restrictions of school life, the teenager looks for style rather than durability. She has had enough of gym tunics and good strong sensible Oxfords. Now she looks for the prettiest shoes she can find, for the most delicate pastel colours, the highest heels, the most pointed toes. But though appearance is all to her at this stage, and though her desire for style must be fulfilled, she must not be disillusioned about quality. She may not look for durability but, if her pretty new shoes fall apart at the first summer shower, she is not likely to spend her money on that particular make again.' This, then, is the perennial problem of the industry, to provide style, glamour, elegance, and lightness, and combine them with serviceability, waterproof qualities, and strength, all at

Fig. 1 *In the new unit at the Howlett & White branch of the Norvic Shoe Company Ltd, shoes are now made on a moving transporter. Each pair is on the last for just over 4 hours instead of the normal time of 4 to 5 days. This has been made possible by the introduction of completely new types of machines and equipment, and new methods of work transportation*

Norvic Shoe Company Ltd

reasonable cost. It demands originality as well as receptiveness to world fashion trends (the 'winkle-picker' has already been ceremonially buried) and flexibility as well as skilled workmanship.

It also demands constant technical progress. The traditional Norwich ladies' shoe had a sole of leather stitched to an upper of fine quality leather, and a heel made of wood covered with the same upper material. Today the sole may be made of a composition, which will outlast leather while lacking its important 'breathing' qualities. It must be said, however, that the traditional sole has not lost favour so much in Norwich as elsewhere, and its use is in any case increasing again. This sole is almost certain to be cemented and not sewn to its upper. This upper, though it is still of fine quality kid or calf, lizard or snake, or possibly of some woven fabric for evening shoes, is sewn together with Terylene or nylon, both stronger and cheaper than traditional thread. The heel is now so slender that wood is not strong enough and

is replaced by a grain-free plastic moulding, still perhaps covered with leather, but, if fashion demands, with lacquer or spangles or nitro-celluloid sheeting instead.

Change, it is clear, has also applied to the ancillary industries, both local and national. The British United Shoe Machinery Co. of Leicester, which owns most of the equipment used by the manufacturing firms and rents it to them, keeping a reserve of skilled men in each area to maintain it, has designed, built, and supplied the new machinery required by the latest fashions. The four main local factories which employ about 300 workers in the manufacture of heels have obviously been affected, as have the three factories which turn, from rough maple blocks, the new pointed-toe lasts on which shoes are made in multiple sizes and fittings. The two local tanyards produce nearly 2,000,000 square feet of leather each year now, not only in the traditional blacks, blues, and browns, but in a range of delicate new pastel shades as well. The manufacture of cardboard boxes from raw materials imported from the Netherlands and Scandinavia has also expanded; the largest of three firms will soon have a capacity of 10,000,000 boxes a year.

The shoe industry, then, is the nearest counterpart of the old woollen industry, for the craftsman still predominates. In spite of the most modern of mass-production methods, including ideas freely borrowed from the Continent, each shoe must still be made individually by skill of hand and eye. Designer, production engineer, and craftsman, in an industry renowned for its good industrial relations, must work as a team in order to face fierce national and international competition.

Of the remaining clothing workers of the Norwich area (rather more than a thousand in number), about 150 make men's outer garments for the Cox Clothing Co. Another two or three very small firms make women's dresses, men's hats, plastic raincoats, duffel coats and industrial overalls.

The remainder, mostly women, are employed by F.W. Harmer & Co. Ltd. Using 500 sewing-machines and 100 steam-presses, they turn out over 20,000 garments each week, including trousers and sports jackets in the latest styles, boys' knickers, Service and Post Office uniforms, and blazers and caps complete with badges embroidered in a separate department. The new single-storey factory on the outskirts, replacing the one destroyed in central Norwich during the war, has enabled production planning on the most modern and economical lines to be developed.

Finally, D. McLaren Ltd has a close enough connection with clothing and the leather work of the shoe trade to be mentioned here. Its 200 workers, predominantly female, produce annually over half a million ladies' handbags in both leather and plastic, almost 10 per cent being exported, chiefly to Commonwealth countries. This is a post-war firm which began modestly but is still expanding.

The next local industry by number of workers is construction, which employs over 7,000. Its features are, nevertheless, quite typical of any town of the size of Norwich. The biggest firms employ two or three hundred men apiece – R.G. Carter Ltd, the largest, is exceptional with over nine hundred – and their contracts extend beyond the immediate vicinity; at the other extreme are several dozen small firms. Norwich Corporation itself employs over 600 men in construction, for there are in the city nearly 16,000 council houses and flats, representing 40 per cent of all dwellings. All these building enterprises have been stimulated by the post-war restoration of bomb-damage; by the housing-drive with its completion of over 9,000 new dwellings in Norwich itself; by the industrial expansion which is described in this article; and by various local authority projects, including road improvements, main sewers, and public buildings.

The industry is supported by local sand and gravel workings, which must yield at least 1,000,000 tons a year. Concrete building materials are manufactured and the two surviving brickworks exploit the local brickearths to make up to 3,500,000 bricks per annum. Their product, sand-faced and frequently hand-made, is the pleasing material which faces most of the older and many of the newer large buildings in the district. An interesting development has been the revival by G. King & Son (Lead Glaziers) Ltd of the school of glass-painting which flourished locally in medieval times. The ecclesiastical wealth of the district has so stimulated the restoration and creation of stained and painted-glass windows that such work is now undertaken throughout the country.

The next largest Ministry of Labour category in the Norwich area is that of food, drink, and tobacco, though there are, in fact, no tobacco-workers. The biggest single employer of the 5,700 people who work in this group is the division of John Mackintosh & Sons Ltd whose local origins as A.J. Caley Ltd have been traced on page 121. The making of soft drinks has now passed into other hands, but an interest is still maintained in cracker manufacture, which is carried on by Tom Smith & Co. Ltd, whose 260 full-time employees and 100 outworkers are responsible for at least one-fifth of the national output. Mackintosh's chief product, however, is chocolate confectionery, and such good progress has been made in this highly competitive field that 2,100 people now work in premises rebuilt and extended since the war; women constitute over half of this total and of these about 15 per cent are under eighteen. A considerable export trade is carried on, especially with North America, while several overseas factories have been established.

Another old-established local firm, J. and J. Colman Ltd, is now part of a larger national, even international, company, that of Reckitt & Colman Holdings Ltd. Carrow Works in Norwich is concerned with food products. Active research has steadily widened their variety, while increased mechanization has permitted record productivity with a labour force of a little over 1,300, compared with 2,200 at the turn of the century. Mustard-milling retains its old importance; the seed now comes from an improved strain, developed by the firm's own plant-breeding section, which grows to only half the height of the old brown mustard plant but gives a 50 per cent greater yield of seed. The milling of local and imported grains – the riverside site is still valuable, for 12 per cent of the inward traffic comes by water – is the basis of various processed cereals and baby foods. The manufacture of soft drinks has now been extended beyond the original Robinson's lemon barley-water to cover a range of various barley-waters and squashes.

Only two other city firms undertake grain-milling on a significant scale: R.J. Read Ltd and C.E. Woodrow & Sons Ltd. While rather more than half of the wheat comes from within a 20-mile radius of Norwich, Read's riverside site again facilitates the import of foreign grains (not only for flour but also for animal foodstuffs) up the Yare in small motor-vessels which trade mainly with the great continental *entrepôts* of Antwerp and Rotterdam. An unusual feature of this company's outward transport is the use of two bulk-flour lorries which supply biscuit and other food manufacturers in the London area.

Norwich's rich agricultural hinterland calls for supplies of animal foodstuffs. To the output of the grain-millers and the skim-milk of the local Milk Marketing Board Creamery must be added the food-stuffs processed by Case & Steward Ltd, who deal also in artificial fertilizers and employ about 100 workers.

Situated in excellent barley-growing country, with supplies of water from deep wells sunk into the chalk, and with a large local market for their products, the three Norwich breweries of Bullard's, Morgan's and Steward & Patteson's employ a total of over 900 persons and supply about 2,500 licensed premises, not only in Norfolk but in such neighbouring counties as Suffolk, Lincolnshire, and Cambridgeshire.

Soft-drink manufacture, which has expanded considerably since 1945 and which now accounts for about 400 employees, is also carried on by Steward & Patteson's and by Morgan's, through its subsidiary, Delecta Table Waters Ltd; J. and J. Colman's products have already been noted. The latest comer to this field has been Thomas & Evans, Ltd (now part of the Beecham Group) which in 1956 opened a Corona factory on the outskirts, with employment for about 100 people. Coleman & Co. Ltd, with a staff of about 200, manufacture two other types of drink: Wincarnis tonic wine, which has been made for over seventy years, and the food beverage Vitacup, which was introduced in 1933. The import of wine to form the basis of Wincarnis has resulted in the shipping of wine as a specialized activity, and Colemans' agencies for sherry and table-wines command a national market. Through its subsidiaries the company also manufactures mouth-washes and dentifrices, such as Odol.

If clothing, construction, and food-processing are the three largest Norwich groups, the largest single employer is in the field of engineering. Laurence, Scott and Electromotors Ltd now employ about 3,000, of whom more than a third are skilled male craftsmen, an important local employment factor, and only 500 women. About a quarter of this labour force is engaged in producing a wide range of high-quality specialized equipment for government departments and especially for the Admiralty. Another quarter makes ships' winches and the associated control gear. By far the majority of ships leaving British yards in recent years have had at least some Laurence, Scott equipment, and much is exported to foreign yards. The remaining half of the labour force makes medium and heavy electrical rotating machines, and the control gear and control systems for them. These motors perform functions both routine and pioneering at home and overseas, pumping water and sewage in Norwich and Melbourne alike, powering the latest British Railways prime-movers, helping in the manufacture of Terylene and Polythene for I.C.I., driving vital installations in new steel works at Consett and Llanwern and in most post-war power-stations, and providing the main gas circulation drives for the Advanced Gas-cooled Reactor at Windscale. A large new workshop, bringing the total area to nearly 700,000 square feet, has just been completed to facilitate the fabrication of the much heavier plant now in demand. Having developed the first safe and practical workshop motors and the first electric winches and steering gear for marine use, having patented the 'N.-S.' stator-fed variable speed A.C. motor, Laurence, Scott are still among the pioneers in supplying industry's latest demand, highly complex comprehensive units of drives and control gear with automatic feedback that can to some extent think for themselves. So far from the normal sources of raw-materials, and even from the normal sources of home contracts, Laurence, Scott must obviously have a high reputation for individually engineered products in all three branches of their activity in order to survive. Such is the Government's confidence that the firm has just been entrusted with the order for the design and manufacture of the electrical propulsion machinery and control gear of the first all-British nuclear submarine.

The rest of the engineering firms of the Norwich area overlap so many of the Ministry of Labour categories that they are best taken together. In categories V (Metal Manufacture), VI (Engineering and Electrical Goods), VII (Shipbuilding), VIII (Vehicles), IX (Other Metal Goods), XIV (Timber) and XVI (Other Manufacturing Industries) there are about 8,500 workers, of whom only the 3,000 Laurence, Scott employees have so far been accounted for. The remaining 5,500 work for well over fifty significant enterprises, only some of which can be mentioned by name.

In descending order of size, the Boulton & Paul Group, with 1,300 Norwich employees, comes first. Nearly all the workers are male, and two out of three skilled. Thirty-five per cent of them are employed in the fabrication and erection of structural steel, for which there is an increasing demand as building techniques have developed. There are three other local competitors, all smaller, in this field. The bulk of orders booked are nation-wide rather than local: a recent £700,000 contract for 7,500 tons for the Pressed Steel Company has just been fulfilled by Boulton & Paul. This firm's

Fig. 2 *A good example of the ability of Laurence, Scott and Electromotors Ltd to manufacture individual and highly specialized products. Four of these 1,570 h.p. motors have been supplied to the United Kingdom Atomic Energy Authority to drive the centrifugal impellers which circulate the carbon dioxide in the Windscale Advanced Gas-cooled Reactor. They are located in the gas flow itself under a pressure of 270 lb per square inch and must operate reliably for long periods. The design provides for any necessary maintenance to be carried out without depressurization of the main carbon dioxide circuit. A previous contract for the Atomic Energy Authority covered a considerable number of motors which were designed to operate continuously for two years without shut-down*

success may be partly due to the semi-automatic mechanical handling and drilling plant for structural steel which it has developed and which is now a product in its own right. Systems are being manufactured and sold, many of them overseas (to the U.S.A. and Western Germany, for instance), and this section of the firm may grow considerably. About a half of the rest of the workers make builders' joinery. The remainder are occupied on fencing contracts and in the manufacture of chain link fencing (plastic and zinc covered) and wire netting. As so often in the past, Boulton & Paul compete in this field with Barnards Ltd who have perhaps the most modern netting factory in Europe and who are now 'foreign-owned'. Between them, these two firms make about half the British total product, and still enormously assist undeveloped areas of the globe as the capital resources to make progress are found. Young cacao trees in Sierra Leone, sugar plantations in the West Indies, farms in Australia and New Zealand, water-courses in Thailand – all these make use of Norwich netting.

Mann Egerton & Co. Ltd, with over 600 workers (550 male and 300 skilled) also have more than one type of product. Closely connected with the motor trade, they use a quarter of their labour force on the manufacture of garage equipment – such as axle stands, wheel trolleys, jacks, and lifting gear – some of which is exported, and another quarter on the building of vehicle bodies. They have been encouraged to specialize in refrigerated and insulated vehicles by the growth of the frozen food trade. The remaining men, except for a small group engaged in making precision-built metal cases for the electronics industry, manufacture school and office furniture of all kinds. Between them, in fact, Boulton & Paul and Mann Egerton account for a majority of the local woodworkers but mention must be made of Remploy Ltd, who provide employment for over a hundred disabled men, office desks and kitchen furniture being their main products, and of Arthur Brett & Son Ltd, whose restored antiques and reproduction furniture are finding a ready dollar market.

Heatrae Ltd come next in order of size, with about 500 workers of whom 400 are men and over 200 skilled. Nearly half their output is the domestic equipment with whose manufacture they started business: electric fires, immersion heaters and storage heaters in sizes from $1\frac{1}{2}$

gallons upwards. A further significant portion is of catering and laboratory equipment. More and more, however, the firm is fulfilling contracts for individually engineered heating processes in industry, like flame-proof heaters for oil-refineries, gas drying plant in chemical factories, and batteries of precisely controlled heaters for the drawing and twisting process in the manufacture of synthetic fibres. This firm's willingness to tackle a wide variety of heating problems has contributed towards its growing success.

The firm of Autowrappers Ltd, employing today about 180 men, a third of them highly skilled, compared with the six when it was founded in 1947, can claim a similar enterprise and competence in the field of wrapping machinery. The great increase in pre-packing in the food, confectionery, drug, and cosmetic trades has provided the market for this expansion. Nearly half the product is exported to over forty countries in competition with German and American firms, which had a pre-war monopoly in these complicated precision-engineered machines. An almost twin firm, in size, composition, date of origin and post-war expansion, and equally engaged in the field of highly skilled fabrication, is the Balding Engineering Co. Ltd, which manufactures machine-tools, especially milling machines, and exports them all over the world. Yet another post-war firm is Marston Caravans Ltd, established by London capital on the Salhouse Road industrial estate. A labour force of about 160 men, mostly skilled woodworkers, is divided roughly equally between the manufacture of caravans and of commercial vehicle bodies from bought-in processed materials and manufactured accessories. Next door is its sister firm, Regency Covers Ltd, which makes car seat covers. Nearby too is J. Billig & Sons, another London firm that has moved to Norwich in the post-war period and is expanding rapidly. Colour printing its own tin-plate, it manufactures in varying sizes nearly a million cans a week for the paint, oil, and chemical trades.

The Miller Organ Co. is on the same estate and employs about eighty people in the construction of electronic organs and carillons. While faithfully reproducing the tones of the pipe-organ and the traditional carillon, these instruments are considerably cheaper and more compact. They have therefore become very popular in the building and renovation of places of worship and many Miller organs have been installed in this country, for example, in the Roman Catholic Cathedral in Northampton, and overseas, notably in Khartoum Cathedral.

The most recent factory to be built in Norwich is that just completed by Roneo Ltd, also on the Salhouse Road, where there is ample space for expansion. It produces steel office equipment for the home and world markets, using the most modern production techniques. In its reliance on mechanized handling and repetition work by unskilled labour, it more closely resembles a Midland mass production unit than the normal Norwich engineering works with its more varied and more individually engineered product.

Over 2,000 workers in this group of categories remain to be accounted for, but only a few more firms may be mentioned by name. A.W. Hunton, for instance, with only thirty-five male workers, contrive to produce at least half the axles and undergear for the farm trailers made in this country. A patented hydraulic-ram tipping-gear for trailers is also sold extensively. F.W. Frost (Engineers) Ltd, with seventeen men, make all kinds of non-powered trucks and barrows and other transporters, and have developed a new but related line in the manufacture of such airfield equipment as mobile passenger-steps, luggage trailers, and maintenance platforms. Only last year, the small engineering firm of E.G. Reeve & Sons Ltd was approached to build a 50-feet steel wherry, which, with a diesel engine, has proved to be a most economical transporter of loads, especially sugar beet, of up to 40 tons. More wherries are to follow this first successful venture into marine engineering. Hill & Dolman (Engineers) Ltd, staffed literally by a man and a boy, are perhaps the smallest firm, and make a range of bag opening and filling machines, some of them patented.

As for the rest, few generalizations may be made, but it is possible to detect, amongst the many precision workshops, sheet metal shops, and subcontracting firms, that constant response to changing economic conditions necessary for survival. Some firms respond by their specialization, like the sheet metal company which meets brewers' special requirements, or the grinderies which service press knives for the shoe trade. Some have taken their skill into fields less vulnerable to modern mass-production techniques; for instance, plastic domestic holloware has driven many sheet metal firms into the construction of the individual dust extractors, ventilation ducts and machine guards on which Factory Acts and workers more and more insist. Other such firms supply the demand by farmers for sheet metal goods like pig and calf feeders, food and water containers for poultry, and hen batteries for which plastic may perhaps be insufficiently robust.

There remain two main groups of industrial workers to describe, those in printing, who number about 2,000, predominantly male, and those in chemical engineering, who at present are fewer than 500.

Much the largest firm of printers and bookbinders is Jarrold & Sons Ltd, the printers of this survey, with nearly 1,000 workers. This company has earned an international reputation for colour-reproduction, based upon its highly skilled craftsmen, the research conducted by the firm itself, and a large and varied range of equipment, which includes what is probably the world's biggest single-colour lithographic machine and certainly the largest four-colour machine in Europe. Increasing holiday traffic has stimulated the demand for the publicity literature, picture-postcards, calendars, and souvenir booklets for which the firm has become noted, while the printing of fine art publications, children's books, and mail order catalogues are other specialities. Jarrold & Sons are also publishers in their own right and their work includes many books of local interest. Of the couple of dozen local printing firms, Page Bros. and Fletcher & Sons Ltd are the only other enterprises whose labour force reaches three figures: the former specializes in technical books and journals and in large colour brochures, while Fletchers, who were among the pioneers of lithography in this country, are mainly concerned with book-production and colour-printing. Norwich claims the first provincial newspaper in the *Norwich Post*, started by Francis Burges in 1701; today, newspaper production is entirely in the hands of the Norfolk News Co., with a total staff approaching 600, whose daily and weekly publications cater for most of the county.

Printing may be described as an old-established Norwich industry. Chemical engineering, on the other hand, is almost one of the future – though three-quarters of the country's model aircraft fuel has for some time been made by a local firm! May & Baker Ltd acquired a 180-acre site on the edge of the city in 1956, and employ at the moment fewer than 200 people in a mere 70,000 square feet of factory space, making chiefly weed-killer and insecticides, together with a few pharmaceutical chemicals and veterinary and poultry products. Eventually it is contemplated that the factory will occupy 2,000,000 square feet while the future nature of its products will depend upon developments in research and market demands. The advent of May & Baker has been called 'the largest and most important industrial development in the city for a hundred years'. It symbolizes that new economic growth in Norwich which has joined with the already great diversity and flexibility of the older enterprises to ensure the continued success of the local 'Industrial Revolution' of last century.

GREAT YARMOUTH

The functions of Great Yarmouth are three-fold: as a port, a holiday resort, and a manufacturing centre. The first two functions, including the fishing industry, are dealt with elsewhere. The third is dealt with here.

Of about 10,000 persons employed in manufacturing in Great Yarmouth district, over 3,500 are employed in the food and drink industries, with over 2,000 of this number in food canning and freezing establishments. Henry Sutton Ltd and Marshall's are both old established firms with interests in the fishing industry. Birds Eye Foods Ltd, a Unilever firm, have carried out considerable development at both Great Yarmouth and Lowestoft since 1945; while fish freezing is a major interest of this firm, the plant is also an important producer of frozen vegetables, especially locally grown peas. The importance of this plant is illustrated by the recent import of American peas. Further expansion is planned, including plant for meat-processing and for research purposes. A further notable food firm is Smith's Crisps Ltd, who manufacture at Great Yarmouth. Brewing and malting are represented by two firms: Lacons, the local brewers serving north-eastern East Anglia, and Watney Mann & Company, whose maltings at Gorleston process barley grown in Great Yarmouth's hinterland and serve the firm's London, Alton

(Hants) and Brighton breweries. Two firms, Matthes Ltd and W. Purdy Ltd, account for most of the 345 employees in bread and confectionery manufacture, serving an area extending far westwards in Norfolk.

The second most important industry in terms of the labour force involved is radio engineering, employing over 3,400 workers, including nearly 2,000 women. One firm, Erie Resistors Ltd, employs most of these and is the largest firm in the town. Its post-war growth has radically altered the employment structure of the town, as subsidiary firms of Pye Radio have done at near-by Lowestoft.

The remaining third of the industrial labour force is distributed over a wide range of industries. Perhaps the most notable of these is Grout & Co. Ltd, a firm of artificial silk manufacturers, originally established by continental refugees in 1815. Another textile firm, Ungar Fabrics Ltd, which manufactures brocades, was set up when Great Yarmouth qualified for government assistance for the establishment of industry during the period 1958–60.

The Hartmann Fibre Company Ltd, whose labour force manufacturing packaging materials exceeds 500, is one of the few manufacturing firms in Great Yarmouth employing a substantial majority of male labour. By broadening the industrial structure of the area, such firms have helped to avoid chronic unemployment in the town; indeed, the Boulton & Paul project for a joinery works at near-by Lowestoft is comparable in this respect.

Among other important firms in a wide variety of industries are Johnson & Sons Ltd, an old-established firm, with extensive interests in clothing manufacture, from hosiery to oilskins, the latter being an appropriate product for manufacture in a port. Precasters Ltd of Gorleston produces concrete goods mainly for domestic use, including garages, coal bunkers, and fencing posts. The firm also has a smaller works at Thetford. The V.G. Porcelain Company, associated with a London firm, manufactures insulating apparatus for electrical goods.

The port provides a measure of quite distinctive industrial employment, apart from that directly associated with fishing. The firm of Fellows & Company Ltd undertakes the repair of coastwise trading ships and the construction of small commercial craft. Shipbuilding in

Great Yarmouth, however, does not compare in importance with the industry in the sister port of Lowestoft, where Brooke Marine Ltd and Richards Ironworks Ltd are notable builders of trawlers. Timber, one of the principal imports of Great Yarmouth, provides employment for 500 men in three main firms – Jewson & Sons Ltd, Orfeur & Bellin Ltd, and Brown, Palgrave & Son Ltd.

KING'S LYNN

King's Lynn is a port, manufacturing centre, and business and commercial centre. Its major industries are food packing, heavy chemicals, and engineering, while other industries established in the town include malting and brewing, sawmilling, and vehicle repair.

In general, it is true to say that the industries of King's Lynn–save engineering–are connected with agriculture. This is most clearly the case with the food industry, represented by four large firms, producing between them soup, canned and frozen fruit, and vegetables, and a sugar refinery. Campbell's Soups Ltd has an international market and is of American origin. Beaulah's (King's Lynn) Canners Ltd is an independent firm, while Lincolnshire Canners Ltd at West Lynn has connections with factories in other parts of the country. Fropax Ltd, also at West Lynn, operating both a cannery and freezing plant, is of a slightly different type, being one of a group of associated firms having a wide range of interests, including meat transport, soap manufacture, animal food preparation, and a shipping line.

The sugar refinery, dating from 1927, was one of the earliest beet-sugar factories to come into production in England. It is one of three in Norfolk, and has an obvious affinity with present-day local agriculture.

The food industry employs about 1,200 men and 1,700 women at peak periods, and imposes a well defined employment régime, characterized by highly seasonal demands for labour and a high proportion of female workers. Furthermore, the canners and freezers all need additional labour at the same period of the year. Generally, buildings are modern and, with the exception of the soup factory, which has private rail sidings, have road access only, but the factories differ widely in their detailed siting in relation both to the local road pattern and convenience for tapping the female labour market.

The sugar refinery, working a 'campaign' from September to February, dovetails its peak labour demand of 300 or more reasonably well with that of the canneries, and forms one leg of an annual migration of casual labour in the district: to the sugar factory in the autumn, to the chemical works in the spring, to the cannery in the summer. The factory provides a special example of railside location; whereas large quantities of sugar-beet are brought to it by road hauliers according to a well devised plan of input of beet, it is desirable to retain a proportion of rail-borne beet, since the yield of the crop may vary in different parts of the country and Norfolk beet, loaded in rail trucks, may be sent elsewhere for processing. For example, King's Lynn beet is often diverted to Colwick (Notts.) since it forms a welcome return load for empty wagons returned from Whitemoor marshalling yard at March to the east Midland coalfield.

The heavy chemical industry is represented by two firms. The older firm, West Norfolk Farmers' Manure and Chemical Co-operative Co. Ltd, producing fertilizers, is a large production unit employing 500, but is fairly small in comparison with some of the multi-branch firms in this industry. It had its origin in the nineteenth century, before the introduction of the Fertilizers Act, when a co-operative organization was started by local farmers in order to produce fertilizers of an established quality and efficiency; the basic organization of the firm is still the same as at the time of its foundation. The other firm, Dow Agrochemicals Ltd, which started full production in 1960, has a very modern, highly automated factory, producing selective weed-killer for the western European market; it is another example of the advantage of the location of King's Lynn for international commerce.

One major firm, the Cooper Roller Bearings Co. Ltd, dominates the engineering industry with almost 700 employees. It specializes in producing ball bearings of a particular type, and may be regarded as a highly individual development of the traditional metal working and blacksmithing trades for which rural areas formerly formed a large market. Alfred Dodman & Co. Ltd employs about eighty people in the manufacture of machinery for the food-canning industry. Marine-engines formerly constituted an important proportion of this firm's production and boilers are still built.

THE REST OF NORFOLK

THETFORD

Thetford deserves separate treatment since it is the only town in Norfolk where a Town Development Scheme is being carried out. Under this scheme the Borough of Thetford is receiving 'overspill' population and industry from the area administered by the London County Council. Before the inception of the scheme in 1959 the industries of Thetford were quite varied, including canning (Norfolk Canneries Ltd), papier mâché manufacture (Patent Pulp Manufacturing Co. Ltd), electronics (Cathodeon Ltd), and the manufacture of road signs (I.R.S. Ltd), and the industries now being set up are adding to this diversity. Two factors have influenced most of the firms developing in Thetford: inability to expand their premises in London and a ready supply of fairly skilled labour, since industrial development must necessarily go hand-in-hand with the movement of population to the town.

Forty years ago, Thetford was virtually a one-industry town, dominated by the steam tractor works of Burrell's, whose closure in 1932 substantially retarded its economic life. The current pattern of industry in Thetford provides a marked contrast. There are two principal industrial areas, a discontinuous line of older-established industries along the Little Ouse river, some of them occupying parts of Burrell's site, and the L.C.C. estate, which is being developed comprehensively with made-up roads and main services. Certain mill premises – in recent use as a coffee mill – have proved useful for temporarily housing firms pending the erection of new premises on the L.C.C. estate. A notable result of the experience of the larger firms in having been restricted regarding expansion in London is their eagerness to acquire sites sufficiently large to accommodate considerable future expansion. Much of the land allocated for industrial use is, therefore, likely to remain undeveloped until individual firms reach the later stages of their development programmes. Road access alone is available to the estate, but this has not so far deterred industrialists from going to Thetford, and reflects the growing tendency towards transport of goods by road. At present there are sixteen firms with a total labour force of about 250 on the estate. Their range of products includes coal-handling machinery, refrigeration equipment, music printing, and women's underwear and outerwear. Perhaps the most significant fact arising out of any analysis of the new industrial structure of Thetford is the comparatively 'heavy' character of some of the industries concerned. Whereas, since 1945, some comparatively remote areas have attracted industries producing goods having a high value but little weight, with low distribution costs, and generally requiring female labour, Thetford has been able to attract firms dealing in quite bulky materials. Two reasons probably account for this: the smooth working of the L.C.C. organization whereby firms are advised to examine the practicability of a site at Thetford, and the comparative proximity of the town to the consuming population of Greater London and the Midlands. Thetford is, on this latter basis, less remote than almost all the other Norfolk market towns. Furthermore, it enjoys exceptionally good road communications with some of the least impeded main roads in England in its immediate vicinity, while by rail it is but a short distance from March, a key point in the organization of British Railways freight services. In short, in the planning of industrial development on a national scale the advantages of Thetford are considerable and are being increasingly realized.

MARKET TOWNS AND RURAL DISTRICTS

The market towns of 3,000 to 6,000 population, evenly distributed throughout the county, are characteristic of rural Norfolk. While the administrative and commercial functions of the towns are similar, their manufacturing industries are quite diverse in both type and size. Nevertheless, industries serving agriculture are found in all the towns; these are either food industries or engineering.

The food industries include malting, grain milling, seed cleaning, and the compounding of cattle food, which is often associated with dealing in fertilizers. Such industries, mainly manufacturing ingredients for consumer food industries, are distributed fairly evenly through the county. They depend on the local acreage of cereals and legumes and, save in the case of malting, their plant is highly mechanized. Production is often for local consumption, though brewers' malt is dispatched from Norfolk towns to London, Yorkshire or Merseyside. Vertical organization is fairly common in this industry, and much Norfolk barley is malted by brewers. The future of some of the maltings is uncertain, since the productivity of labour working in them is far inferior to that in a large modern malting. Further, the buildings are not readily adaptable to other uses since they receive little daylight and have low ceilings and obstructed floors. Grain mills are, on the whole, fairly small, since the locally produced soft wheat is in smaller demand than the hard, imported grains, which are usually milled at the country's main points of import.

A second major food industry is the preserving of fruit and vegetables. This is found in fewer locations but much larger units than the cereal industries, at North Walsham (Norfolk Canneries Ltd, Westwick Frosted Products Ltd), Thetford (q.v.), Swaffham (Corbatch Canners Ltd), and King's Lynn (q.v.). Freezing as well as canning is carried on at North Walsham. An allied industry is cider making at Attleborough. The canning industry has generated a demand for other industries, notably the manufacture of canning machinery at King's Lynn (q.v.) and of tinplate cans at Wisbech in Cambridgeshire.

Freezing of poultry at Harleston and Fakenham (Waveney Valley Packers Ltd) and Great Witchingham (Bernard Matthews Ltd) is an industry of recent growth. The broiler house is a common feature of the Norfolk rural scene, and, by reason of its price, the frozen chicken is able to compete successfully with red meat; ducks and turkeys are also becoming important in the quick freezing trade, for the market, as for preserved fruit and vegetables, is nation-wide, while the regular supply of broilers throughout the year is a considerable advantage, since the processing plant is in constant use.

Norfolk has three of the country's eighteen beet-sugar refineries, at King's Lynn (q.v.), Wissington, and Cantley, for a considerable acreage of sugar-beet is grown locally, and is especially popular with farmers since it is a cash crop, a 'cleaning' crop on the land, and has agriculturally useful by-products.

The second important group of industries in the county may be classified under the general heading of engineering. In sheer number of firms, agricultural engineering is probably the most evenly distributed, both as regards major firms in the towns and small businesses in the rural areas. Indeed, the manufacture and repair of agricultural implements is an industry that has grown naturally in this arable county. Nevertheless, there are few firms which have a national market for their products.

Outside Norwich and King's Lynn, East Dereham shows the most remarkable concentration of general engineering, with over 900 people employed. There are four firms in engineering or woodworking, a foundry, and the largest firm of tractor dealers and repairers in Norfolk. The size of firm is comparatively large, and the demand for male labour is in conspicuous contrast to the food industries' requirements of female labour. Crane's, with their production of specialized heavy road trailers for a world market, are probably the most notable firm, but, in terms of the labour force employed, the woodworking (Hobbies Ltd), furniture (Jentique Ltd), and electric clock (Metamec Ltd) factories are no less significant. Not so large, but highly important among East Dereham industries, is the firm of Dreibholz & Floering Ltd, manufacturing beet-slicing machinery and established in 1930 by reason of the high import duties charged on Dutch machinery. Anglian Building Products Ltd, of Lenwade (a member of the Boulton & Paul Group), has devised another highly specialized engineering product, pre-stressed reinforced concrete components for civil engineering projects, including component members for the construction of motorway bridges. Like Crane's it provides a good example of a firm producing specialized goods of quite considerable bulk for a wide market; in addition, the industry depends on local mineral resources. Yet the rise of the firm clearly owes much to local technical and commercial enterprise.

New engineering firms are still being set up in Norfolk. Harleston Industries Ltd, which recently started production of light agricultural implements, was attracted to the town by reason of the labour force available, for, at the time of the inception of the project, the Waveney Valley was recognized at national level as a distressed area; a more detailed aspect of location was the need for easy access to the parent factory is south-west Essex. The electronics industry and the manufacture of high frequency welded plastic goods have been introduced to Norfolk recently – a sign of Norfolk's share in the changing techniques and emphases in engineering.

Alma Components Ltd, at Diss, transferred the whole of its production from Holloway to Diss in 1960, to a site affording generous room for expansion. Pye Radio, through subsidiary companies, is established at Thetford and Harleston; indeed, this firm has done much to provide employment in some of the smaller East Anglian towns since 1945. Capital expenditure was minimized by the Pye firms, which took over existing empty buildings. It is quite usual in the electronics industry for a factory's production to be dispatched by post; in the case of the Diss firm the facility of a late night post to its London sales office was an important attraction. East Coast Plastics Ltd, at North Walsham, also set up in 1960, manufactures a very wide range of plastic goods, from metatarsal pads to beach balls, and, as in electronics, the clean and quiet work is highly attractive to female labour.

Outside the food and engineering industries there are certain large firms which have taken advantage of the rural craft tradition and have evolved modern manufacturing methods in its place. Nationally, the brush industry consists of a few large firms: two of these, the C.W.S. and Briton Brush Co. Ltd, are represented in Wymondham and, indeed, dominate the employment structure of that town, giving work to over 500 people. The C.W.S. factory also produces garden furniture, while Briton Brush has another works at Attleborough. Aldrich Brothers Ltd, at Diss, also makes coir matting and is a wholesale distributor of linoleum.

Other commodities produced in Norfolk which are also of high value and little weight, and require a substantial labour force, include cardboard boxes and display material, manufactured by the Argent Box Company Ltd (attracted from London to establish a branch at Cromer), and fireworks (manufactured by Brock's Crystal Palace Fireworks Ltd at Swaffham). Fakenham, where Wymans Ltd employs over 200, is a printing centre of national importance, as are Beccles and Bungay in east Suffolk.

The availability of labour in the rural areas has also stimulated the development of branch factories by Norwich firms. F.W. Harmer Ltd has clothing factories at Watton and Fakenham, while Edwards & Holmes Ltd maintains a closing room (for the stitching and shaping of shoe uppers) at Sheringham. The latter example, where only one intermediate process in shoe making is carried out, is paralleled in Kendall's umbrella factory at Cromer, to which umbrella fabric segments are brought from Leicester for stitching to frames, and are returned to the parent factory for finishing.

RURAL CRAFT INDUSTRIES

Norfolk Rural Industries Committee provides technical and marketing advice for craft industries. This, together with the national Rural Industries Bureau's building and equipment loan fund, does much to assist viability of the smaller craft firms. These include such traditional activities as thatching, saddlery, farriery, and basketry. Agricultural engineering businesses, the successors of the village blacksmith, are the most numerous, and, provided they can practise such modern techniques as arc-welding, small firms can make a living. Although farm mechanization has reduced the number of horses, there is a demand for farriery by reason of the popularity of riding schools. Reed thatching is a notable rural Norfolk craft, in spite of the relative cheapness of unsightly alternative roofing materials. Furniture making and pottery are examples of non-agricultural rural crafts depending on a demand for individual handicraft goods. A newcomer of marked recent growth is boat building. There has long been a boat-building industry concerned with cabin cruisers in the Broads area, but the growing demand for outboard runabouts has stimulated expansion of the industry. It is one of the most prosperous in the county, and includes a number of quite small firms. This industry is particularly alive to the possibilities of new techniques, such as the use of fibre-glass. It also has a lively export trade, particularly from such important yards as those of Graham Bunn Ltd at Wroxham and Herbert Woods Ltd at Potter Heigham.

After this description of present-day manufacturing industry, it is now possible to discuss in general terms the factors which have influenced its structure.

Norfolk's mineral resources are limited. The Chalk has for long provided agricultural lime and its harder layers ('clunch') have been used locally for building. Its flint content was an essential element in prehistoric cultures, and later a valuable material for the construction of foundations and walls. The Carstone of the Lower Green-sand formation may have been a source of iron to early man and it may still be seen as a building-material in west Norfolk, while the Sandringham Sands which constitute the lowest beds of the formation are exploited near King's Lynn for glass making. The Kimmeridge Clay and glacial brickearths have been the basis of relatively small and scattered brickworks in the area. Finally, the Crag deposits and fluvio-glacial gravels are a source of aggregates.

This catalogue reveals Norfolk's lack of those minerals which were the basis of large-scale industrial development in other parts of the country: coal and metalliferous ores, particularly iron. The nearest sources of coal lie in the east Midlands, and the poor state of west–east land communications in the initial period of industrial growth hindered its transportation to the county. The longer sea haul from the north-east coalfield was, and to some extent still is, an easier route for the movement of this vital mineral. The peat resources of the fens and of Broadland, though of domestic importance as a fuel, were no remedy for this deficiency.

The lack of coal and other minerals was, then, a handicap to the area at the time of the Industrial Revolution. It has not remained so. The linking of all parts of Norfolk by means of the grid system with power stations not only in the locality (where waterside sites facilitate the import of coal and oil) but with the rest of the country, has solved the problem of power supply, and has given freedom of location to a manufacturing industry which makes extensive use of small individual motors. Indeed, it would not be unreasonable to correlate the post-war industrial development illustrated in fig. 5 on page 209 with the post-war growth of electricity production shown in fig. 6 on page 221.

The former limitations have, however, left their impress upon the industrial structure. There is no metallurgy and little heavy engineering, while textiles have disappeared from a position of dominance. Farming has survived on a large scale because of the lack of industrial competition for land, and the processing of its products is an important element in modern manufacturing industry, which is for the most part light in character.

Industrial development has been encouraged by the cheapness of sites. The lack of such development in the past in many parts of the county has held down site-values to a relatively low level. Increasing interest in the area is now causing an upward trend in land prices (most marked in central Norwich) but this price factor still remains an attraction.

Physically, also, the sites are often attractive. The relative flatness of the land makes their development inexpensive; yet the land is sufficiently undulating and its structure usually permeable enough to permit good drainage. Water supply is, on the whole, adequate, though difficulties appear to have arisen recently in the provision of additional supplies for Norwich. Not only do the rivers maintain a fairly even flow but the underlying chalk yields an ample supply. The water is, admittedly, hard and some firms have had to instal softening equipment, but its abundance remains a real attraction to industry. On the other hand, effluent disposal, while presenting no problems in such places as Norwich, is proving a difficulty in some of the smaller centres, particularly in connection with such food-processing industries as canning and broiler-processing. Its noxious quality and great quantity may require heavy capital expenditure to extend the small domestic sewage disposal systems which are typical of the market towns. Effluent disposal facilities are a more important factor in the location of certain industries than is generally realized: while such industries as creameries are, with more modern plant, tending to reduce their requirements for water supply and trade waste disposal for a given volume of production, such newer industries as those which wash and process fresh vegetables for retail sale need phenomenal supplies of water and produce equal quantities of effluent. The impact of this trend in such areas as Norfolk may well cause future location problems.

Finally, because of the relative cheapness and abundance of good building sites, industrialists are able to buy comparatively large and contiguous areas which will provide not only for their immediate needs but also for all foreseeable future developments. A number of firms have opened branch factories in Norfolk on account of their inability to obtain such room for expansion in their original locations.

The value of the various factors just discussed is well illustrated by the choice of a site on the outskirts of

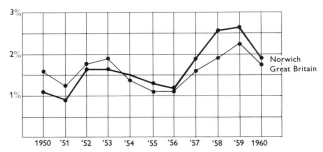

Fig. 3 *Unemployment percentages, Great Britain and Norwich, 1950–60*

Norwich by the firm of May & Baker, which was unable to expand further on the parent site at Dagenham. After examination of eighty-nine sites throughout the country, this spot was chosen because it offered, among other things: 180 acres of gently sloping land on which two million square feet of factory space might eventually be developed; the supply of three million gallons of water daily, partly from the mains and partly from bore-holes in the underlying chalk (with the nearby river

Wensum as an emergency source of supply); and the disposal of a corresponding amount of effluent.

Turning next to the factor of labour, Dr Allison has shown how the nineteenth century development of new industry in Norwich was based upon a pool of redundant textile workers. Today, no such pool exists. Fig. 3 shows that the post-war unemployment percentages lie close to the national average, in comparison with areas that depend heavily on one industry, for example, the Lancashire cotton area (Bolton 16.4 per cent unemployed in 1952) and the tin-plate area of S.W. Wales (Llanelly 7.8 per cent unemployed in 1958). This suggests that Norfolk's diversity of industries, many of them concerned with such consumer goods as food and clothing, for which there is a rising demand, has contributed to these low percentages. Furthermore, consumption of these goods, unlike that of consumer durables, is not so readily affected by changes in hire-purchase regulations and indirect taxation.

Nevertheless, the general state of labour supply remains an attraction. Though some categories of worker

TABLE I

AVERAGE EARNINGS, OCTOBER 1959 (*Source: Annual Abstract of Statistics,* 1960)

Ministry of Labour Order No.	Occupation	Weekly wage rate: Males and Females	Per cent of Local Labour Force	Weekly wage rate: Males over 21	Per cent of Local Male Labour Force	Weekly wage rate: Females over 18	Per cent of Local Female Labour Force
II	Coal Mining	300s. 3d.*	Nil	Figures not available	—	Figures not available	—
V	Metal Manufacture	282s. 11d.	0·26	303s. 4d.	0·37	147s. 7d.	0·03
VIII	Vehicles	271s. 8d.	0·46	304s. 8d.	0·67	163s. 3d.	0·03
XV	Printing	253s. 7d.	2·01	322s. 6d.	1·88	150s. 5d.	2·29
VI	Engineering and Electrical Goods	241s. 2d.	5·63	279s. 7d.	5·97	152s. 5d.	4·93
III	Food, Drink, and Tobacco	195s. 10d.	7·78	248s. 4d.	6·56	133s. 9d.	10·29
X	Textiles	179s. 9d.	0·93	248s. 1d.	0·59	139s. 1d.	1·62
XII	Clothing	149s. 9d.	5·67	235s. 11d.	3·68	134s. 4d.	9·74
I	Agriculture and Fishing	Figures not available	16·67	199s. 7d.	22·48	128s. 1d.†	4·76
	Average of all industries	**228s. 6d.**		**270s. 9d.**		**140s. 4d.**	

* Including value of allowances in kind.   † Women and girls

in some areas are scarce, the situation is not, on the whole, so difficult as in certain parts of Britain. Furthermore, the area is remarkable for its lack of industrial disputes: in Norwich the efficient machinery of labour relations in the shoe industry may set the tone for other sectors; in the county, the rural ethos and the relative scarcity of alternative employment may be influential. In addition, the general level of wages appears to be low. Table 1 shows that the most highly paid industrial categories are scantily represented in the area and that, conversely, the rewards of the most important occupations locally fall below the national average. To the employer this is reflected not only in lower operating costs but in lower building outlay as well. To the worker, the lower money wages may be offset by cheaper housing, the low cost of the journey to work and, in Norwich, the amenities of a large centre without their attendant high costs.

There has been little influx of foreign labour, either white or coloured, and therefore none of the social problems which have been so marked in certain parts of Britain in recent years. It seems likely that male immigrants, often with families to support, prefer those regions where a shortage of labour has made earnings unusually high. One Norwich clothing factory, some local hospitals, and domestic service are among the exceptions and, in these cases, the labour is entirely female and European in origin.

With reference to female labour, a rather sharp distinction may be drawn between full-time and part-time workers. In Norfolk generally, the proportion of females in the labour force is somewhat below the national average, and so far as the rural areas are concerned this has, in part, been attributed to the heavy domestic demands on females in an agricultural community. So far as permanent work is concerned, it may also be a reflection of the inability to amass a labour force of sufficient size to be an efficient unit of production. Nevertheless, if there are no undue difficulties about the journey to work, most areas can produce a reasonable female labour force, although an individual small town may not; the journey-to-work range of the bicycle is a somewhat critical factor in determining labour catchment areas. Employers in the county have made considerable provision for the transport of female labour and some of the journeys are considerable – Hingham to Wymondham, Aylsham to Norwich, and, in the case of canning, Hunstanton to King's Lynn, Downham Market to Wisbech, and even Methwold to Long Sutton (Lincs.). While such daily journeys are more usually necessary in the case of professional and clerical employment to obtain a wider choice of job, comparable journeys for factory labour are more extraordinary.

In general, the market for part-time labour is distinctive. Such jobs appeal to the married woman who wishes to work only for a short period in the year and who, in canning at least, has hours suited to her domestic duties; or they may appeal to the woman who habitually has a seasonal change of job – from canning in the summer and autumn to working in the fenland bulb fields in the spring. Many seasonal jobs in the holiday industry are undertaken by people such as students from other areas. In Norwich a declining amount of 'outworking' is carried on in shoe and cracker manufacture.

It may be seen, then, that Norfolk can offer certain advantages in terms of land and labour. Although these advantages are found throughout much of the county the industrialist's precise choice of site may be influenced by other factors. Despite good road communications between most major settlements and London and the Midlands, sites in the south and west of the county are inevitably better placed than those in, say, the north coast area. Thus a newcomer may well prefer Thetford or Diss to Cromer or Sheringham. Again, the growth of the rail network in the nineteenth century determined the precise location of those industries which handled bulky raw materials and products, such as the maltings and beet-sugar factories. The more recent contraction of the rail network (see fig. 4) may conversely limit the sites for certain types of new industry.

The sources of capital for industrial development have tended to change. Most of the old-established firms began as local enterprises and their early growth was financed largely by the 'ploughing-back' of their own profits. Such capitalization was adequate for small concerns and, indeed, some post-war businesses have made a successful debut by such means. But frequently growth has had to be accompanied by the recruitment of outside capital. Many private companies have become public and control has passed outside the district:

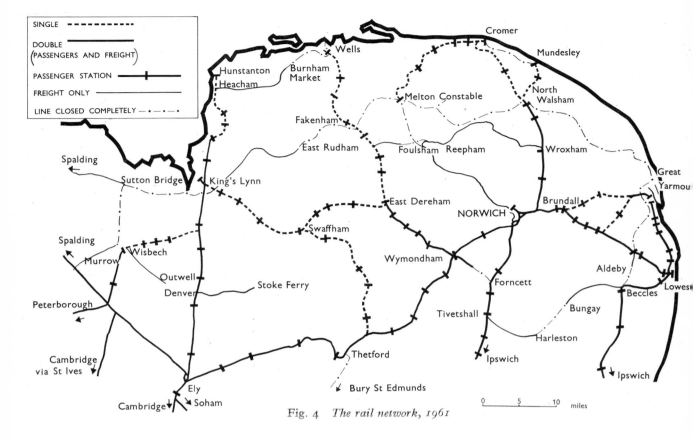

Fig. 4 *The rail network, 1961*

J. and J. Colman and Barnards, both of Norwich, are good examples of this process of development. A substantial proportion of post-war enterprise has been financed by outside capital from the start: Campbell's Soups (an American firm) at King's Lynn, May & Baker and Roneo Ltd in Norwich, many of the new Thetford firms, all illustrate this tendency.

Government assistance in the establishment of industry has been limited. The encouragement of rural industries has already been discussed. Apart from this, the only intervention which has taken place occurred in the years 1958–60, when the coastal stretch between Blakeney and Great Yarmouth with its hinterland and the Waveney valley qualified for Government assistance. This led to the establishment of factories at Cromer, Pulham, and Harleston. There has been an absence of, for example, the Government 'speculative' building, which is taking place in Northern Ireland, the L.C.C. site at Thetford being unique; the Urban and Rural

District Councils have no powers, and the private builder has shown little inclination, to anticipate industrial expansion, the Salhouse Road industrial estate on the outskirts of Norwich again being exceptional.

Since the area must import so much of its raw-materials in a partly or completely worked-up form the development of vertical organizations has been limited. Such organization is, however, seen in those industries based on locally produced foodstuffs – maltings and breweries, for instance, and the cultivation, canning or quick-freezing of garden-crops and fruit on estates such as that at Westwick near North Walsham. Shoe manufacture is the only factory industry to display a fully developed structure, with its tanning, last and heel making, and cardboard-box manufacture; but these activities are usually carried on by separate firms. Horizontal organization may be found among firms in, for example, construction, the timber trade, and food-processing, but it is somewhat exceptional. It may be

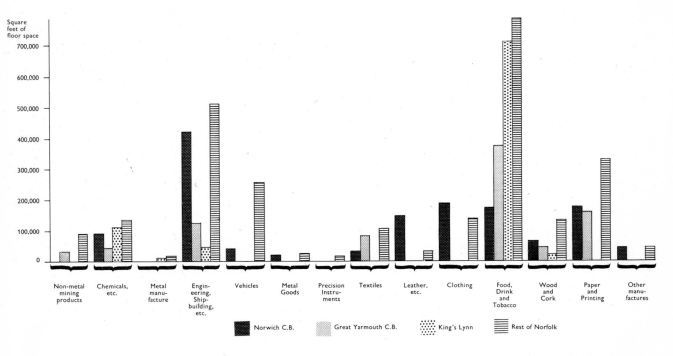

Fig. 5 *Square feet of floor space authorized by industrial development certificates 1949–61. Classified by Ministry of Labour Employment Orders*

concluded that while some firms constitute, in effect, a multiple factory on a single site and others are part of bigger local or national organizations, the majority exist as solitary units. Furthermore, they do not look to Norwich as a supply and marketing centre in the same way as would, for example, the textile towns of south Lancashire or the West Riding towards Manchester or Leeds respectively. This feature in manufacturing industry contrasts with Norwich's importance as a centre for service industries, illustrations of which have been given by Mr Thomas.

Account must finally be taken of that enterprise which is necessary to weld the factors of land, labour, and capital already considered into an effective organization. Dr Allison has shown how many of today's thriving businesses started life in the last century on the initiative of an individual or a small group of partners. It was personal enterprise that ensured success in the face of lack of raw materials and the remoteness of the region.

The descriptive parts of this section make it clear that such enterprise still exists today.

Future economic development can, of course, only be guessed at, but the tendencies shown in fig. 5 may well persevere. Food-processing, in an agriculturally rich area and with an increasing market, is likely to expand further, provided the phenomenal seasonal demand for labour can be met. Further mechanization may be the answer to this problem. Engineering, in its many forms, with its production of goods of high value for the weight of imported raw materials involved and with its reputation for quality and enterprise, should continue to prosper. The reputation of local printing firms will perhaps further their opportunities. Together with Beccles and Bungay, Norfolk is already responsible for about one-fifth of the country's book-production. In chemical manufactures, we may look confidently for continued expansion both in Norwich and King's Lynn. Increasing automation in the shoe industry, with its attendant need for large-scale

TABLE II

MAJOR DEVELOPMENTS OF 5,000 SQUARE FEET OR OVER COMPLETED IN THE FOOD INDUSTRY 1948–61

	Grain Milling	Baking	Dairying	Sugar Refining	Fruit and Vegetable Products	Other Food Industries	Brewing and Malting	Soft Drinks
Norwich C.B.			78 (2)			17 (2)	59 (4)	
Great Yarmouth C.B.					213 (8)	114 (8)		
Norfolk (Admin. County including King's Lynn)	71 (6)	10 (1)	34 (3)	70 (7)	753 (29)	323 (9)	9 (1)	29 (1)

The left-hand figure in each column indicates floor area in thousands of square feet, the figures in brackets the number of projects

operation and heavy capitalization, may lead to a greater amount of amalgamation in this sector than has taken place in the past. The industry will be faced with the problem of maintaining its reputation for design and craftsmanship while making increasing use of machinery. This, in its turn, will involve not only precise control in the tanning of natural raw materials so as to guarantee, for instance, uniform stretch, but also a greater standardization of last shapes and measurements. A further problem may well be that of mounting foreign competition, and the industry's representation in the recent British Trades Fair in Moscow symbolizes its determination to maintain and, if possible, expand its overseas markets.

Norfolk News Co. Ltd

The Port of Norwich by night

commercial and professional services

P. G. THOMAS

ITS DISTANCE from other large towns and cities and the rural nature of the county of Norfolk are factors which have encouraged the growth of Norwich as the capital of a large provincial area and as a centre providing many types of services. It follows, therefore, that in a survey of commercial and professional services in the region, Norwich should occupy a position of great importance. The diagram of employment quotients in the introduction to this section (fig. 3b) illustrates this importance by comparing the numbers employed in the

of its working population than Norwich employed in the Transport category as a whole.

There follows a survey of each of the Commercial Services in Norwich and of the work of the ports of Norfolk. The scale and nature of Professional Services in Norwich are described, and the section concludes with a survey of the Health Services, the Public Utilities, Entertainment, and the Holiday Industry in Norwich and its region as a whole.

	Population	No. of Shops	Population per Shop	Total Turnover	Average Turnover per Shop
Norwich	118,800	1,510	78·6	£17,384,000	£11,512
Oxford	104,100	1,033	100·8	£17,159,000	£16,611
Plymouth	216,300	1,808	119·6	£20,358,000	£11,260
York	105,600	1,465	72·1	£13,996,000	£9,553

Norwich area with those in Great Britain as a whole. In the categories of Transport, Distribution, Insurance and Banking, the Public Utilities (Gas, Electricity, and Water Supply), and Professional Services, Norwich is above the national average except only in Transport and even in this category, if the comparison is confined to the numbers employed in Road and Rail Transport, it is found that 5.4 per cent of the working population of the Norwich area are in these groups, compared with a national figure of 3.9 per cent. Norwich has no Air Transport services, and the numbers employed in Water Transport services in the Norwich area are small, thus producing a different picture when all forms of transport are compared. King's Lynn, because of its Docks and Harbour services in particular, has a higher proportion

Distribution–Retailing. The hinterland of Norwich, i.e. that area in which public transport carries passengers more conveniently to Norwich than to any other centre, has an estimated population of approximately 131,000, larger than the population (118,000) of the centre itself, and much larger than the hinterlands of comparable centres such as Oxford (64,000) and York (48,000). Plymouth, with a population of 216,300, almost double that of Norwich, has a hinterland of only 55,000.

The Table above shows the scale of retailing in Norwich as compared with Oxford, Plymouth, and York. Figures are taken from the full Census of Distribution, 1950.

It will be seen that Norwich is well served with shops,

P.G. THOMAS is a Lecturer in the Department of Commerce and Management at Norwich City College

having the second lowest population per shop, though having a much lower average turnover per shop than Oxford. This may well be the result of lower average earnings in Norwich and its hinterland compared with Oxford. However, the corresponding figures for Plymouth and York are even lower, so that it may be said that retailing in Norwich is relatively flourishing.

The breakdown in character of the retail outlets is shown below:

NUMBER OF SHOPS

	Norwich	Oxford	Plymouth	York
Grocery Group	362	228	445	332
Other Food Shops	380	220	567	399
Confectioner, Tobacconist, Newsagent Group	180	122	175	140
Chemist Group	42	45	67	51
Hardware Group	69	68	76	56
Booksellers and Stationers Group	19	28	33	28
All other Retail Outlets	458	322	445	459
Totals	**1,510**	**1,033**	**1,808**	**1,465**

The estimates for the 1957 Census of Distribution, which was a sample survey, and Ministry of Labour returns show the following picture when Norwich is compared with Great Britain as a whole:

	Population per shop	Average Turnover per shop	Employees per shop	Turnover per employee
Norwich	81·8	£17,117	5·7	£2,990
Gt. Britain	87·2	£13,586	4·5	£3,036

Although the figures for the 1957 census are subject to small sampling errors in respect of the smaller independent traders, Norwich appears again above average in its number of shops and in average turnover. Employment per shop is higher than the national average and turnover per employee 1.6 per cent below the figure for Great Britain as a whole.

There is an open Provision Market in the Market Place, with approximately 200 stalls, about eighty of which sell fruit and vegetables, with a general assortment of other traders selling goods such as grocery, fish, drapery, and books.

On Mondays and Thursdays it was customary for no market stalls to open, but during 1960, weekly tenants have been opening their stalls on these days in increasing numbers for the sale of fruit and vegetables. The majority of greengrocers and fruiterers are now selling a large proportion of foreign produce and out of ten growers who have stalls, only two now sell solely their own produce, the result of the large variety and cheap price of foreign produce. The volume of trading seems to be increasing, judging by the difficulty faced by Norwich Corporation in moving increasing quantities of stall refuse, though the increased use of pre-packing and non-returnable boxes and crates is no doubt responsible for some of this.

The supermarket has not yet appeared in Norwich, although branches of well-known multiple grocers have followed the recent campaign to cut prices and self-service is increasing. The majority of department stores and large drapery and fashion houses are members of the Debenham Group, although one large store still retains its independence and its own individual character. The customers patronizing the main Norwich stores appear to be divided fairly evenly as between city and county dwellers, although one or two stores cater particularly for a county clientele and report that 60 per cent of their account customers live in the county. An interesting feature of business in the last year or so has been a tendency towards a more even spread of the week's trade at the expense of Saturday's previous preponderance. Many retailers feared the effect on trade of moving the Livestock Market outside the city to Harford Bridge in 1960, believing that the customary shopping expeditions made by farmers' wives and others, whose menfolk had business at the Cattle Market on Saturdays, would no longer be convenient. However, trade has not been noticeably affected in volume, although the tendency to a more even spread of the week's business may well be partly explained by this move. Since the Old Cattle Market site has been levelled as a car park, 2,000 more cars per week are being parked there, and this may prove to be significant for business in the immediate vicinity.

City stores have a very wide delivery area, since customers from such a large area do their shopping in Norwich, particularly for furniture, carpets, and other household durables. There is no competing shopping centre of any size in the immediate vicinity so that it is quite common for customers to travel 40 miles to Norwich, whereas in the Midlands, for example, there would be several alternative shopping centres. This gives rise to heavy delivery costs and a large weekly mileage. One store with two delivery vehicles averages 1,200 miles per week for delivery, and 750 miles per week for staff cars and its carpet-fitting van. Most stores deliver to the whole of Norfolk and parts of neighbouring counties.

The Norwich Co-operative Society had a membership of 42,924 in the half-year ended 5 March 1960 and assets of £1,298,516. The net sales for the half-year were £1,941,833, an increase of 5.7 per cent over the corresponding period in 1959. There was a record net trading profit of £124,416, the dividend on members' purchases being 11d. in the £, the average dividend over the whole country having fallen below 1s. in the £ for the first time during the same period. A major problem facing the Norwich Co-operative Society is the considerable expenditure which will be made necessary by the Norwich Corporation's proposals for the widening of St Stephen's Street, where several of the Society's older central shops will have to be demolished and replaced by larger modern ones.

Apart from the main shopping centre of the city, there are two sub-centres which have declined in prosperity in recent years. The first is St Benedict's Street, a narrow street leading to Dereham Road and the main exit from the city to King's Lynn. The second is Magdalen Street leading to Botolph Street and St Augustine's on the north of the city and just over the river.

In 1957, the Civic Trust proposed to the Norwich City Council a joint project which would show how the appearance of a given area of the city could be improved, and in 1959 Magdalen Street was chosen for this, a pioneer experiment, which has since been repeated successfully in Holt, Diss, and Cromer, in several other towns inside and outside Norfolk, and more recently in St Benedict's Street.

The work of improvement took about two months and the average cost was less than £80 per property. In only four cases was the expenditure greater than £175; in twenty-two cases it was less than £50. Properties were repainted in a co-ordinated scheme, fascia boards over shops were altered and some re-lettered. Unsightly projecting name signs and advertisements were removed, new blinds and curtains were installed where necessary, and street 'clutter' tidied up or removed. On 8 May 1959, the street was formally opened by Mr Duncan Sandys, President of the Civic Trust (see Front Cover and page 7).

In a survey carried out in August 1960 retailers were questioned concerning the effect of the scheme on trade in Magdalen Street. Out of thirty-nine who were willing to give information, twenty-one reported an increase in turnover, eighteen of whom found that the increase was maintained after the early period of public interest in the scheme had passed. Increases were substantial in thirteen cases, varying between 5 per cent and $33\frac{1}{3}$ per cent, whilst in eight cases increases were only slight. Allowing for variations in hire purchase restrictions and purchase tax rates, also changes in prices and wage rates, some revival of interest in Magdalen Street by the public is quite clear and shopping there has become more pleasurable. Shops with a substantial degree of casual trade profited most, whilst retailers of food, shoes, and expensive shopping goods reported no gain. Only three of the retailers questioned felt the expense had not been worth while.

Other advantages which have accrued are that traders have become more conscious of the need to decorate and to maintain their premises in good condition. The scheme has also brought traders together to discuss common problems, and the Magdalen Street and District Traders' Association has been revived. However, it is certain that a scheme such as the Civic Trust Scheme in Magdalen Street cannot change the planning pattern of an area. Any radical change in the volume of trading in the street seems unlikely until the road and traffic problems of the area have been solved.

The Norwich Co-operative Society, multiple shops, department stores, and independent traders have made use of the new advertising medium – television – since Anglia Television began operating in 1959. The effect on sales has not been very appreciable, although one retailer who advertised his annual sale reported a record first day. Another, a multiple, reported a very favourable reaction when advertising a speciality such as quilt re-covering. A fur company felt that the wider area of customers reached by a television advertisement made it worth while. Apart from sales promotions, other retailers believe that their television advertising has been good for their prestige generally. Two observations of interest are that few retailers reduced their Press advertising when using the television medium, and most carried out an additional Press campaign to back up the television feature. Also, where a television announcer gave the advertising details, the personality and popularity of the announcer had, in some cases, a noticeable effect upon public reaction.

The attraction of television advertising to the local retailer is explained by the fact that 363,000 homes receive Anglia transmissions out of the 695,000 house-holds in the Anglia area which covers all Norfolk, in-cludes Boston (Lincs.), and in the west Wellingborough (Northants.), and Maldon (Essex) in the south. By February 1961 an estimated 400,000 homes in the area will be receiving Anglia. At the news time at 6.15 p.m. approximately 150,000 viewers are watching and this figure is larger during the winter months. This pro-gramme is followed by an advertising session patronized by local retailers, who pay £12 for a 7-second slide with the announcer's voice giving a commentary. Prices vary upwards according to the popularity of the viewing time to a maximum of £91 per 15-second period. The cost to a retailer to reach a thousand homes actually viewing varies for a 30-second flash from 2s. at off-peak times to 12s. at peak periods.

Livestock Market. The new Livestock Market occupies a site of 32 acres near the southern boundary of the city at Harford, and was opened on 1 July 1960. It has parking accommodation for 650 cars and 160 cattle floats. There is also a special railway siding leading directly to the site.

There is space available to handle on one day 3,000 cattle, 400 calves, 2,500 pigs, 850 sheep, and 4,000 head of poultry. Auction sales can go on simultaneously in four rings, and there is an open area for those wishing to offer stock directly to the buyers. There are six blocks of offices, shops, and display areas which have been leased to merchants, bankers, and insurers, meals can be obtained in a restaurant and there is a licensed bar and saloon. It is expected that the cost of construction of the market will have been about £520,000, and for several years, notwithstanding tolls and rents, £13,000 will have to be found from the rates annually to cover this expenditure.

Although it is early to judge the effect of an enlarged market on the amount of business coming forward, the figures of stock for sale for the first three months com-pared with the same period in 1959 on the old Cattle Market are encouraging:

	July–September 1959	July–September 1960
Fat Cattle	2,649	3,559
Barren Cows and Bulls	2,132	2,212
Store Cattle	2,387	4,104
Dairy Cows	317	548
Calves	2,007	2,023
Fat Sheep	2,306	3,218
Store Sheep	1,332	1,628
Fat Pigs	10,338	9,836
Store Pigs	7,442	8,242

Wholesaling. A Wholesale Fruit and Vegetable Market is held on the Old Cattle Market Car Park on Tuesday and Friday mornings with a lesser market on Wednes-days and Saturdays. Many of the market traders also have local depots, to which retailers go for supplies. English produce is carried by road from local growers, or from Wisbech and the Fens, and both English and foreign produce comes from Covent Garden and Great Yarmouth Docks. Market gardeners and farmers also bring in their own produce. There are fourteen specialist wholesalers on the market, of whom six deal almost exclusively in foreign produce, whilst two handle potatoes only and celery in season. The scale of market-ing is seen from the average weekly loads of one of these potato merchants, who brings in 100–120 tons and sometimes up to 160 tons from the Fen areas such as Southery and Ten Mile Bank.

There are over 230 wholesale firms in the city and many of these, including larger firms, are in the food trades; of the remainder, the smaller firms are in the leather and hairdressing supplies business.

Two forces are tending to reduce the number of wholesalers in Norwich, especially the number of mixed wholesale businesses. The first is the growth of the business of multiple shops and the reduction of the business of the small independent trader who was the wholesaler's main customer in bygone years. The second is the growing cost of distribution involved in supplying fewer and smaller orders in the large rural area of Norfolk. The high mileage cost is only worth while for small wholesalers in those commodities with a higher profit margin such as hardware, stationery, toys, and patent medicines. However, the small village shop can often make a traveller's call a profitable one, since such a wide variety of goods must be stocked.

The outstanding trend in the wholesale grocery business has been the extension of Voluntary Group Trading, the two main groups having over 300 retail members in Norfolk. The largest wholesale firms have upwards of 500 retail customers and one has over 900. The volume of goods delivered to retail customers is illustrated by two wholesalers, who, between them, supply 275 tons of sugar and 16 tons of butter weekly. One of these with fourteen delivery vans has an average weekly mileage of 3,392.

Insurance. Some sixty insurance companies have branch offices in Norwich, but many of these are small. This is true even of branches of several of the leading companies and is the result of the pre-eminence of one institution, the Norwich Union Insurance Societies, whose Head Office has a staff of 1,600 and whose Branch Office employs a further 100 people.

The Norwich Union Insurance Group, whose President is Sir Robert Bignold, is one of the largest in the country and consists of the 'parent' company, the Norwich Union Life Insurance Society, with its associated offices, the Norwich Union Fire Insurance Society and the Scottish Union and National Insurance Company. The Life Society is a Mutual Office, with no shareholders, and is the largest institution of this type founded in Great Britain. The early history of the Societies has been described by Dr Allison on page 122, and today there are more than 120 branches and offices throughout the United Kingdom, and all classes of life, fire, accident, and marine insurance are transacted through branches or agencies in more than seventy countries, including western Europe, the Commonwealth, the United States, South America, India, the Middle East, the Far East, and Japan. The Societies have their own training schools for staff and there is a very wide use of mechanical and electronic aids for accounting and recording purposes.

The total group assets now exceed £250,000,000 and the acquisition in 1959 of the shares of the Scottish Union and National Insurance Company has brought the total premium income in respect of fire, accident, and marine insurance business to more than £31,000,000 per annum. More than one-half of the Fire Society's business comes from overseas and the proportion of the Life Society's business is about one-third. Because of the continued expansion of business, extensive rebuilding of Head Office premises is taking place, consisting of a nine-storey office block designed to accommodate a staff of 2,000. One wing of this has been completed and the other is expected to be ready for occupation in 1962.

Banking. Branches of all the large banks are to be found in the area and the character of their work reflects, as is to be expected, the life of the community and the business activity of the area. A large proportion of business comes from agriculture and forms of business ancillary to farming, such as the supplying of feeding-stuffs, fertilizers, and equipment. The boot and shoe industry and light engineering provide a good deal of the banking business in Norwich, while the tourist and holiday business of the county is an important factor. Hotels, holiday camps, caravan sites, and the Broadland motorcruiser firms are all features of this business. The fishing industry of Great Yarmouth and the general port activity require the services of the banks, though services for the fishing industry have decreased as herring fishing itself has declined.

The leading position of Barclay's Bank in the area is almost entirely the result of its amalgamation with the

Gurney Bank of Norwich in 1896. The system established on the acquisition of the small banking firms which had been absorbed into the Gurney Bank and at the amalgamation in 1896, was that the former partners of the old business should be offered positions on the local board of directors, so as to retain local connections and to maintain personal service to customers. This principle has remained in what is now known as Barclay's Bank. Dr Allison has referred on page 122 to the maintenance of local interest which has been a characteristic of the growth of Barclay's Bank: members of the Gurney family are still local directors at Norwich, which is a Local Head Office for branches in Norfolk and along the Suffolk border. This decentralized system of Local Head Offices is a feature of Barclay's Bank. The Bank Plain, Norwich, branch of Barclay's Bank is one of the largest in the country, with a staff of eighty to ninety. In addition, there are staffs employed in the Trustee and Income Tax Departments and there is a small Local Head Office staff.

Road Transport. There are numerous road hauliers in Norwich and district, several of whom have large fleets of vehicles. Some of these vehicles are on permanent contract to particular firms, others being used seasonally, or for the transport of such loads as sand and ballast, but one of the largest of the independent operators, who concentrates on the distribution of industrial and agricultural commodities, has upwards of eighty vehicles and handles an average of 10,000 parcels per day. This operator carries an average annual load of 40,000 tons of fertilizer for agricultural use and large consignments of other freight, providing 600,000 cubic feet of warehousing accommodation, including temperature-controlled facilities, for buffer stocks of a wide variety of foodstuffs and other consumer goods.

The largest group of 130 vehicles is controlled by the B.R.S. (Parcels) Ltd Area Office in Surrey Street. This Area Office controls the Eastern Parcels Area, with two depots in Norwich and others at King's Lynn, Cambridge, Ipswich, Chelmsford, Clacton, and Southend. From Norwich there are regular nightly trunk services to Birmingham, Boston, Cambridge, Halifax, Ipswich, King's Lynn, Leicester, London, Manchester, Nottingham, Rushden, Sheffield, and Southampton, linking all Parcels Depots throughout the country. Two of the most important types of consignment are ladies' shoes and canned goods, reflecting two of the major industries of Norwich and Norfolk. In 1959, the Eastern Parcels Area handled 8,746,053 packages.

The heavy haulage depot of British Road Services has a fleet of sixty-six vehicles with a total carrying capacity of 839 tons. The major consignments are soft fruit, grain and canned goods, and in 1959 the tonnages collected in these groups were 1,009, 22,000, and 23,000 respectively. Whilst approximately three-quarters of the tonnage is

PRINCIPAL RAIL TRAFFICS (1959)

Forwarded		Received	
Confectionery	4,100 tons	Steel and Steel Scrap	35,500 tons
Wine	2,100 tons	Cement	14,500 tons
Boots and Shoes	1,900 tons	Bricks	16,000 tons
Wire Netting	5,000 tons	Fuel Oil and Bitumen	17,000 tons
Iron and Steel Scrap	24,200 tons	Roadstone	11,000 tons
Roses and Bedding Plants	1,500 tons	Feeding Meals	10,000 tons
		Glass Bottles	9,000 tons
		Wire	4,000 tons
		Flour	4,000 tons
		Mustard Seed	4,000 tons

'tramp' traffic, regular services are operated to London, Birmingham, Nottingham, and Manchester.

Rail Transport. The Great Eastern line of British Railways provides freight transport services by means of a system which designates Norwich (Thorpe) as a Zonal Centre, subsidiary to which are fourteen railheads which cover an area extending from Great Yarmouth and Lowestoft as far south as Ipswich, Colchester, and Chelmsford.

Fast freight services run regularly for consignments of over 1 ton to twenty-one large cities and ports all over the country, and a daily service of through wagons of consignments under 1 ton is provided to forty-nine destinations, and on three days a week to four others. The work of the railheads is to send goods by direct routes, but where full loads are not possible, consignments are loaded to Norwich, whence they are re-routed.

The Ports (see fig. 1).

Norwich. The port of Norwich suffers from the disadvantage of lying 27–28 miles inland from Great Yarmouth, the river Yare having a narrow channel with only a safe draught of 10 feet 6 inches, the cost of

dredging swallowing up most of the revenue received from shipping tolls. Careful navigation is required to avoid grounding on river bends and the five-hour journey for a laden ship involves the negotiation of four bridges. There is about 400 feet of public quay and there are several private wharves.

Main imports are: coal, grain, meal, granite chippings, paper, structural steel, and wood, with scrap-metal being the main export from Norwich and sugar and molasses from Cantley.

Great Yarmouth (see fig. 2). The port has a 200-foot channel at the entrance and an average width of 270 feet along the 2½-mile channel to the Haven Bridge, which

SHIPPING USING THE PORT

	Number	Registered Tonnage
1959	465	80,157

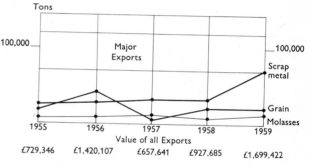

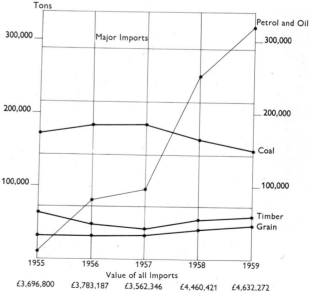

Fig. 2 *Port of Yarmouth graph*

Fig. 1 *Vessels using Norfolk Ports*

GREAT YARMOUTH

MAIN FOREIGN IMPORTS

	Coal (Tons)	Grain (Qrs.)	Manures (Tons)	Timber (Standards)	Salt (Tons)	Strawboards* (Tons)
1959	—	147,918	27,414	20,064	7,085	4,410

MAIN COASTWISE IMPORTS

	Coal (Tons)	Meal (Tons)	Grain (Qrs.)	Oil and Petrol (Tons)	Stone (Tons)
1959	157,030	8,918	55,792	335,904	6,750

MAIN FOREIGN EXPORTS

	Grain (Qrs.)	Herrings (Tons)	Live Cattle (Head)	Scrap Metal (Tons)	Molasses (Tons)
1959	78,319	189	3,655	59,027	3,294

MAIN COASTWISE EXPORTS

	Grain (Qrs.)	Molasses (Tons)	Sugar (Tons)	Coke Breeze (Tons)
1959	1,374	7,414	7,820	3,433

* For box making for the Norwich Boot and Shoe Industry and Mackintosh Caley Ltd

is a double-leaf opening bridge. Vessels up to an overall length of 320 feet and not exceeding 18 feet 6 inches draught can enter the harbour under suitable weather conditions at normal high water.

There are five principal quays under the jurisdiction of the Port and Haven Commissioners with a total length of 12,180 feet.

Regular services run from Great Yarmouth to Rotterdam and Antwerp, and until 1 January 1960, a tug and lighter service was in existence for cargoes unloaded over the side at Great Yarmouth and then carried up-river to Norwich, but with the growth of the coal-carrying trade by small motor-vessels the tug and lighter service became uneconomical, as coal was the major traffic.

King's Lynn (see figs. 3 and 4). The accommodation at King's Lynn consists of the harbour which is under the authority of the Conservancy Board, and the docks which are administered by the British Transport Commission.

The harbour is about 1,000 yards long and 200 yards wide at high water. Vessels cannot enter at low water.

The docks have a water area of 17 acres and a quayage of 1 mile, the entrance lock being 50 feet wide.

Regular shipping services operate from King's Lynn to Hamburg, Rotterdam, and Gothenburg.

Norfolk News Co. Ltd

Fig. 3 *King's Lynn Docks*

Imports 1959 (tons)	Coastwise	Overseas
General	—	27,963
Grain	4,571	4,924
Potatoes	—	2,626
Petroleum	289,689	11,856
Timber	—	70,240
Fertilizers	1,150	105,880
Miscellaneous	2,431	8,731
Total	**297,841**	**232,220**

Exports 1959 (tons)	Coastwise	Overseas
General	—	16,033
Grain	28,278	23,305
Sugar	30,687	—
Miscellaneous	1,401	1,332
Total	**60,366**	**40,670**

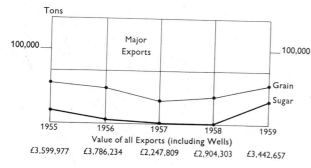

Wells. This small port in north Norfolk provides an outlet for cereals grown in the area. Potash for agricultural use is virtually the sole import. As the following figures show, the number and size of vessels using the port is small, since the depth of water falls from 14 feet at the high spring tides to 8 feet or less at other times.

WELLS

	No. of Vessels	Total Reg. Tonnage	Cargoes In	Cargoes Out
1959	14	2,032	Potash	Barley

Professional Services. The city is well supplied with professional services as this comparative table shows:

	Norwich	Oxford	York
Pop.	118,800	104,100	105,600
Solicitors (Practices)	34	18	26
Chartered Auctioneers and Estate Agents (Firms)	15	11	10
Chartered Accountants (Practices)	33	13	19

These figures emphasize the distance of Norwich from other large towns and cities, the figures for solicitors particularly illustrating the distance from London, which encourages the prospective client to consult a local solicitor. In addition, the fact that Norwich is a Cathedral city means that there must be, for example, a Diocesan Registrar and Registrars for the Archdeaconries. Norwich is an Assize town and has its own ancient

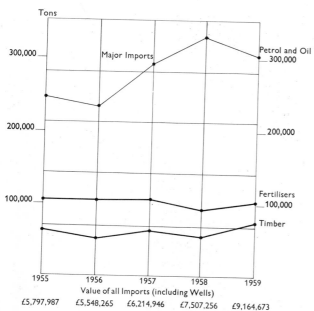

Fig. 4 *Port of King's Lynn graph*

Guildhall Court of Record, one of the few of its type still in existence. Solicitors' practices in Norwich are essentially general in character and are the type to be expected in a provincial capital of an agricultural county with landed estates.

Health Services. The rural nature of the region affects the health services of the county, 78–9 per cent of patients living in rural districts, so that mileage payments to doctors under the National Health Service are extremely high. Out of 360,000 registered patients, 174,000 have their prescriptions dispensed by their own doctors because of transport difficulties and the figure of 114 doctors who do their own dispensing is higher than for any other county. The difficulty of reaching the small market towns from some of the isolated areas of the county keeps the number of dentists' practices small outside the larger towns, so that in many areas there is only one dentist to as many as 10,000 of the population as against a national average of one dentist to about 4,000 of the population.

Medical and dental services in the county are on the following scale:

2,323 patients per doctor
7,147 patients per dentist

In the city of Norwich two figures are significant. In the inner city area there is an average of 2,537 patients per doctor, and in the fringe areas of the city the average figure is 2,397 patients per doctor. The national figures are:

Average number of patients per doctor (Rural) 2,049
Average number of patients per doctor (Urban) 2,284

Great Yarmouth has an official population of 51,400, but because of holiday visitors this increases from the end of May, until it reaches a peak of about 250,000 at 31 July, reaching normal again after the third week in September. This increase and the influx of several thousand persons connected directly or indirectly with the fishing industry from the end of October until mid-December, gives rise to large numbers requiring temporary medical treatment and emergency dental treatment during these periods.

PUBLIC UTILITIES

Gas Production. The Norwich Division of the Eastern Gas Board serves the whole of the county of Norfolk and part of east Suffolk. At the time of nationalization in 1949 there were twenty-seven works producing gas in the Division. This number has now fallen to fifteen and a study of fig. 5 shows that this has been achieved by a

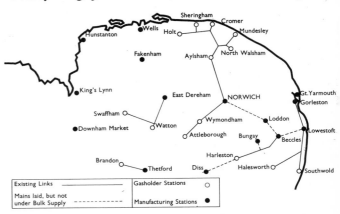

Fig. 5 *Eastern Gas Board. Norwich Division Gas Grid*

process of rationalization; the smaller and less economic works have been converted to gasholder stations, and supplies have been brought in by a grid from the larger, more economic, manufacturing stations. Thus, Norwich will eventually send gas throughout the eastern half of Norfolk, and connect with the grid in east Suffolk; a smaller scheme is centred on East Dereham.

Special mention should be made of developments at Norwich and Thetford which are part of the scheme of modernization. At Norwich additional equipment has been installed to pump supplies to the outlying districts. It is proposed to increase productive capacity by the installation of two reforming units, each with an output of 1.5 million cubic feet per day, at the Cremorne Lane site, making gas from oil refinery products. At Thetford supplies are now made available for Brandon and for Thetford itself by means of an oil gasification plant with a capacity of 300,000 cubic feet per day.

The output in the Division has increased over the past decade by about 7 per cent, rising from 13,519,724

	1948–9	1959–60	% Increase
Generated in England and Wales	42,824 million kW. hours	100,556 million kW. hours	138%
Consumed in Norfolk	334,476 thousand kW. hours	881,456 thousand kW. hours	163%

therms in the year 1950–1 to 14,524,895 therms in 1959–60. Somewhat over half the output comes from Norwich, where each week about 1,100 tons of coal are imported by water and a further 500 tons by rail. The sources are the north-east coalfield, Yorkshire, and the east Midlands. Industrial uses account for only about 14 per cent of consumption (though this represents a 2 per cent increase on 1951), because of the lack of heavy engineering. Food processing is the main industrial consumer.

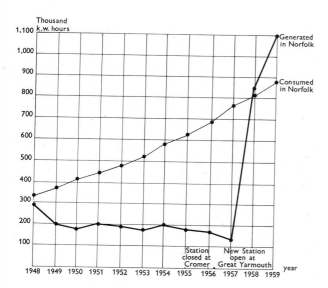

Fig. 6 *Electricity production and consumption in Norfolk*

Electricity Production. Electricity supply in Norfolk has, like gas supply, undergone a process of rationalization since the service was nationalized in 1947. The generating stations at present operating are an oil-burning station at South Denes, Great Yarmouth, with a 240.0 megawatt installed capacity, which was commissioned on 26 September 1957, and a coal-burning station at Norwich with a 73.5 megawatt installed capacity. Since nationalization, smaller, less efficient

stations at Cromer, King's Lynn, and Great Yarmouth have been closed down, and the Board's policy of generation of electricity on an efficiency basis will mean that the new station at South Denes will have priority over the older Norwich station, though the latter will still have a useful part to play for many years to come, mainly as a peak-load station.

Electricity consumption in Norfolk as compared with England and Wales as a whole can be seen from the figures above.

As fig. 6 shows, prior to the commissioning of the South Denes Generating Station at Great Yarmouth in 1957, power was taken from the National Grid to make up for a deficiency in production in Norfolk, but since that date, in spite of the large increase in consumption in the county, there has been a surplus of power available for the grid to supply to other areas.

Water Supply and Sewerage. The City of Norwich Water Department supplies an area of 178 square miles which embraces, in addition to the city itself, large parts of the surrounding rural districts, the total estimated population served being about 180,000. Water is also supplied in bulk to other parts of these rural districts which are not within the statutory area.

Water is obtained from the river Wensum at Heigham on the north-west side of the city, where, around the point of intake, the river drains 256 square miles of agricultural land which is studded with villages and small towns. In the circumstances, the raw water is polluted and requires treatment at the Heigham Waterworks before being passed into supply.

The distribution system is based upon a high-level pressure zone with two reservoirs at Mousehold having a combined capacity of 2,788,000 gallons and a lower level pressure zone with two reservoirs at Lakenham having a combined capacity of 2,620,000 gallons. A further reservoir of 3,000,000 gallons capacity is under construction at Mousehold. There are five electrically driven pumps at the Heigham works, two of these being used for the lower zone and three for the higher, though normally only one pump is in use at any one time in each zone, the others being on stand-by duty. During times of peak demand an additional pump is necessary in the Mousehold zone, where a large elevated reinforced concrete water tower is used for the supply of an extra high-level zone. For the supply of outlying rural areas a system of booster stations has been constructed.

The average daily quantity of water supplied during 1959–60 was 6,754,023 gallons, annual consumption having increased from 2,210,000,000 gallons in 1958 to 2,471,000,000 gallons in 1960. If consumption continues to rise at the expected rate of over 2 per cent per annum it is probable that the water undertaking would find it difficult to continue to meet all domestic and industrial demands for water. Indeed, in a survey carried out for Norwich Corporation in 1960, it was estimated that as a source of supply the river Wensum would, by 1980, be fully utilized and demand could only then be satisfied by taking supplies from water-filled gravel pits at Costessey, or from the river Yare. Parliamentary powers would be required for the latter. Rising domestic consumption accounts for the greater proportion of the increasing demand for water, but the probable future needs of industry have also been taken into account by the Water Committee, which has recommended to the Council that an additional intake at Heigham, two pumps and filtering and supply facilities, should be considered as urgent works, to be followed by further extensions for completion by 1966. The question of a five million gallon service reservoir at Mousehold is also recommended for consideration after the completion of the other projects.

In the county of Norfolk in 1944, there were 383 rural parishes out of a total number of 523 without a public piped water supply, a proportion worse than that of most counties. Since that date, local authorities in Norfolk, assisted financially by grants from the County Council and the Government, have made great progress in providing a piped water supply, and among the rural counties Norfolk is now one of the areas best provided for. Excluding the statutory supply areas of the Norwich Corporation and the Borough of King's Lynn, almost £5,000,000 have been spent in the county and nearly 1,500 miles of main have been laid.

There is little risk of serious water shortage in Norfolk, for with the exception of certain water undertakings such as Norwich and Great Yarmouth which derive their supplies from rivers and broads, the majority of the remaining undertakings rely upon about twenty-five major underground sources and a large number of smaller sources. The most important water-bearing stratum of the county is the chalk and it is computed that this source of supply is replenished at the rate of 172,000,000 gallons per day, the amount being drawn for distribution being only a very small fraction of this. If shortages occur, they will be the result of mechanical limitations or failures rather than of any shortage of supplies at initial source.

Sewage disposal is bound to create serious problems following extension of water supplies, especially in a county in which the need to protect underground sources of water supply from pollution must be a paramount consideration. Since the war, the Boroughs and Urban Districts have spent about £800,000 in installing new systems of sewage disposal or in improving and extending existing ones to serve 44,000 people. The Rural District Councils have already spent about £2,250,000 to serve an estimated 53,000 people. Many Rural District Councils have substantial schemes in course of preparation and the next decade is expected to see a great extension of this service.

ENTERTAINMENT

The trend in local entertainment services is that which is common in other parts of the country, namely the decline of the cinema in the face of competition from television, and of the growing popularity of car and motor-cycle owning, which diverts cash from the box-office. Since the end of the war, six cinemas have closed in Norwich, one having been demolished to make way for a modern store, the remainder having been converted to alternative uses or left to stand idle. The Hippodrome, which used to be a music hall, was for a time used for repertory productions, but the sole representative of the live theatre is now the Maddermarket, where high-class amateur productions are presented during the winter season. The Theatre Royal shows mainly films, but from time to time opera is played there by London companies, occasionally ballet performances may be seen, or pantomime at Christmas. There are five other cinemas still in existence. A steady decline in the number of cinemas in the market towns of Norfolk has also taken place in recent years.

In contrast, the popularity of television and the decline of sound radio is illustrated by the figures of licences issued in the Norwich postal area. The trend has been even more marked since the opening of Anglia Television on 27 October 1959.

	Wireless	Television and Wireless
1955	62,676	13,295
1956	56,492	24,055
1957	49,034	33,789
1958	39,229	42,582
1959	33,068	50,788

The success of Norwich City Football Club in gaining promotion to the Second Division of the Football League has been reflected in their 'gates' which averaged 26,500 during the 1959–60 season, and continuing success in the 1960–1 season has brought similar crowds to the Carrow Road ground from the city and a very wide area around Norwich.

THE HOLIDAY INDUSTRY

To many people outside Norfolk the holiday industry is one of the most prominent of the county's economic activities. Norfolk has a wide variety of holiday amenities, including the lonely marshes of the north coast, the popular resort of Great Yarmouth, the historic city of Norwich and the unique Broads, which have the distinctive appeal of a holiday afloat in an area where access to the waterways is decidedly limited, save by boat, which is the only practicable means of transport.

A sample survey carried out by the British Travel and Holidays Association in 1955 showed that about 2 per cent of the population of Great Britain had a holiday in Norfolk, representing approximately 1,000,000 people. Of these, almost one-half stayed at Great Yarmouth, while the Broads and coastal caravans each accounted

for rather more than one-fifth. The average holiday expenditure per head (excluding the cost of travel) was of the order of £12, a figure approximating to the national average for home holidays, so that the total income from the holiday trade was about £12,000,000.

A large proportion of Norfolk holidaymakers come from the east Midlands, but London and the north also provide a good many visitors. A notable feature of the appeal of Norfolk holidays is the difference between the coast, with its comparatively short 'season', drawing its clientele from comparatively short distances, and the Broads, with a considerably longer 'season', drawing holidaymakers from a much wider area, probably due to the energetic publicity of the two associations of boat-yard owners, comprising the majority of the participants in the industry, and, of course, the highly distinctive nature of the area.

While the number of holidays taken in Norfolk is apparently being maintained, it is doubtful whether the area is taking its proportion of the increasing national holiday trade, for it has a number of problems to counter. Though attractive to the static family holidaymaker, Norfolk's position and scenery have not encouraged that heavy car tourist traffic which has become such a feature in some parts of the country. Its 'season' is very short, for summer weather comes late to Norfolk; consequently there is little movement in the holiday industry until June and the coastal area hardly partakes of the April 'honeymoon' or Easter trade. The resorts, excepting Great Yarmouth, are small and the possibility of expenditure on publicity and amenities is necessarily fairly limited. Moreover, towns such as Cromer and Sheringham have traditionally depended on the hotel and boarding house trade, whereas in post-war years these forms of accommodation have declined sharply in popularity while the static caravan has been constantly gaining favour for a number of reasons.

Caravan holidays have grown in popularity as a result of their informality and comparatively low cost, within the means of people who might not be able to afford a holiday in the older established types of accommodation. Moreover, for the site operator and caravan owner, capital costs are very modest, while the high return is attractive. Surveys made in 1959 revealed that about

8,500 holiday caravans were in use in Norfolk, with over 85 per cent of the total concentrated in four areas:

Caister–Hemsby	2,700
West Runton	700
Hunstanton–Heacham	1,400
Great Yarmouth	2,500

While the increasing number of holiday caravans in Norfolk has been significant, this side of the holiday industry has not yet reached an advanced stage of development as it has in the south and south-west of the country. This fact is illustrated by the difference between site rents per caravan, varying from £10 to £20 per season in Norfolk and from £35 to £40 on the south coast. Hitherto, planning permission for caravan sites has been given on a short-term basis, but the Norfolk County Council has recently adopted a policy regarding holiday caravans whereby it is hoped that the grant of planning consent for longer periods – 10 years – will encourage investment in caravan sites to provide a higher standard of amenities. In addition, the provision of further sites is to take place mostly in the areas where caravans already provide the bulk of holiday accommodation.

The growth of the Broads holiday trade has resulted in very extensive development of some centres, notably Wroxham–Hoveton and Horning; indeed, at the peak of the season the Bure is a rather crowded waterway. There remains room for expansion of the industry on the other waterways of the area, and new boatyards have been opened in recent years at Stalham, Brundall, and Ellingham. There is sporadic local agitation for extension of the navigable waterways of the region, in particular for the restoration of the Waveney navigation to Bungay, the Bure navigation to Aylsham, and the reinstatement of the North Walsham to Dilham canal. Such projects might prove expensive, however, and are unlikely to take place before such rivers as the Yare and Waveney are more intensively used.

Another aspect of the Broads holiday industry is the possibility of the creation of a National Park. Although suggested for designation by the Hobhouse Committee in 1946, no active steps have been taken to this end, for any National Park scheme would have to take into account the complex administration of the waterways, responsibility for the maintenance of which is divided amongst a number of bodies. Nevertheless, there is no doubt as to the national and growing importance of the Broads as a holiday area.

Throughout Norfolk's economy, development will tend to centre upon existing towns and 'Greater Norwich' will almost certainly expand so far as is permitted by the 'Green Belt' Plan (see fig. 7): there is room for a population of 200,000. These same limitations may, in turn, stimulate separate growth in near-by centres such as Wymondham.

The continued prosperity of Norfolk's economy has been shown to be based upon a variety of products and services for which there is a relatively stable demand. The energetic activities of the local Planning Departments, particularly that of Norfolk County, have done much to encourage a further diversification, and it may well be that the research departments of the proposed University of East Anglia will suggest still more ways of using the area's resources.

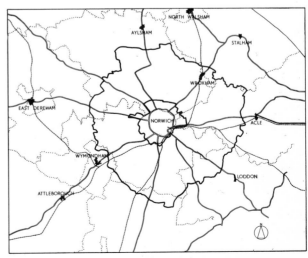

Fig. 7 *Proposed Green Belt for Norwich*